D0436839

FROM HIROSHIMA TO THE MOON

CHRONICLES OF LIFE IN THE ATOMIC AGE

BY

DANIEL LANG

SIMON AND SCHUSTER
NEW YORK
1959

PUBLISHED BY SIMON AND SCHUSTER, INC.
ROCKEFELLER CENTER, 630 FIFTH AVENUE
NEW YORK 20, N. Y.

FIRST PRINTING

LIBRARY OF CONGRESS CATALOG CARD NUMBER: 59-13877
MANUFACTURED IN THE UNITED STATES OF AMERICA
BY GEO. McKIBBIN & SON, NEW YORK

TO FRANCIE, NIKI, CECILY

With the exception of one poem, "Spaceman's Song," all the contents of *From Hiroshima to the Moon* originally appeared in *The New Yorker* in somewhat different form. Substantial portions were previously published in book form in *Early Tales of the Atomic Age* (1948) and *The Man in the Thick Lead Suit* (1954).

My thanks are extended to William Shawn for suggesting the idea of this book and to Tom Torre Bevans, Robert Gerdy and Spencer Klaw for their invaluable aid in its preparation.

D. L.

CONTENTS

FOREWORD

SHORTLY AFTER the B-29 *Enola Gay* raided Hiroshima, on August 6, 1945, I went to Oak Ridge for *The New Yorker* Magazine to write a story about a worker in one of the esoteric factories there who had spent the war trying to figure out what he was doing. The assignment, as far as I was then concerned, was just another job of reporting, and one reason I had been asked to do it was that I had run dry of ideas of my own. *The New Yorker*'s editors were certainly under no illusion that I possessed a scientific background. I didn't and don't. I was glad enough, though, to arrive in that raw Tennessee town that hot summer, and not because I attached any special significance to the atom. The idea at hand—it turns up as Chapter Three in this book—struck me as a good one, particularly since its interest would be heightened by the headlines. It was then the Year One of what has come to be called the Atomic Age, and the newspapers were full of stuff about how far a piece of U-235 the size of a pea could drive the *Queen Mary* and their pages were laid out with pictures of Dr. Oppenheimer and his colleagues—so many secret weapons, the captions suggested, whose gray matter had cleverly done in the enemy.

Paradoxically, those same headlines kept me—and most people, I suspect—from comprehending the portentous nature of the *Enola Gay*'s mission. The war had put us all through years of exciting headlines, and this new one about an atomic bomb was, like my assignment, hard to look upon as something special and apart from all the others to which we had become accustomed—D-Day, Dieppe, Doolittle. The news of the bomb, nevertheless, was not lightly received by the public. The casualty estimates at Hiroshima and Nagasaki were astonishing, and the sudden capitulation of a government that had withstood fire raids for so long was plain evidence of the weapon's influence. But caught up in the exhilaration and relief of knowing that the fighting was finally at an end, most of us, I believe, concluded that the Japanese had been knocked out by a mighty weapon but one that was essentially an addition to the gunpowder family, a kind of super-blockbuster. This impression, in retrospect, may have derived, at least in part, from President Truman's well-meaning attempt at popularizing the magnitude of the new weapon in terms of T.N.T. tons—as if that familiar explosive could scatter fallout for cows to nibble on, as if the effects produced by chemical energy, quickly over and done with, could compare to the lingering incursions of radioactive elements.

In Oak Ridge, my mystified worker told me how he had vainly sought to learn the purpose of his job. The rest of the country, too, had been in the dark on the bomb, so, embarking on a second article, I asked counter-intelligence agents for the Manhattan District how a $2 billion undertaking had been kept a secret from Americans over a period of years. The chief agent told me, for publication, that the secret had not been perfectly maintained. Espionage in behalf of a foreign power had been attempted during the war, he said, and its spies were continuing their activities. I decided to do a third article, one that dealt with life in Oak Ridge, and canvassed its residents on what they guessed would become of their factories now that the war was over. There was no guesswork. Everyone assured me, matter-of-factly, that the plants were still in business, that bombs, for the present, at any rate, were continuing to be made. I was startled. Here it was, a moment of hallelujah—the Emperor's emissaries were only then preparing to ratify their surrender aboard the *Missouri* in Yokohama harbor—and not only was the manufacture of a bomb that could wipe out thousands upon thousands proceeding apace but a foreign power wanted it. I checked what I had heard with the highest officials in Oak Ridge, civilian and military, and it was when they said it was so I realized that the headline about the atomic bomb was no transient affair, that the world had contracted a chronic condition that would last long after the *Missouri* raised anchor.

I expected that a weapon capable of instantly supplanting a war with a counterfeit peace would bear watching, but I did not imagine that I personally would do the amount of watching I seem to have done, to judge by this bulky volume. I had always, as I do today, considered myself a general reporter, covering whatever came up and temperamentally chary of pounding a particular beat. But then I did not anticipate the profusion of ancient themes and modern variations that would unfold as atomic energy and, later, space rocketry engaged us in questions of good and evil, life and death. Time and again, since that trip to Oak Ridge, I have been drawn to look into yet one more facet of these old struggles—some intellectual or absurd turn of events, something gay or idealistic. A physicist who has worked on the bomb is ordained a member of the Episcopal hierarchy, and I am prompted to go ask him why. One of Hitler's chief military scientists becomes one of America's chief military scientists, and, wondering whether a man who knows how to kill will always be sure of a job, I find myself bound for Wernher von Braun's home, in Alabama, to hear that rocketeer's moral views. How can one resist seeking out Paddy Martinez, of Grants, New Mexico, an illiterate sheepherder whose life is transformed when, riding to a trading post for cigarettes, he stumbles upon an immense uranium strike? Now and then, as the reader will note, I have had to inform myself on some technical situation or other, but it is the human comedy of our scientific age that engrosses me, and I am emboldened to explore it by the thought that I stand as good (or poor) a chance as the next fellow of guessing an individual's motives and objectives.

This book, then, represents the chronicles of a layman who, by virtue of his occupation, has been able to wander through the bewildering maze of developments since the Year One, and it is these very wanderings that lend the book whatever shape and form it may possess. Perhaps its contents will afford historians to come a clue as to what went on in the tumultuous era through which we have already lived, an almost perfectly carved-out period of history in which we have gone from Hiroshima to the moon (and beyond), from earthly ruins to the unspoiled heavens. We will probably be centuries, or whatever time is left us, assessing the consequences of these past few years, and it may be that one useful way of coping with so concentrated a burst of history is to handle it journalistically. Perspective may come later, and I say this with a sense of authority as well as of chagrin, for in rereading certain sections of this book I can see where I might adopt a different tone here, a sharper emphasis there were I writing them today. I am permitting such shortcomings to remain, however, and I am neglecting to indicate, at the point where certain individuals make their appearance in the book, that they have passed on—a necrology that includes the important scientists Fermi and von Neumann; Miss Edith Warner, the transplanted Philadelphian who for many years befriended the Indians dwelling in the environs of Los Alamos; and her neighbor, Cady Wells, the artist, who has ceased to ponder how to flee atomic energy. I am refraining, too, from bringing various facts up to date, nor am I tampering with opinions that have become archaic with the passage of time, such as one engineer's prediction, stoutly ventured to me in 1947 at a military proving ground, that a day of supersonic aircraft would yet come to pass. To do otherwise, it seems to me, would undermine the scheme of the book, which, as I have mentioned, is possibly to supply some future historian with a footnote. I hope there will be such a man, and I wish him a quieter day than the one we are now knowing.

DANIEL LANG

Martha's Vineyard, Massachusetts

CHAPTER 1 | AUGUST, 1945

THE WAR'S TOP TOP SECRET

THE ATOMIC BOMB proved to be the war's biggest surprise, but it took two and a half years of daily suspicion, hunch-playing, soft-soaping, and double talk on the part of the Counter-Intelligence Corps of the Manhattan District—the Army's cover name for its secret undertaking—to keep the bomb from becoming prematurely famous. Some members of the C.I.C., in fact, were amazed that President Truman's announcement, on August 6th, 1945, was a sensation instead of an anticlimax, for by the time the steel tower in New Mexico was vaporized, well over a million Americans knew of the existence of the Manhattan District. The vast majority of them weren't aware what the project was trying to produce, but, at that, nearly two thousand known instances of loose talk, dangerous and close to home, had been investigated. Hundreds of breaks in newspapers, on the radio, in pulpits, and on lecture platforms had nearly spilled the beans. Furthermore, definite attempts at espionage had been made by foreign countries.

Against these threats to the Army's top wartime secret, the C.I.C. (whose agents were known among project workers as the creeps) adopted an extremely simple policy: to try for a complete blackout on any publicity and talk even indirectly related to the subject of atomic energy. "The idea," a C.I.C. officer explained to me, "was to be able to separate the wheat from the chaff. If everybody was talking about the project, well, we'd have to suspect everybody. But if everybody on our side kept quiet, then only those against us would be talking." Another reason for this approach was to get the Axis to underestimate the United States. If America had bragged in advance, in the Goebbels manner, the Germans might have stepped up their work in the atomic-energy field instead of diverting so much of their efforts to such relatively harmless affairs as the V-1 and V-2.

So bent was the C.I.C. on its campaign of silence that it would not court-martial Army personnel who had talked carelessly or committed some other indiscretion. Even a closed trial, it was pointed out to me, would have meant that the defense counsel, assistant defense counsel, members of the court, and a stenographer would have had to learn about the project. If the defendant chose to appeal, still more individuals would have had to live with the secret. What happened instead was that the culprit, after promising to keep still in the future, was sent to a replacement pool with a set of secret orders that instructed the commanding officer to assign him to a rear-echelon post or a remote Pacific island where there was no chance of his being captured by the Japanese or Germans. Civilian employees engaged in the project who violated security regulations were fired, but tactfully, so that they wouldn't go away angry and talk too much. Even espionage agents who were detected were not arrested. The creeps would put the spy under surveillance twenty-four hours of the day, make friends with him, even "help" him with his mission. Details about the spies still cannot be disclosed because military security is involved.

The creeps had a couple of peculiar problems to face from the start. In the first place, the project might need years to complete its work. "It's different if you're trying to keep a new tank under wraps," a C.I.C. captain told me. "A tank doesn't take long to put together, and once it goes into combat, you can kiss the secret good-by, because the enemy captures it." Another problem for the C.I.C. was the fact that both atomic energy and the possibility of an atomic bomb had been discussed in scientific and popular journals for years and could quite reasonably be ordinary topics of conversation. Nothing, however (including an atomic bomb), is supposed to be impossible in the Army, and so the creeps set out, among other things, to keep the United States from talking for an indefinite period about something Einstein had announced to the world in 1905.

The way the C.I.C. people saw it, they had several so-called zones of information to protect. First, they didn't want either the existence or the location of the Manhattan District installations known. The cost and size of the project had to be kept secret. So did the fact that plants in the States of Washington, Tennessee, and New Mexico were related to each other. If an outsider had known, for example, that the end products manufactured at Hanford and Oak Ridge were being shipped to Los Alamos, the trucks carrying them might have been sabotaged en route. The fact that men such as Dr. Bohr, Dr. Compton, Dr. Fermi, and other eminent nuclear physicists were involved had to be kept secret, too. Finally, the various methods by which the District was processing uranium, the properties of the end products, and data on our equipment and techniques had to be kept under cover. "The longer it took them to have that bomb dropped," I was told by the C.I.C. head, Colonel William Budd Parsons (known as *the* creep), "the less chance we had of preventing the enemy from hearing about it. Most of us felt that we had a losing fight on our hands, but we could never concede that. If we had, we might as well have closed up shop."

The C.I.C. never had much chance of keeping the existence of the Manhattan District a secret. The project was simply too big. Thousands of workers were needed, and that meant that the Army had to ask the War Manpower Commission to recruit labor, skilled and unskilled. All sorts of critical materials were required, which necessitated getting the help of the War Production Board. The W.P.B. had to tell manufacturers to rush the completion of certain machinery for the District's plants. The Post Office and telephone companies had to hear of a new town by the name of Oak Ridge. Railroad spurs had to be built, so railroad people knew about it. Native farmers, forced off the project sites, had to explain to relatives in other regions why they needed temporary shelter.

By the time the project was a few months old, still more people were finding out about it. When a young scientist was called up by his draft board, the Army tried to keep him out of the Army by requesting his draft board to defer him. The District often had to tell Selective Service that a young man was working on a project that had a No. 1 labor priority and an essential rating by the War Department, but it could say nothing about the nature of the employee's job. Frequently draft-board members would decide that the Army was taking itself too seriously and order the scientist to an induction center. When this happened, the District usually was able to grab the man after his thirteen weeks of basic training and put him right back on the job he had held as a civilian, at an enlisted man's pay. The War Labor Board's assistance had to be asked, too. When unions and contractors involved with the project negotiated agreements before the Board, C.I.C. agents read the briefs both sides had prepared to see if censoring was necessary. Sometimes, in the heat of an argument, a spokesman might forget that he was discussing a secret project and the C.I.C. man in the room would have to jump up and caution him. "We kept their briefs down to essentials," an officer who had been a labor-relations man before the war said. "And I must say our censoring seemed to help. I can't remember hearings that had less unnecessary haggling."

As a result of huge District contracts, corporations would float new issues of stocks and bonds to finance themselves. Ordinarily they would have had to let the Securities Exchange Commission know why, but the District asked the S.E.C. to waive its rule until the nature of the project was no longer secret. The S.E.C. was agreeable, but it had got in on the fact that the Army was up to something big and very secret. Thousands of District employees, whose families got tired of the elementary living conditions in the newly built communities, quit their jobs. When they did, they signed a pledge promising that they would disclose nothing about their work until the War Department gave them permission to do so, but it was a gamble just the same. One officer told me that four hundred thousand workers, about three times more than the peak payroll, had been investigated. Additional thousands of people in subsidiary factories all over the country, making telltale equipment of one sort or another, couldn't help getting wind of the project.

The Counter-Intelligence tried its best to control gossip and curiosity in the Manhattan District plants. The employees were lectured almost every day on the importance of secrecy. Posters, among them such items as "DON'T BE A BLABOTEUR," were hung all over the District's reservations. Trailers urging silence were flashed on the screens in the District's movie houses. "Most of it was straight corn," an officer told me. "It had to be, because we couldn't tell them they were making a brand-new secret plane or super-duper submarine. All we could do was to ask for their loyalty and patriotism—pretty abstract matters, when you get right down to it." Former Secretary Stimson and other high War Department officials paid morale visits. None of these things prevented a syndicated humorist from writing that he had heard tell that the Army was sponsoring a huge project in Tennessee where the front ends of sawhorses were being manufactured.

All personnel on the project were reinvestigated every three months, every six months, or every year, depending on the importance of their jobs. C.I.C. men found themselves investigating each other. "You know how a structural steelworker gets?" Lieutenant William Huisking asked me rhetorically. "He walks on those girders every day and he's liable to forget there's hard ground several hundred feet below him. Well, in the same way, a fellow with top secrets in his head can get to take them too much for granted." Some of the creeps took civilian jobs in plants to keep an eye on the employees; at Oak Ridge such C.I.C. men earned sixty thousand dollars in extracurricular pay, all of which was turned over to the U.S. Treasury.

The principle of what the C.I.C. called "compartmentalization of information" was rigidly followed. In shorter words, this meant that no one was to know more than he had to. Maintenance men in one plant at Oak Ridge, for example, were dressed in blue uniforms, while operations employees wore white ones. Thus, if a maintenance man wandered into a room full of white uniforms, he was immediately spotted by a supervisor, who either ordered him to leave or, if he had been called to fix something, watched him closely until he finished his chore. So assiduously was this principle followed that today an astonishingly small number of people have the over-all picture of the District's work.

Trucks bound for the District sites with valuable equipment and materials took circuitous routes. Most of the drivers never knew where their cargoes were headed for. They would drive a certain distance and then a fresh driver, waiting in a safe, lighted neighborhood, would take over. "A truck that's on the road for only twenty-four hours," I was told by Captain James Haley, who handled this phase of security, "is twice as safe as one that's on the road for forty-eight hours."

Armed officers and enlisted men rode as guards on the trucks and also in the cabooses of freight trains hauling strategic metal. Despite the speed with which the Army was working, the end products were never flown to New Mexico, because of the risk attached to airplane travel. Top-secret data that had to be transported were given to officers, who rode on trains in locked compartments, their pistols in hidden shoulder holsters and the documents in rubberized pouches strapped to their chests. Code, needless to say, was used in all official communications. Some of the code vocabulary was: "top" for "atom," "topic" for "atomic," "boat" for "bomb," "topic boat" for "atomic bomb," "urchin fashion" for "uranium fission," "spinning" for "smashing," and "igloo of urchin" for "isotope of uranium." The word for U-235 was "tenure," and I learned how perfectly obvious it was from an eager lieutenant. "You see," he told me, "two and three are five and five make ten. Right? O. K., that's where the 'ten' comes in. The 'ure' stands for uranium. So, 'ten' plus 'ure' equals 'tenure.' A cinch."

One of the special headaches for the C.I.C. was handling the top scientists. Most of the people the Army was trying to keep quiet didn't actually know what the District wanted to produce. The scientists, however, knew more about it than the Army did. An inadvertent tidbit from one of them to an enemy agent, or even to a patriotic gossip, about the state of the District's plutonium research or some new idea that had been figured out for its electromagnetic separation process might undo everything. Nor could the Army afford to fire its civilian geniuses for talking loosely. The nuclear experts wanted very much to co-operate, but free interchange of information had been a lifelong practice with them, and they were itching to discuss their work. Also, they didn't take care of themselves, which disturbed the Army, since it was vital that the scientists stay alive at least until the first bomb was dropped. "Some of the world's lousiest auto drivers developed the bomb," a lieutenant told me. He added that they didn't walk so well either. Professor Ernest O. Lawrence, of the University of California, often visited in Chicago, where the District operated an important laboratory in an armory. He would cross streets waving his arms in the air and exclaiming, "God, what a city! Smell that smoke! What air! Beats any air we've got in California!" Dr. Bohr was quite a jaywalker too. They used to say down in General Groves' office, in Washington, that they could always tell when he was coming to call by the sound of screeching brakes. Bohr was a problem from the beginning. When the British smuggled him out of Sweden in the bomb bay of a Liberator, they had to fly very high on the way to England to avoid being intercepted by the Luftwaffe. The crew put on oxygen masks and tried to put one on Bohr, too. The scientist's head, however, proved to be so massive that it wouldn't go on. The plane landed with its precious passenger out cold.

The Army, doing its best to meet a trying situation, assigned young intelligence officers to protect its troupe of nuclear specialists. The officers were primarily supposed to serve as bodyguards, but actually their duties ranged from that of gentleman's gentleman to guardian to equerry to companion. Their personalities were supposed to go well with those of their wards. The man who watched Professor Oppenheimer, for example, could not be a conversational drip, and he had to ride well. Compton's man had to be prepared to recite the latest baseball batting averages. Fermi had John Baudino, an Italian-speaking American, for his aide. Their relationship was particularly congenial, so much so that after a while, Baudino got to know more about the atom than he had ever wanted to know. Fermi would introduce Baudino to his fellow-scientists as "my colleague," and say, "Soon Johnny will know so much about the project he will need a bodyguard, too." Another creep, Charles Campbell, quietly chauffeuring his physicist, Professor John von Neumann, of the Institute for Advanced Study at Princeton, was suddenly asked by the Professor where he was studying his theoretical physics these days. The intelligence man replied that he was a little too busy to be doing any studying. Von Neumann was horrified. "It is my fault!" he exclaimed. Campbell, who has little interest in physics, said it wasn't worth getting upset about, but that didn't soothe the Professor. "That is the trouble with you Americans," von Neumann said, "you are too kind. You will come with me and together we shall study theoretical physics in New Mexico."

Another of the Army's handicaps was the flattering but unrealistic faith the scientists had in intelligence agents. "They had this notion," one tired-looking bodyguard told me, "that we could know whatever they were doing even if they didn't tell us." The scientists never ceased to wonder when they were recognized by a C.I.C. man whom they hadn't met before. When Professor I. I. Rabi, of Columbia, a short man with distinctive features, was met in a Chicago station by a lieutenant of the creeps, he congratulated the young officer effusively. "How did you know it was me?" he asked. The C.I.C. man started to explain, but the Professor said he was too modest and wouldn't listen. "What I wanted to say to him," the officer told me, "was that I had studied six very clear photographs of him taken from every angle and that the initials 'I.I.R.' were painted on his suitcase." Most of the scientists were delighted with themselves when they succeeded in eluding the C.I.C. men. "Mine would tease me," one aide recalled morosely. "He'd tell me, 'How come you let me get away? You're slipping.' "

It was during one of these escapes from a bodyguard that a celebrated physicist, sitting in the lounge car of a Tennessee-bound train, got into a conversation with two young Army officers. The scientist was cagey to the extent of not disclosing his name, but that was all. He was in the groove that day and nothing in the world could have stopped him from discussing the problems that were holding up the large-scale unleashing of atomic energy. The officers listened respectfully, and, without his being aware of it, walked off with two bulky briefcases he had with him. When the scientist arrived at one of the gates in the fence around Oak Ridge, he was surprised to see the same two officers standing there. They handed him his briefcases and told him that it was just luck that they happened to be working under him in one of the plants and knew who he was. "Sir," one of them told him, "you talk too much. We'll have to report you to the C.I.C."

Various other threats to security took place. Late in 1943 some Columbia scientists decided to get rid of a mixture of scrap uranium and sodium by tossing it off the George Washington Bridge. It would have burst into flames and burned briefly before sinking. The plan never came to pass. When Captain Bernard Menke, of the C.I.C.'s New York office, heard of it, he hired a motorboat and had the stuff thrown into the ocean far from land, where it made a sizzling but less public bonfire. "I had visions, dashing up to Columbia," Menke told me. "I saw suspicious guards on the bridge shooting at the scientists just as the sodium was plummeting down toward the river. I saw bright-yellow flames and big black headlines, in which reporters quoted Police Department authorities as saying that the first saboteurs in New York City had been caught."

The scientists were given code names, but most of them were so passionately, or so absent-mindedly, devoted to their real ones that the Army had to keep reminding their secretaries to see that all letters and telegrams were signed with the assumed ones. Occasionally, however, these names, for some reason, became too well known. When it was feared that Professor Lawrence's code name, Ernest Lawson, was getting to be as famous as his own, the C.I.C. dreamed up a brand-new one—Oscar Wilde. It was selected, I was told, because Wilde had written a play called *The Importance of Being Earnest*. There is at least one incident on record in which a scientist used code names resourcefully. In the winter of 1944, Dr. Fermi (Mr. Farmer) and Dr. Wigner (Mr. Wagner) appeared at an Oak Ridge gate and were stopped by a guard. Wigner told the guard he was Mr. Wagner, and the guard, after running his finger down a special list of approved names, decided to admit him. But the guard didn't believe Fermi, who speaks English with an Italian accent, when he identified himself as Mr. Farmer, although that name was on the list too. He asked Fermi to show him letters addressed to Mr. Farmer. The Italian didn't have any. At that point, Wigner announced that he was prepared to vouch for Mr. Farmer. "Do you believe my name is Wagner?" he asked the guard. "No question about it," the guard answered. "Well," Wigner said, "if my name is Wagner, then I swear to you by the heavens above that this man's name is Farmer." The guard waved Fermi in.

In addition to its domestic work, the Manhattan District did some spying on the Germans. A special unit known as Positive Overseas Intelligence handled this work. It was small but it gathered a lot of information, much of it from correspondence between German scientists, who are uninhibited letter writers. (Occasionally the C.I.C. would have these letters read to District scientists as object lessons.) The Germans were looking for a way to use atomic energy, but their efforts, I was told, have impressed certain newspaper correspondents much more than they did the heads of the Manhattan District. The District's intelligence reports during and since the war indicate, in fact, that the Germans did not even try for an atomic bomb. Rather, they seem to have had ideas of harnessing atomic energy as a form of fuel. The Nazis' work, indeed, was held in such poor esteem by American military authorities that certain German laboratories, whose locations were known, were left unbombed to enable Hitler's experts to continue their failures. "By the end of the war," Major Francis Smith, a member of the Positive Overseas Intelligence, told me, "the Nazis had not yet reached the stage we were at when we started our project."

The Reich laid out no more than $1,500,000 for nuclear experimenting, a piddling sum compared to America's expenditure. Two hundred thousand dollars went for uranium, a hundred thousand for heavy water, and a half million for cyclotrons and high-voltage apparatus. Only twenty-four of the Reich's leading scientists were occupied with 811-RFR-111, the Reich's code for its equivalent of the Manhattan District, as against the hundreds the United States used. Nor were the few scientists assigned to it well organized. They bickered among themselves and, according to one newsy letter, two of their leaders, Heisenberg and Diebner, had a first-class grudge against each other. The Germans performed thirteen experiments, mostly in Leipzig, Berlin, the Heidelberg region, and the Joliot Laboratory in Paris, in attempts to get a chain reaction going. Even had they succeeded, I was told in Washington, they wouldn't necessarily have known that plutonium was the end product within their reach. That would have entailed making another discovery. When the United States tried for a chain reaction, it knew perfectly well what its end product was going to be, plutonium having been produced in a cyclotron within its borders as long ago as 1939. As for U-235, the Germans were even farther behind. The U-235 research that did take place was conducted in Hamburg and Freiburg.

Unlike President Roosevelt, the Nazi leaders vacillated about the advisability of nuclear experimentation. In 1940 and 1941 the group around Hitler was moderately interested. Between 1941 and 1943 they were skeptical, and believed that their best bet was perfecting V-1s, V-2s, and jet-propelled planes. Then, toward the end, when only a miracle could have saved them, they turned around and began to assign top priorities to the atomic physicists for materials and transportation. The constant reshuffling of 811-RFR-111 reflected this governmental uncertainty. Before the war, the Ministry of Education had organized a team of scientists to look into the possibilities of harnessing atomic energy. When Poland was invaded, the Reichswehr's ordnance section took over the work. In February, 1942, at a meeting in Berlin, the State Research Council was ordered to assume control. The Army didn't like this and set up its own scientific group under Dr. Diebner. This led to rivalry, which Goering took cognizance of in the spring of 1943 by appointing a man named Esau, of the State Research Council, to run the whole show. In January, 1944, according to one piece of intercepted correspondence, a Dr. Walther Gerlach was appointed to succeed Esau. Early in the winter of 1945 it was agreed that a Government Institute for Nuclear Physics Research and Development should be established in May, but that was a little late in the game.

Despite the fact that they weren't in the same league with the United States, the Germans, displaying their traditional cockiness, were comfortably sure that they were doing all right. On December 16, 1944, Dr. Gerlach wrote a letter to Martin Bormann, one of Hitler's right-hand men, in which, in the course of asking for draft deferments for his assistants, he put down an interesting thought: "I am convinced that we are at the present time considerably farther ahead of America, both in research and development, although we are operating with a progressively smaller percentage of help as compared with America. . . ."

As the months went by in 1944 and 1945, the C.I.C. people began to feel a kind of edginess. Things were going too well. None of the trucks carrying materials night and day over the highways were sabotaged. The trainloads of metal were coming through on schedule. The security campaigns in the plants were yielding fruit, as the C.I.C. could tell by the increasing number of tips, nearly all of them duds, which they were receiving from employees. "Any time a wrong-number party phoned them, they'd tell us the Germans had arrived," a creep told me. Also, some of the more troublesome foreign espionage activity had fallen off sharply early in 1944. Those spies already spotted were under control. "The way some of us felt," one Oak Ridge lieutenant said to me, "we didn't mind spies so much. Spies were a black-and-white deal. But we were flying blind when it came to knowing how many unauthorized people were in on the secret or who might take it into his head next to talk too much. It was like taking a poll without interviewing anybody. That was how things were going to have to stay, too, until the day the bomb was dropped on Hiroshima."

The C.I.C. men continued their shadowboxing to the end and, thanks to a variety of happenings, were kept busy enough to be spared boredom. They even had two cases to work on that involved enemy military action. Both of these came toward the end of 1944, at the Hanford works in Washington State. One day a Japanese balloon floated down onto, of all things, the power line running from Bonneville to Hanford. "It stayed there a fraction of a second and fell to the ground," a major told me, "but you can put it down that production of the atom bomb was definitely interfered with by enemy action. Inside the plants the motors hesitated a little, just like in an auto when you're shifting from second to high." The other incident came about 3 A.M. one night, when the Army got a radar fix indicating that a small plane, not resembling any American model, was slowly moving over one of the Hanford plants. The Army immediately asked the Naval Air Station at Pasco to send up fliers after what might have been a Kamikaze plane launched from a vessel off the Coast. The Navy pilots went up and reported that they could find nothing. The next night the radar screen showed the same image over the same plant. Again the Navy pilots went up and found nothing. Creeps from all parts of the country were ordered into the area. They checked and double checked every airstrip in the region. After two weeks, during which a mysterious plane was still occasionally reported in the air, it was discovered that the radar had been picking up flights of geese.

The newspapers and radio also provided the C.I.C. with work. Byron Price, U. S. Director of Censorship, had sent two confidential memoranda to editors, asking them not to print anything about atomic research, but either the requests didn't reach all the editors or some of them forgot about them. Usually, when a break occurred, a C.I.C. man would drop around to see the editor or radio-station manager, discover that the slip was unintentional, and be assured that it wouldn't happen again. Letters to the editor criticizing the Army for not getting busy with atomic weapons were frequently printed. "Hints point to the earlier realization of the atomic bomb," a wide-awake reader wrote to the Toledo *Blade* in December, 1944. "A special substance said to have amazing potentialities could, if it is automatically exploded the right way, ensure victory." The University of Chicago *Maroon,* in an outburst of school spirit shortly before V-E Day, lauded Alma Mater for having a monopoly on Nobel Prize winners and then said, "Compton and his colleagues are working on problems, fraught with tremendous possibilities to mankind, of releasing atomic energy." A congressman sounded off on atomic energy in the *Congressional Record* and mailed five thousand copies to his constituents. A Cleveland reporter, after spending a vacation near Los Alamos, New Mexico, came home and wrote an excited story entitled "The Forbidden City." He said, "The Mr. Big of the city is a college professor, Dr. J. Robert Oppenheimer, called the 'Second Einstein.' . . . [A] widespread belief is that he is developing ordnance and explosives. Supporters of this guess argue that it accounts for the number of mechanics working on the production of a single device and there are others who will tell you tremendous explosions have been heard." The C.I.C. took care of that matter in a hurry.

Probably the break that threw the District into its greatest tizzy came in the summer of 1944, when a nationally known radio announcer got on his nationally known network and told his listeners that the United States had a "Columbia University Project" which was experimenting with atomic energy, and, "If Germany knew what is now known here, she could still win the war." The commentator and his boss were hailed to Washington and dressed down, by order of General Marshall. "But no tongue-lashing could undo the broadcast," Colonel William Consodine, the District's public-relations chief, told me in Washington. "We just closed our eyes tight and waited for the deluge. I don't know," the Colonel said, shrugging. "That fellow's got a pretty high listener rating, but he doesn't seem to have many listeners. The backwash was practically nil."

Plenty of other matters kept the C.I.C. hustling. Several employees at the Oak Ridge project broke out in red rashes and, convinced that they had suffered burns from radioactivity, dropped their work and made for their home towns to see their own physicians. The physicians, of course, asked them what could have caused the rashes and the workers, in their panic, told everything. The C.I.C. men got busy and asked the doctors to be sure to regard what they had heard as a professional secret. Then they persuaded as many of the employees as they could to return to work, assuring them that the Oak Ridge hospital had several radiology experts on its staff. (The rashes turned out not to be serious.)

The clergy also contributed its share of trouble. During the spring of 1945, it seemed to the C.I.C. that every minister in the country had suddenly decided to consider the comparative might of the Lord and U-235. In New York a Lutheran pastor told his flock, "One of the developments in the field of science today is a new source of energy called U-235, but regardless of its power, it will never be powerful enough to comfort us in affliction or strengthen us in despair." The same reasonable sentiment was voiced from dozens of other pulpits, but the preacher who concerned the creeps most was one near Oak Ridge, whose parishioners included many plant workers. "You cannot see God," he told them one Sunday in an awesome voice, "and you cannot see atoms, but their power is energy." The minister had no idea that Oak Ridge was involved with atomic energy, but some of his hearers assumed that he knew what he was talking about and accepted his words as a tipoff. A C.I.C. officer immediately talked things over with the preacher and asked him to stay away from nuclear matters in the future. The minister said he would be glad to, although any fool knew that rockets, gas, and bacteriological weapons, not U-235, were being made at Oak Ridge.

In Chicago the Army once found itself locked in battle with the Anti-Vivisection Society. The District was buying up all the dogs in the Chicago pound and using them to discover if there were any radioactive rays or lethal gases in the armory laboratory its scientists were working in. The Anti-Vivisectionists had a measure passed by the City Council which required full reports on all dogs used for experimental purposes. The Army complied, but with a vagueness that attracted the suspicions of the Society. One of its ladies came around to the armory and said that she wanted to investigate the dogs' kennels to make sure they were clean. She was assured that they were and was also assured that she could not come inside and see for herself. A few days later she turned up again, disguised with sunglasses, and applied for a job in the laboratory, which she did not get.

Then there was a crop of rugged individualists to handle. A young New Yorker who knew nothing about science except what he had read in the popular-science magazines wrote to dozens of chemical supply houses asking for uranium, heavy water, and the loan of a cyclotron or two. "I am a Ph.D. and a Doctor of Philosophy," his letters began. Interrogated by the C.I.C., he said, "I think there's a great future in atomic energy and I want to be a pioneer." Another would-be pioneer was an Oklahoma oil man who was trying to buttonhole Conant, Dunning, Urey, or any other scientist who could give him the inside story on nuclear physics. The C.I.C. had a hard time coaxing him to give up his undertaking. "Damn it," he told his Army visitors, "those capsules are going to ruin the oil business and you're asking me to sit still." An optimistic Chicagoan advertised that he had discovered something that wasn't fuel, as we know it, but would drive an airplane at a speed of three thousand miles an hour with two hundred passengers aboard. He wanted backers. Two C.I.C. plainclothesmen went around to see him, representing themselves as patent attorneys passing through Chicago on their way to their homes on the West Coast. The man let out only a little of his secret. "In my plane," he said, "there's a hole in the front. Then there are two tanks, which I call Tank No. 1 and Tank No. 2. Well, the air keeps coming through that hole in the front and passes through the two tanks, and the plane goes like hell." At that point the man stopped his explanation. "I'll tell you some more," he said, "if you put up some cash." The two C.I.C. men said they were broke and the deal was off.

In the midst of all this intricate detective work, the C.I.C. was jolted one day shortly before Hiroshima was demolished when it learned from a project employee in Chicago that a friend of his had told him at dinner the previous evening that the Chicago laboratory was doing research on plutonium, a top secret at the time. Two C.I.C. agents hurried over to see the friend, who was startled at their interest. "Why, I was riding home on a trolley," he told them, "and I heard it from two passengers who were sitting near me. What's all the fuss?" Lieutenant

James Vaughan, who told me about this, trembles at the memory. "Just like that!" he said. "He heard about it on a trolley car. 'My God!' we thought to ourselves. 'On how many trolley cars in this country of ours are people talking about plutonium?' "

One of the last incidents to plague the creeps before the detonation of the bomb involved an elderly Chicago lady who phoned the Sixth Service Command to say she had some important and secret information she wanted to let the Army in on. She must have got an impressionable officer on the phone, for he went so far as to request an investigation by one of the District's agents—Herschel Oliff, to be specific. Oliff found the lady in an agitated condition and waited patiently for her to impart what was on her mind, which she finally did. She wanted a bodyguard, she told him, because she had had a dream the night before that was full of secret stuff. "I saw the invasion of America," she told Oliff. "I saw Japs and monkeys and the Statue of Liberty." Oliff politely declined an invitation to stay for tea and left. That was not the end, however. A relationship—at least in the lady's mind—had been established, and she kept calling Oliff about further dreams of high strategic matters. After a couple of weeks of this somnolent intelligence work, the old lady phoned to say she'd had the dream of dreams. Oliff dutifully went around to see her and, to his astonishment, learned that the lady *had* had the dream of dreams. She had dreamed that the way to topple Japan was to drop an atomic bomb. Oliff was puzzled as to how to handle the situation, but the old lady herself provided the solution. "Sir," she said sternly, "seal your lips. Tell no one about this, not even your superiors." Oliff swore he would not. "And, Madam," he replied, "you, too, must pledge yourself to secrecy." The two of them shook hands on it.

CHAPTER 2 | AUGUST, 1945

THE ATOMIC CITY

ONCE THE SECRET was out, back in the summer of 1945, the Army's Manhattan District, which was then still in charge of America's atomic project, permitted one of the sites—Oak Ridge, Tennessee—to be visited. That community was then less than three years old, but it already had a tradition: secretiveness. A stranger in town, like myself, casually mentioning U-235 or plutonium, was likely to receive a stare fit for an enemy agent. I got acquainted with one of the more persistent starers, a physicist, and, after pointing out that the atomic bomb had become a widely known matter, asked him to explain his suspicious looks. "Two years' worth of being told and warned and ordered not to talk about the project," he said. "I remember I was working the night shift August fifth and the next day a friend of mine woke me up with a phone call. 'President Truman says it's an atom,' he told me. I hung up quick. I thought my friend had cracked." The physicist giggled self-consciously. "I still don't see precisely how my job ties up with the bomb," he said, "and I don't really know much more than you do just from reading the papers. I wouldn't know what to say even if I did open my mouth, but I'm going around not talking."

The higher-ranking Army officers at Oak Ridge were cautious, too, but, being in positions of authority, they unbent to the point of reminiscing and imparting scattered, unrelated information. Unlike the science columnists, these officers said they hadn't any idea how close America's nuclear race with the Axis was, but they suspected that it got off to a later start than the Germans. The Manhattan District,

I was told, set up, in 1942, a long-range timetable for the production of the bomb, and kept so close to schedule that its horrible product was dropped practically on time; that is, only a few weeks late. Looking back on the project, the officers regarded it as quite a calculated risk, to use the Army term, and one hell of a nervous strain, to use plain English. In addition to the distracting knowledge that Goebbels wasn't necessarily just employing propaganda when he talked about a secret weapon, there were other worries. For one thing, the scientists weren't certain that they would be able to split atoms on a large enough scale to use in the war. However, at any given moment, a majority of the men in charge—the majority wasn't always the same men—had been in a sufficiently confident mood to keep things going full tilt. But their uncertainty dogged them right into 1945, when they were well over the hump and knew that they could soon turn out atomic bombs. "That was the period," an anonymous colonel recalled, "when we began to sweat out the idea that the Germans might develop a terrific short cut. Maybe, we thought, one of those Nazis would wake up one morning and produce U-235 or plutonium right in his bathtub." Even after the Germans, who seem to have worried the Army much more than the Japanese, surrendered, one fear remained. "Supposing," the colonel said, "we hadn't been able to make the bomb before the war ended. Why, we'd have been called a two-billion-dollar boondoggle."

It was still impossible to learn from the authorities how many bombs the District had manufactured or just how they were stored. However, the officers, in the summer of 1945, went so far as to say that the Manhattan District was still turning out U-235 and plutonium to make atomic bombs. Also, they disclosed that America was still trying to figure out whether U-235 or plutonium was the more effective, and a few of them ventured the guess that the final form atomic energy would take might be a blend of the two. Whatever the form, a certain amount of it would probably be available for limited public use, according to these cautious gentlemen, by 1960. There was no restriction, either, on the information that the entire processing, measured from the time the ore is dug out of the earth, takes a matter of many months. The preliminary refining of the ore, I was told, is done in various spots outside Oak Ridge, but well over half the processing goes on there. The Army, incidentally, was holding on to its accumulating store of uranium from which U-235 and plutonium had been extracted and was going to give the stuff a second going-over sometime in the future in an effort to determine possible additional uses. I was informed that after the uranium, which is brought into Oak Ridge in cardboard boxes and cylindrical metal containers, is refined, it is sent to New Mexico for what the Army calls the "utilization phase."

There were several plants in Oak Ridge, and they were widely separated. It took thirty-five miles of circuitous driving—a trip I made in the company of a civilian official and a young Tennessee country girl, who was our chauffeur—to see what they all looked like. The names of the plants sounded like the combination to a safe—X-10, Y-12, S-50, and K-25. All the plants except X-10, a plutonium research laboratory, performed the same function—extracting U-235 from U-238—but each unit had its own method. At S-50, what was termed a liquid thermal-diffusion process was employed. "Before Hiroshima," the official told me, "we called that place the Fox Farm—a cover term. A colonel by the name of Fox was in charge." At Y-12 an electro-magnetic process was applied, and at K-25—for all the difference it makes to a layman—the process was gaseous diffusion.

Each plant consisted of a number of buildings. K-25, while not the biggest plant, did include the biggest building in Oak Ridge. Twelve thousand employees worked in it day and night seven days a week. There were three shifts, starting at 7 A.M., 3 P.M., and 11 P.M. The night shift was on when we got there. A high ridge formed a backdrop for K-25, and beside the plant there was a small hill. We drove up the hill to look down at its immense, sprawling structure. The windows were brilliantly lighted by thousands of bulbs, and its white cement-asbestos exterior added to the brightness. I listened closely for any sounds, but I could hear nothing. I mentioned this to the official, and he said, "Oh, there's one floor where you can hear motors turning over if you're inside, but it's really a pretty quiet place. No big compressors stamping anything. Nice and clean, too. No grease to speak of. An awful lot of piping. Just miles of pipes. The equipment's like nothing you've ever seen. Right out of Rube Goldberg. Nothing standard about it one bit. Nothing like it ever built before."

"Who's in there?" I asked.

"Mechanics to keep equipment in condition," he said. "Electrical and chemical and other kinds of engineers. Foremen who ride bikes to get from one part of a floor to another to check operations. Fitters and men who bring in uranium to feed the apparatus. Girls out of college supervising girls out of high school who stand in front of a dial watching to see if a needle jumps from zero to ten. Ph.D.s who turn knobs."

We hung around a few minutes staring at the silent, glowing mass below us. "Doesn't anything come out of that place?" I asked the official after a while. "Man," he said pleasantly, "they're not making anything in there. They're just extracting." Several hundred lights suddenly and inexplicably illuminated a corner of the building that I hadn't noticed was dark. The girl chauffeur ah'd at that. "Bright lights," she said in her slow Southern voice. "Tennessee's got the bright lights now, just like Broadway."

To set in motion the mystifying manufacture of a mystifying product, the sudden town of Oak Ridge, population seventy-five thousand, came into being. It took up fifty-nine thousand acres of Roane and Anderson Counties and was completely fenced in. The plants were off by themselves, in doubly restricted zones, anywhere from three to eleven miles from the center of town, and away from residential districts. The houses were scattered, too, but at intervals there were clusters of shops, movie houses, and ice-cream parlors that the people in Oak Ridge liked to refer to as "neighborhoods." Villages disappeared to make way for Oak Ridge. Scarboro, Wheat, and Robertsville were the names of vanished places where the hill folk of this region went in for what amounted to non-profit farming —some tobacco planting, a couple of hogs, some poultry, perhaps a head or two of cattle, and a little moonshine-making. The Army forced them to sell their land, and they hated to do it. A small percentage of them took jobs with the project, but most of them migrated to new farms. However, the Army has let them return, whenever they wish, to visit their cemeteries. It was the second time

some of them had become displaced persons; they had been evicted from other sites several years ago by the T.V.A., when it bought up land not far from Oak Ridge. One tough old gentleman, whose farm was in a particularly remote corner of this great acreage, decided to stay where he was as long as he could. He managed to hide out on the Army's top-secret reservation for a full year before a Piper Cub pilot, on patrol duty, spotted him feeding his chickens.
responsible for the picking of this particular spot as the setting for

The natives of this Bible Belt country maintained that God was
the Army's diabolical factories. The Manhattan District, however, offered some man-made reasons. Electric power, which is used in large quantities, was supplied by T.V.A. The Clinch River, which skirts the area, provided water for the inhabitants of Oak Ridge. The land was low-priced, selling, on the average, at forty dollars an acre. Knoxville, only eighteen miles east, was considered an uncritical labor area by the War Manpower Commission and the Army figured it could hire a fair amount of civilian personnel there. Transportation facilities in Knoxville, both rail and air, were adequate for bringing in supplies. High ridges surrounding the plants made things hard for snoopers. Finally, the Luftwaffe would have had to penetrate well past the Atlantic coast to raid the plants.

The Army engineers and contractors arrived on the scene late in 1942 and went to work on the scrubby, unattractive, practically roadless terrain. Quail roamed the place then, and the guards picked off skunks with their rifles. The guards also had to shoo away curious people who turned up at the entrance gates. Among them was a bearded fellow, a religious fanatic, who said he understood that a Vatican was being built on the site. He told the guards he wanted to have a go at being the American Pope and asked them where to apply for the job. "Beat it," the guards told him. "We don't know what's getting built here." The old man couldn't be brushed off that easily. "Well," he asked the watchmen, "if you don't know what's being built, how do you know it isn't a Vatican?"

One of the things that complicated the project was that the Army frequently changed its plans. The first blueprints did not provide for the mammoth plants that have since been erected. As for housing, no more than three hundred dwellings were planned at the start, though eventually there were over fifteen thousand. "All we wanted to do," an Army lieutenant told me, "was take care of the longhairs. You can't expect a high-powered scientific joe like Dr. Compton to sleep with ants." The approach to atom-splitting was to try every conceivable method that might work, and to try it in a hurry. The scientists kept thinking up new ideas, with the result that Oak Ridge went through a series of expansions. The summer of 1944, when construction reached its peak, must have deeply impressed the children of Oak Ridge, for that Christmas they didn't ask for electric trains but wanted toy bulldozers and roadscrapers. A certain amount of building was still going on during my visit, but no one thought about it much; by then it was perfectly clear that another of those American construction feats that most of us have become tired of marveling at had been brought off. By the time the Japanese surrendered there were good roads, bus lines, taxicabs, and lots of neon lights in Oak Ridge. One could play pin ball, roller-skate in a rink, and watch night baseball games. According to a mimeographed Army handout, Oak Ridge had thirteen supermarkets, seven movie houses, and nine drugstores, and there was no reason to doubt that these counts were entirely accurate.

The dominant architectural note of the town was something that might be called Early Alphabetical Cemesto. Thousands of houses in Oak Ridge were of Cemesto Board, a trade name for a mixture of cement and asbestos rolled into sheets that can be thrown together in a great hurry. There were six types of Cemesto homes—"A-House," "B-House," and so on. "F-House," the largest of the models, had six rooms and rented for seventy-three dollars a month. Many people lived in prefabricated plywood houses (they were called "A-1," "B-1," and so on), and even more lived in trailers which the Army had scrounged from the T.V.A., the Federal Public Housing Authority, and other government agencies. Visitors permitted on the reservation, such as scientists and journalists, were put up at the Guest House, a rudimentary but comfortable enough hostelry. Most of the trade at the Guest House, where I stayed, seemed quite definitely to be scientists. I was addressed as Dr. Lang by the lady desk clerks as soon as I checked in. After I had been there a few days I asked one of them to forget the "Dr." She took to my suggestion at once. "O.K., Doc," she said.

The city, for all its newness, was fairly cosmopolitan in character. People with all sorts of backgrounds had come from every state to work for the Manhattan District. There were men in Oak Ridge who came from towns in which it was perfectly all right to hold crap games in the street, and they continued to roll the dice on the reservation, too, amazed that anyone should stop and stare at them. And there were fellows who had been boosters all their lives and had taken to boosting Oak Ridge. They attached small metal signs to their automobile license plates that said, "OAK RIDGE: THE ATOMIC CITY." A man named Bill Feldman organized a Junior Chamber of Commerce. "I want to see this town beautified," he told me. "I see the day when the Lions, the Elks, Rotary, and Kiwanis will be holding luncheons in Oak Ridge." There was also quite a concentration of Ph.D's, as well as other educated folk, who in their off hours played chamber music, studied foreign languages, and sat around their B-Houses discussing the more technical aspects of nuclear energy. These different groups kept pretty much to themselves, but their offspring were thrown together in school. There the children from rural districts blinked with bewilderment when precocious metropolitan brats, fresh from progressive education, told their teachers, "That's not the way we learned long division in Chicago."

The residents of Oak Ridge had no voting say about how their town was run. The Army ran it. That was not quite as bad as it might sound; the Army didn't want its civilian employees, who had been assembled with great difficulty, to pick up and return to the more comfortable communities from which they came, so its policy was one of considerable solicitude. The lieutenant colonel who administered the community, a pleasant, unwarlike individual, thought it was probably a simpler proposition to be mayor of an ordinary city. "Then," he said, "all you have to do, if you want to be re-elected, is to try and please fifty-one per cent of the people. But I have to worry about one hundred per cent. If somebody complains that her neighbor's dog barks too much, I have to go out and ask the dog to stop barking."

The Army probably didn't know it, but it was operating Oak Ridge on a downright radical principle. Only Manhattan District employees, and their families, were allowed to live in the area. Consequently, Oak Ridge was possibly the one American city in which there was full employment, a situation that should have brought a senatorial investigating committee charging down here. The Oak Ridge crime rate was one of the lowest in the country. There had been only three homicides since the project was started. There hadn't been one decent robbery, and what thieving went on involved shirts, cigarette lighters, and fountain pens. Needless to say, there were no panhandlers. Everybody had enough money to invest in a group medical plan, and it was excellently managed. For an annual forty-eight dollars, a worker and his family could count on thirty days' hospitalization, if necessary, and the worker himself could get medical treatment any time he felt like visiting his doctor. As a result, the population, despite the somewhat elementary nature of living conditions, was extraordinarily healthy. The Oak Ridge schoolteachers had had to work hard to get their educational system under way, but there was one thing they did not have to worry about. "This is the first place I've taught," a primary schoolteacher told me, "where I haven't had to handle relief cases—youngsters who have to be helped out financially to buy their books and pencils and lunches. You try to keep the other kids from finding out such matters, but they always do and then you have a problem on your hands to stop them from teasing their classmates who aren't well off. Conditions here make teaching a little easier."

Some of the residents who were up on their Lenin said that Oak Ridge was one of the better tries at a classless society. Both extreme wealth and poverty were non-existent. A number of construction workers lived in crowded trailer camps, but the issue was blurred because a good many of these workers were among the highest-paid men on the reservation. Certain members of the community had private incomes and were therefore better off than others, but money couldn't buy much in Oak Ridge. "Supposing you decide to splurge and get yourself a mansion to live in," an electrician transplanted from Chicago said to me. "So you look around and discover that an F-House is the best they've got in stock. And you can't get that unless you apply to the Housing Section and prove that you have a big enough family to fill up the rooms. And if you have, they tell you a lot of other people who can also afford seventy-three dollars a month are already in line in front of you."

Nobody, late in the summer of 1945, knew what lay ahead for Oak Ridge. The city was waiting to see what Congress decided. Some people, confident that the project would be made permanent, had started small flower gardens in front of their homes. Others, more dubious, had let the weeds grow tall. In the meantime, K-25 and the other plants continued to produce U-235 and to ship the stuff out to New Mexico to increase America's stockpile of atomic bombs, now that peace had come.

CHAPTER 3 | SEPTEMBER, 1945

CAREER AT Y-12

WHILE I WAS in Oak Ridge, I spent an evening at the house of one of the workers who was engaged in the world's newest and possibly last industry: atomic energy. This man, whom I will name Edward Jackson, told me about his career in what someone will inevitably call the atomic game, and also about the life he, his wife, and their infant son had been leading in the new town of Oak Ridge. Jackson was an inspector at a huge plant run under government contract by the Tennessee Eastman Corporation. In this plant, known to Oak Ridgers as Y-12, an electromagnetic separation process was used in the complex, precise production of U-235. Jackson examined certain incoming equipment to see whether it conformed to blueprint specifications. If he thought a piece was not up to standard, he listed the defects he had found, and the government rejected it. Frequently he disapproved equipment in which a single part was off by as little as one ten-thousandth of an inch, and occasionally the tolerance was even smaller. It was a responsible job. A favorable word from him on a defective piece of equipment could have slowed down the country's production of atomic bombs.

Jackson was a pudgy, black-haired man of thirty-five from near Pittsburgh. Before he came to Oak Ridge he had driven a truck for his father, who owned a fleet, and, after getting a ground instructor's license, had taught the students of a small Harrisburg technical school how to repair a plane's sheet-metal parts and read blueprints. His wife, Betty, and their baby were in the house the evening we talked, and I saw a good deal of them. It would have been hard not to. Like thousands of other Manhattan District workers, the Jacksons live in a prefabricated plywood house whose main feature is compactness. It is about the size of a caboose, I would say, but, because of a Venetian-blind arrangement in the middle of one room, the Jackson home is officially considered a three-room dwelling. Mrs. Jackson, a slender, pretty girl, is enthusiastic about it. We had scarcely been introduced before she showed me the numerous closets, contrivances that pulled out of the walls and from under window seats. "This house would be perfect to take along on a camping trip," she said. "It's what the Oak Ridge housing section calls an A-6 model," Jackson told me.

Jackson heard about the chances of getting a Manhattan District job in November, 1943, when he was teaching at the Harrisburg school. The school was about to close and the boss assembled his small faculty and, waving a bunch of application blanks, informed them that Tennessee Eastman was looking for men like them to work on an important project, about which he knew nothing. Most of the instructors didn't want to go South, but Jackson and another man stepped forward and took the forms. "I had another offer from some Miami outfit," Jackson said to me, "but a second iron in the fire couldn't hurt me. I couldn't afford to be out of work too long. Betty was in a family way." On Thanksgiving Day he got off a train in Knoxville to investigate Tennessee Eastman, at the company's invitation. He felt blue about being away from home on the holiday, and the sight of Knoxville's dreary railroad station didn't console him any. He was met by a company car and driven out to Oak Ridge, eighteen miles west, to be interviewed by a personnel man named Welch. "At the entrance gate," Jackson said, "guards searched us, checked the auto's pockets, and even lifted the hood, looking for weapons." Jackson did not penetrate deep into Oak Ridge. All he could see, on his way to the personnel office, was vast stretches of red clay being churned up by bulldozers making roads, and a few wooden buildings. When he got out of the car and stepped into a gooey mass of thick, red clay, he felt even more depressed. Welch told Jackson that he could get on the payroll at once but that he couldn't know what the project was. He said that the work would help shorten the war and that Jackson stood a chance of learning a lot about some rather revolutionary machinery. "I asked him," Jackson said, "if this job could lead to postwar opportunities. Welch just smiled and said he thought so."

Jackson said he'd think it over. He went back to Knoxville and phoned his wife that he hated Oak Ridge. "Then don't take the job," she said. He hopped a train to Miami to see about his other iron in the fire. That job, it developed, was a State Department project for sending American mechanics to Brazil to teach Brazilians how to repair planes. He called Betty again, and she said she wouldn't dream of going to Brazil. "Are you *sure* that Tennessee place isn't O.K.?" she asked her husband. "I was phoning her from a booth that looked out on the Florida beach," Jackson told me. "It was a beautiful day. Blue sky and the temperature just right, and people were parading by in orange-colored beach clothes. I forgot all about that mud in Oak Ridge. When Betty asked me that question, I took one more look at the Florida beach and told her, 'Oh, Betty, it's beautiful.' "

Jackson spent his first three days as a Tennessee Eastman employee getting settled in the drafty dormitory to which he had been assigned and being processed. He was given a medical examination, was photographed and fingerprinted, and had to fill out innumerable forms. "Eighteen feet of paper!" Jackson said. "Every time I poked my nose around a corner, somebody stuck something at me to sign. Had to tell them my jobs for the last ten years, where I'd been, if I'd ever done time, and promise that if I invented anything on the job the rights belonged to Tennessee Eastman."

On the fourth day, Jackson was told to report, along with a couple of hundred other newly recruited men and women employees, to a training school, where they were herded into a large, bare room, full of benches, known as the "bull pen." Jackson was sitting there, waiting, when a man called out his name and asked him to come to the front of the room. The man, who turned out to be the superintendent of the school, told Jackson that because of his teaching experience, he ought to be a good man to address the gathering. He briefed Jackson on what to say, and Jackson stood up before his fellow-novices. "I told them to keep their mouths shut about Oak

Ridge," he said, "or it might mean a ten-thousand-dollar fine or ten years in the cooler. I told them a lot of things like that. I started off rickety, but I warmed up as I went along, and by the time I finished I was pounding the table. I might have done even better if I'd known what I was talking about."

For the next couple of weeks, Jackson continued in his state of authoritative bewilderment. "I'd lecture five, six times a day," he said. "I was a professor of security. All kinds of people were joining the project—architects, electricians, chemists, and young kids who were college graduates. Illiterates, too. I know that, because everyone had to sign an attendance sheet and there'd always be a few who'd ask me to write their names down for them. I always gave the same lecture, and they were as bored as I was. We were all getting investigated and waiting to be cleared. That could take quite a while. Sometimes I'd be in the middle of my spiel when an M.P. would walk into the room, tap someone on the shoulder, and I'd have one less pupil. The same thing could have happened to me, but there I was, sounding off on security." The recruits for the school had come from all over the country. There was a group of girls just out of Grinnell College; construction men who had been working on the Alcan Highway; middle-aged women who had read ads declaring, "When You're a Grandmother You'll Brag About Having Worked at Tennessee Eastman." There was also a large group of men who had worked in a magnesium plant out in Las Vegas, Nevada. The plant had shut down and a Tennessee Eastman man had flown out there to tell them about Oak Ridge.

After some weeks of specializing in security, Jackson's horizon was broadened. He was asked to tell his classes about the bus lines that were now operating on the reservation and to do a bit of morale work by assuring his listeners that any inconveniences they were suffering from, particularly in housing, were temporary and that a little patience and fortitude were necessary. "That was a hell of a thing for me to be lecturing about," Jackson told me. "Betty was writing me every day from Harrisburg bawling me out for not getting us a place to live. I'd kick to Welch and he'd recite my own lecture back at me." Two months after Jackson's arrival at Oak Ridge, his housing problem was solved. He was shown a huge map on which hundreds of squares, each one representing a plot of land, were drawn in pencil, and told to pick out his home. Jackson pointed to one of the squares, more or less at random. "An excellent choice! That means you're going to live in East Village," a housing official told him. Jackson, curious about what he had put his finger on, drove out to East Village just in time to see his home being unloaded in sections from a truck that had hauled it from Indiana. With the help of a crane, a crew was lifting pieces of it from the truck and gently setting them down on wooden foundation blocks. "You're getting a furnished demountable," one of the crew said.

Jackson took a train to Harrisburg and drove back to Oak Ridge with his wife in their car. He spent much of the trip warning her not to be troubled by her first impressions. It was pouring when they arrived, and the clay quagmires were at their softest. The car got stuck in the mud just as they pulled up in front of their house. "This is it," Jackson said, and, lifting his wife out of her seat, he carried her over the mud and into the A-6. In mid-March, two months later, their child, a boy, was born, at the Oak Ridge hospital. "That makes him a hillbilly," Jackson said.

Shortly before Jackson got his house, he was at last cleared by Military Intelligence. He promptly informed the school superintendent that he wanted to work at Y-12 instead of hanging around a training school. "I told him," Jackson said, "that I was a first-class aircraft sheet-metal man and wanted to help make plane parts out at Y-12. That's what I thought they were making." The superintendent suggested patience and assigned Jackson to a new lecturing post—teaching people how to read blueprints. It wasn't until just before his child was born that Jackson got his break. A personnel man at the plant who had heard and liked his lectures asked him if he wanted to be a maintenance-and-operations engineer at Y-12. Jackson enthusiastically said yes, and the next day he was sent out to the plant.

His first job had to do with the converting of a small building that had been used for chemical work into what was called a product-control unit. "I was warned that it was a very secret building," he said. "I was given a special badge without which no employee could enter it, no matter how many other buildings he could get into. The badge had a letter and a number on it. The letter O.K.'d me for the building, and the number showed how much could be discussed with me. The numbers ran from one to five, five being for the top dogs. My number was only one, but just the same I got a kick out of having the badge." Jackson's job was to help with the installation and maintenance of fluorescent lighting and air-conditioning and to oversee the repainting. He was also to act occasionally as a liaison man for his supervisor, Dr. Angus Cameron, which meant that he would be able to get around to other units of Y-12. In addition, he would have the opportunity to become acquainted with some of the machinery being used.

"It made all the difference, being at Y-12," Jackson said. "There was real activity. The grounds covered twelve thousand acres, and construction gangs were busy putting up new units." The building to which he was assigned had glass-brick walls. "No machinery in the place," he said, "but there were a lot of dials and meters." The temperature was kept constant and the air-conditioning purified the atmosphere. As Jackson continued to work for Dr. Cameron, he discovered the reason for all these precautions. It was the existence, in a small room in the building, of a delicate instrument used to determine the quality of something extremely important (U-235, but he didn't know that then). Thus, there could be no machinery in the building, because its vibrations might affect the instrument. Dust in the air could also have thrown it off. The entire building was painted white and the workers wore white uniforms; only chemical workers were supposed to wear white uniforms, to distinguish them, for reasons of security, from other classes of workers, each of which wore uniforms of a different color, and Dr. Cameron's product-control section, though not strictly chemical, was considered to be under the chemical people. However, the white uniforms served a purpose. "The place reminded us of a hospital, and that sort of kept you on your toes. You worried that if you got careless you'd mess up the whiteness and maybe something would be hurt."

Jackson thought a lot about the mystery of the delicate instrument in the small room. "That was one piece of equipment I never got to know well," he said. "Dr. Cameron kept people away from it."

One day the air-conditioning inside the small room broke down, and Jackson fetched two repair men. The mechanics, who were dressed in blue uniforms, instantly caught Dr. Cameron's eye and he swooped down on them. They explained their mission, but Dr. Cameron wanted to know if they had to do their work inside the secret room. "Well, we can't fix it if you won't let us in," one of the maintenance men said. Dr. Cameron asked, "Can't you tell me what to do from outside?" They explained that would take a lot of his time. He finally let one man in the room for a few minutes a day until the air-conditioning was in shape again.

Everything about Y-12 was mysterious, Jackson said, but he found the place exhilarating rather than sinister. "So many screwy things went on," he said. "The workers in the building next to ours couldn't get into their place unless they had gas masks strapped to their sides. Sometimes a loud horn would go off, and that meant they were having a gas-alarm drill. They'd come hustling out with the masks pulled over their faces. There were chemical installations that smelled of ammonia and ether, and places where the employees got down on their knees every now and then to look for tiny bits of metal. In their hands they held Geiger counters, instruments that detect radioactive rays. Sometimes the counters would lead them to a tiny orange or black speck on someone's white uniform. The speck was very valuable. The uniforms of certain workers were always chemically treated before they were laundered or junked, to make sure that none of those precious bits would go down the drain.

"Then there was the huge main production plant," Jackson went on. "Anyone who could go on thinking about aircraft sheet metal after one look at the place was plain batty. There weren't any lathes or drills or presses. Just a mass of copper and stainless-steel pipes of the weirdest shapes you ever saw. It was an enormous building, with pipes all over the place. You'd see two of them running together for a stretch, but then they'd part company and go off to different ends of the building. And there were so many valves that the chains to operate them had to have different-colored tags on them so you could tell which valves they operated. The plant was very clean and quiet. All you could hear was the low sound of generators. The lights were on the end of long, thin poles that came down from the ceiling through spaces between the pipes. You couldn't have the lights in the ceiling, because the pipes were so closely packed that they'd have blocked illumination. Off this area were the control rooms. That's where you found the cubicle operators, young girls who sat on high stools in steel boxes about ten feet high, fifteen feet deep, and five feet wide, with switchboards full of dials and meters. Those dials and meters told us whether or not the separation process was operating smoothly. The girls didn't really understand the readings they made, but they knew that the meter needles had to respond a certain way, that certain red and green and yellow and orange lights had to flash, and that they had to hear certain clicking sounds. If any of those things didn't happen, they phoned their supervisor, who was an electrical engineer, and he'd take over in the cubicle then. He'd check everything to find out where the trouble was, and he wouldn't leave until it was cleared up. Then the girl would climb back onto her stool and go on with her day's work. I didn't know then and I don't know today what all those dials and meters were indicating, but, whatever it was, it must have been the payoff."

Naturally, Jackson said, all the secrecy made the workers do a lot of guessing about what was being produced at Y-12. "We knew it couldn't be very big," he said, "and we were also pretty sure it wasn't mouse traps." One rumor Jackson heard was that the Army was developing a new and revolutionary type of gasoline. A paint that would make planes invisible was another candidate. One of Jackson's friends, certain that the secret product was rocket fuel, showed him a magazine article which said that something called uranium could lend itself to such a purpose. Another notion was that the plants were working on a death ray. "For a while," Jackson told me, "I heard that nylon stockings were being manufactured. I think that one got started because there are a couple of hosiery mills in the vicinity." Some workers believed that the place was the start of a postwar project, and thought it was a shame that so much manpower and material should be expended on it then. A batch of gag guesses were in circulation, too—that the plant was making Roosevelt campaign buttons, face powder for Wacs, dehydrated water for overseas troops, and "the configulator." Jackson handed me a piece of tissue paper on which was typed, "Configlugator T-1 is the newest weapon ordnance has under consideration. Tactical uses are still secret, but it can be safely said the art of warfare will be revolutionized by it. Briefly and in non-technical language, Configlugator T-1 is a combination of totalizer wheels arranged to be propelled through multiple predetermined circumferential superpositions and an intrinsically heterogeneous precomputed taxonomy of abutments controlled by nonconsecutive monodromic sequences of denominational seriatim concatenation. . . . Aw nuts—let's give the damn thing to the Japs!"

Some workers couldn't take all the secrecy. "They wanted to know why they were showing up day in and day out at Y-12," Jackson said, "and they weren't supposed to know, so they quit." The problem never bothered him. To begin with, he was too busy. Then, too, he had always had a passion for machines. "Every time I'd learn something new about Y-12 equipment, I felt good," he said. " 'My God,' I'd tell myself, 'nobody in history has every worked on this equipment before, and here I am fooling around with it.' And then you got into a daily routine, seeing friends at night, picking up the groceries, and such stuff, and the secret product got to be like the question of salvation—you just didn't think about it. Once in a while I'd think maybe I was just wasting my time, but then it became a case of whether or not you had faith. I just couldn't believe the government was pouring all that dough into nothing."

After five months of working for Dr. Cameron, all the installations in this particular unit had been completed, and Jackson was given a choice of two new jobs. Dr. Cameron wanted Jackson to stay with the product-control unit, and he also was offered a chance to spend a couple of months at the Westinghouse factory in East Pittsburgh inspecting devices the company was making for Y-12. "I decided on the Westinghouse deal," Jackson said, somewhat hesitantly, "because I'd get to know more about the machinery." Mrs. Jackson, who had put her baby to sleep some time before and was now listening to us, laughed. "It was my fault," she said. "I got tired of the wooden walks they have here in Oak Ridge. I wanted to see solid sidewalks again. I felt homesick, too, and we've got people—Eddie's family—up near Westinghouse." "It doesn't matter whose fault it was," Jackson said. "It worked out fine." He explained that when they returned to Pennsylvania they realized, to their surprise, that they had become attached to Oak Ridge. Mrs. Jackson even found that she missed the wooden walks and her A-6.

At the Westinghouse plant, Jackson discovered that he was a celebrity to the workers. They asked him to tell them all about the Manhattan District, and they were impressed at the knowing way he inspected what they were making for the project. They said that after the war they wanted to visit the District's installations and find out how the parts they had been making were used. Jackson would smile cryptically and they would be even more impressed. "They sure made me feel as though I were on the inside," he said. "They'd give the parts they were making such names as bazooka, Mae West, bread pan, and sailboat. But I knew the code names and if they were made right for us and how they looked when they were assembled at Y-12." As for Mrs. Jackson, she found her old friends too commiserating. They kept feeling sorry for her because her house was so small and she didn't have a cellar. Finally, she told them off—said that her house saved steps and that the reason she didn't have a cellar was that it never got cold enough down there for people to need a furnace.

After the two months at Westinghouse were up, the Jacksons went back to Oak Ridge. That was in February, 1945. "When we got back," Jackson said, "we looked up all our friends. It was nice to listen again to the Tennesseeans talking in their funny way about that 'storm' of theirs. If one of them is talking, they say he's talking up a storm, or if he's working, he's working up a storm—always that storm. We went on our Sunday auto trips again, with the baby sleeping in a hammock in the back of the car, to the Great Smokies and to see the T.V.A. dams. Sometimes we'd drive down to Chattanooga to see Lookout Mountain. There was still plenty of mud in Oak Ridge, but I was glad to be back." On his return, Jackson was informed that he had been promoted to inspector of equipment, his present job. He liked the job better than his old one with Dr. Cameron because he had even more to do with equipment. The construction work had let up somewhat by then, he said, but the activity in Y-12 was as great as ever. "Everyone was used to his job now," Jackson said. "Employees were trained, assigned, transferred, fired, promoted, and went on two-week vacations." During the months just before Hiroshima was bombed, Y-12 was functioning as smoothly as if it had been going fifty years.

Jackson's own vacation began on August 4th, and that day he, his wife, and the baby started on a leisurely trip to visit Mrs. Jackson's relatives in a small Pennsylvania town near Altoona. Toward noon of August 6th, they were driving along, some thirty miles from his mother-in-law's house, when his wife casually turned on the radio. The big news was just being announced. "I got goose pimples," Jackson said. "I pushed the accelerator down to the floor and I didn't know I was doing sixty-five until Betty asked me where the fire was. She kept dialing all the stations. Every announcer was saying the same thing. After the sixth station, Betty said to me, 'So you were really doing something down there after all.' 'Some nylon stockings I made!' I told her."

When they reached their destination, they found Mrs. Jackson's mother, who had also heard the news, very nervous. "She didn't think that Oak Ridge should have been mentioned on the air," Jackson said. "She said Japanese spies would attack the place and kill Betty, the baby, and me." After his mother-in-law had been reassured, the reunion with family and friends became jolly. A young brother-in-law, home on furlough from Europe, shook Jackson's hand and said, "You saved me from going to Japan." Other relatives and neighbors congratulated Jackson not only for having worked on the bomb but also for having kept quiet all that time. Jackson insisted that he hadn't known what he was making, but everyone thought he was joking. Late that night, after everyone else had gone to bed, he got out an atlas in the living room and looked up Hiroshima. "It's thirty-four degrees latitude, one hundred and thirty-two degrees longitude, and three hundred and forty-three thousand Japs lived there," he told me.

The Jacksons started back to Oak Ridge next day. Jackson wanted to know what had happened in the town when the reason for its existence had at last been disclosed. Some people, particularly those in less responsible positions, had, it seemed, claimed that they had always known that U-235 was being made at Oak Ridge; the run on newspapers had been so big that copies had sold at a dollar apiece; inside the plant, workers had gathered in groups to discuss the news, but their now knowledgeable foremen had persuaded them back to their posts by saying, "Come on, let's break it up—uranium's running all over the floor." The next day the absentee rate was as low as usual. On the whole there had been no particularly spirited outbursts. When Nagasaki was bombed, Jackson and his friends were discouraged. "We began to wonder how many atomic bombs were going to have to be dropped," he said. But then, a few days later, the war ended. "Well, we *had* helped shorten the war, after all," Jackson said.

"Well," Jackson said, "that's the way it's been up to now. You haven't seen much excitement since you've been in Oak Ridge, have you? You're not going to, either. People have settled down here to live and work. It's a funny thing. In the old days they used to have a poster around here that said, 'YOU CAN LICK JAPAN!' Now they've got one that says, 'YOU HOLD THE KEY TO WORLD PEACE.' And we're working the same way with the new poster as we did with the old one. We show up at Y-12 on time, come home, keep a date, wonder if we're going to get a raise, or maybe hear a tip about a bigger house to move into. It's a business now, and I'm in it. I've forgotten all about going back to planes. I used to think they were the coming thing and how I'd open up a plane garage. But this thing I'm in now is basic. I'm in on the ground floor, and so far I've been doing all right."

CHAPTER 4 | JANUARY, 1946

A FINE MORAL POINT

UNLIKE JACKSON, Dr. Philip Morrison, a young physics professor who for three years was one of the key scientists at Los Alamos, the New Mexican center of weapon experimentation, knew right along the objective for which the secret project had been striving. Morrison also had a clearer idea of the results which had been achieved, because he was a member of America's first overseas mission to determine the effects of an atomic bomb—the bomb the Superfortress *Enola Gay* released over Hiroshima. Only twelve men made that trip, they didn't reach their destination until thirty-one days after the bomb had fallen, and they stayed there less than twenty-four hours. Most of the members of the mission didn't even start out as such when they left the United States. They were part of a group of physicists and radiologists who, when Hiroshima was attacked, happened to be stationed on Tinian, one of the islands in the Marianas, where they were supervising the assembling of atomic bombs. They felt sure that the bombs were going to shorten the war, but they believed that the end was a matter of months, not days. Indeed, they were all set to stay on Tinian until fall, when they expected to be relieved by another group of scientists. When Japan quit, eight days after the *Enola Gay*'s visitation, they were hastily mobilized and sent on their way under the leadership of Brigadier General Thomas F. Farrell, who, along with a few physicians, had himself been rather hastily mobilized in Washington by his boss, Major General Leslie R. Groves, the War Department's atom chief. Later on, missions sent to both Hiroshima and Nagasaki stayed longer and did more thorough investigating of the damage. This first group, however, was sent to make only a spot check.

The purpose of the mission was not wholly scientific. The Tokyo radio was claiming that Japanese relief workers who had entered Hiroshima some days after the bomb had been dropped on the city were dying mysteriously, the obvious implication being that the place was still contaminated by radioactivity. The War Department, however, contended that only a small percentage of Hiroshima's hundred and seventy-eight thousand casualties were the result of radioactivity and that any injuries caused by it must have been inflicted within a few seconds after the bomb burst, because the dangerous gamma rays released by the detonation of an atomic bomb soon lose their power unless the bomb is exploded too near the earth. Stories elaborating on the Japanese broadcasts were printed all over the world. One American scientist who had been associated with the Manhattan District expressed the opinion that for the next seventy years anyone who visited Hiroshima would in effect be committing suicide. There seemed to be a tendency in all this to question the humaneness of American methods of warfare, and the Army, sensitive to such criticism, felt called upon to prove as soon as possible that the new bombs were entitled to the same degree of respect accorded by the civilized world to rockets, mines, incendiaries, and sixteen-inch shells. As Dr. Morrison explained to me at dinner one evening, "A fine moral point was involved."

Morrison's trip to Hiroshima seems to have been an unusual mixture of tourism, scientific exploration, and public-relations work. He and twenty-five of his colleagues on Tinian learned about the mission shortly after the Japanese gave up. They were told that they, together with General Farrell and some other experts who were coming on from Washington, were going to Hiroshima. Actually, only twelve of the men reached their destination. "A snafu," Morrison said. "Most of the others were put on the wrong LSTs or found themselves sitting in some place like Zamboanga waiting for a naval port director to let them loose." The twelve who reached Japan arrived in Yokohama the day after MacArthur and followed him to Tokyo. What with one mixup and another, the trip had been a strenuous one, and they were pretty well bushed—all except General Farrell, who, realizing that the heat was on in Washington, was eager to shove right along to Hiroshima, four hundred and fifty miles to the southwest. "General Groves was sending him indignant cables," Morrison said. Farrell's zeal was not shared by MacArthur's headquarters, which told him that American occupation troops had not yet moved into Hiroshima and that the mission would have to wait until they got there, because the theater commander would be responsible for anything that might happen to the scientists while they were in Japan. Farrell replied that his mission ought to make sure the bombed area was safe before the troops moved in. Headquarters, however, couldn't see it that way, and during the delay which followed the members of the mission killed time as best they could.

"I ran into a Japanese scientist named Ryokichi Sagani one day and asked him around to dinner," Morrison told me. "We had K rations, for which he seemed grateful. He hadn't had any meat for fifteen months. Before the war, Sagani spent a year at the University of California, doing some research in nuclear physics, and two of my colleagues on Tinian—Luis Alvarez and Robert Serber—and I had met him there. As a matter of fact, we had tried to communicate with him while we were still on Tinian. When we finished tailoring the Nagasaki bomb there, we decided to send Sagani a note with it, hoping someone would find it and pass it along to him. 'Please make every effort to inform the Japanese government that this is an atomic bomb and that we have more,' we wrote, and signed it 'From Three Former Colleagues.' We addressed it to him and Scotch-taped it to an instrument box that was to be parachuted to the ground at the same time the bomb was dropped." The box contained a device designed to record the force of the bomb's explosion and the altitude at which the explosion took place, as well as an automatic radio to transmit this information to the plane that had dropped the bomb. "Well, Sagani and I talked physics a bit," Morrison went on, "and then he mentioned that the note had been found and that he had been questioned about it by officials of his government. He didn't ask me if I had been one of the authors, and I didn't tell him."

While the members of the mission were waiting around, Dr. Marcel Junod, the Swiss chief of the International Red Cross delegation in Japan, gave them some idea of the conditions they could expect in Hiroshima. "Junod," Morrison told me, "has a sober disposition, and with good reason. For eleven years he had been following all sorts of disasters for the Red Cross—Abyssinia, China, the Spanish Civil War, Poland, and Japan. Now he had an atomic disaster on his hands. It was something new for him, and he was up to his neck in it." Junod fixed things so the mission could look over a file the Japanese had compiled of affidavits made by people who had been in Hiroshima at the time of the explosion. "They were beautifully inscribed on rice paper," Morrison said. "Twenty affidavits with a string around them tied in an elegant bow. An interpreter translated them for us. We always had an interpreter with us." The delicate calligraphy on the sheets of rice paper seemed to indicate that no radioactivity had lingered in Hiroshima.

Through Dr. Junod, the members of the mission met Masao Tsuzuki, a professor of radiology at the University of Tokyo's medical school. "An urbane man of sixty-five," Morrison said. "Very dignified and with an air of gravity, but he could be biting. The first time he came to see us, he brought along his papers to establish his professional position. Among them was a thesis he had published in 1926 while he was doing research at the University of Pennsylvania. It was called 'Deaths Induced by Severe X-Ray Radiation in Laboratory Animals,' or some such, and it described in detail the hemorrhages, oozing of blood through the pores, and other disorders brought on by X-ray radiation. What Tsuzuki had described twenty years ago had now happened to his countrymen. When I handed the thesis back to him, he slapped me on the knee and said, 'Ah, but the *Americans*—they are wonderful. It has remained for them to conduct the *human* experiment.' "

After a week of finagling, General Farrell succeeded in moving his mission out of Tokyo by having its members appointed temporary International Red Cross representatives (who are evidently regarded in Army circles as more expendable than scientists) to accompany thirteen tons of medical supplies that were to be flown to Hiroshima in five C-47s. "Theoretical delivery boys we were," Morrison said, with a smile. "Clinching that deal was a moment of triumph for Farrell, but it was another kind of moment for me. It occurred to me that once we got beyond the protection of our troops, it would be logical for the Japanese to kill us, or at any rate lock us up, and that in either case they would probably steal some secret documents I had on me. So I carefully sealed them up and gave them to an enlisted man who'd been assigned to look after us while we were in Tokyo, with instructions about what to do with them if I didn't get back. Then I sat down and wrote my wife a letter in which I was deliberately cheerful. Just like in the movies. Then we got in those C-47s and took off."

The minute Morrison stepped out of his plane at the Iwi Kuni airport, twenty miles north of Hiroshima, he realized that his anxiety had been needless. Word that the Americans were coming had preceded them, and there, at the edge of the field, was a long table covered with a white cloth on which bottles of beer and pots of tea had been laid out. Seventy-five Japanese soldiers and naval cadets stood at attention on either side of the table, and in front of them was a Japanese colonel, who advanced and invited the visitors to sit down and refresh themselves. General Farrell was, however, in no mood for dillydallying, especially when he learned from an airport employee that a batch of American war correspondents, fresh from a look at Hiroshima, had taken off for Tokyo only a few minutes before in a B-17 put at their disposal by an enterprising Air Forces public-relations officer. What General Groves (two stars) would say when their stories appeared in the press back home while the War Department was still without its own first-hand information, General Farrell (one star) could painfully imagine. He brusquely declined the colonel's beer and tea and herded his party into a bus that the Red Cross had ordered to be ready at the field.

"Poor Farrell," Morrison said. "That bus made ten miles in something like four hours." Sitting beside the Japanese driver was a kind of co-pilot, an assistant whose job it was to fill the machine's makeshift halfgallon fuel tank with gasoline from a big jug, and since he naturally found it impossible to do this while the bus was in motion, it was necessary to make a dozen or so lengthy stops. The trip was further prolonged by a call that the driver decided must be paid on the Japanese commander of the Hiroshima military district. This involved a detour through a Japanese Army camp, where Morrison received further reassurance that he was not going to be killed. "We drove past thousands of soldiers who were cleaning their rifles and they hardly noticed us," he told me. "Things were going to be ironic, I could see." The commander, a sour-looking Bushido product whom they found in his headquarters, offered doleful and elaborate apologies for not personally guiding his visitors into Hiroshima. His excuse was that he didn't know the way very well because he had been assigned to this post only recently, his predecessor having been killed by the bomb. Farrell got his group moving again as quickly as he could, but the mission might as well have stayed around listening to more of the commander's apologies, for as soon as it had resumed its limping journey, the driver announced that, in view of the lateness of the hour and the lack of suitable billets in Hiroshima, the party would have to spend the night at Mia Jima, an island resort about a dozen miles from the city. He forthwith dumped the scientists at a pier, where a ferry picked them up and took them to the island.

"Mia Jima was simply sybaritic," Morrison said. "It was the place where couples used to go for their honeymoons—the Banff of Japan." The Americans were installed in bridal cottages in a cypress grove next to a brook. A hostess handed them white kimonos and directed them to a bathhouse, where attendants scrubbed their backs. They were then served a pretentious but not very good meal of soup, rice, fish, seaweed, gamy meat, and a bottle of Scotch. "The Scotch, I'm reasonably certain, was synthetic," Morrison told me. "The reason I think so is that the label said, 'Made in Japan.' "

When the scientists reached the mainland early the following morning, the bus was waiting to take them into Hiroshima. Morrison naturally looked forward to seeing what was left of the city, but he had an idea that he was going to find it anticlimactic. "For me," he said, "the first and main impact of Hiroshima's destruction had come the day before, when we were flying down there from Tokyo. First we flew over Nagoya, Osaka, and Kobe, which had been bombed in the conventional manner, and they looked checkered—patches of red rust where fire bombs had hit intermingled with the gray roofs and green vegetation of undamaged sections. Then we circled Hiroshima, and there was just one enormous, flat, rust-red scar, and no green or gray, because there were no roofs or vegetation left. I was pretty sure then that nothing I was going to see later would give me as much of a jolt. The rest would be just a matter of details." The bus was still eight miles from Hiroshima when the scientists began to notice that the roofs of some of the flimsier houses were missing. As they got nearer, roofless houses became more common. They entered Hiroshima by crossing the Otagawa River, which winds in and out of the city seven times, over a bridge whose heavy stone balustrades had been blown to pieces. Up to this point there had been vegetation along the road, but now the earth looked seared. Hiroshima is on a delta whose flatness accentuated the effect of the wholesale levelling of the buildings. It was raining. The bus passed several cyclists pedalling along determinedly, and at one point swung out to avoid a small queue in front of a soup kitchen. "What is there to say about damage?" Morrison asked rhetorically. "Perhaps the same dreadful feat could have been achieved by other means and we had simply used a labor-saving device. To an air-power enthusiast like Major de Seversky what I saw might have looked as though a thousand B-29s had hit the place. To me it looked as though a small atomic bomb had exploded."

Hiroshima's port facilities, three miles from the center of the city, were outside the bomb's range, and Morrison noticed that the cargo cranes were still standing. "But the *Enola Gay* sure got the target," he told me. "You mean," I asked, "that there was a specific target in Hiroshima? Precision atomic bombing?" "Certainly," he replied. "The Japanese Fifth Division, the so-called invincible masters of Singapore, were using the grounds of a castle in the city as their headquarters. They were planning the defense of Kyushu there. That was the official justification for the bombing."

The bus finally stopped in front of a sideless shed with a raised floor, a rough structure that had obviously been hurriedly thrown together but that looked remarkably sturdy compared to the ruins around it. Morrison gathered that it was a kind of official center for directing rescue and salvage work. The commander of the military district had managed to find his way to the town and was waiting in the shed for the mission, together with several other Japanese, including Professor Tsuzuki, the radiology professor whose remark about American experimental methods had impressed Morrison in Tokyo. The group had been assembled by the Red Cross, at the request of General Farrell, to tell the mission what had taken place in Hiroshima after the bomb exploded. The Americans sat down on a bench along one side of a plain wooden table, and the Japanese seated themselves on the other side. The commander started things off by gravely explaining that he had asked one of his aides, a young major, to tell the Americans the "facts of the disaster." "They always referred to it as 'the disaster,' "

Morrison said. "It made me feel as though I were a member of an earthquake commission."

The Japanese major stood up and told the mission that on August 6th, the day of the bombing, he had been in Tokyo, where he was attached to the General Staff. At seven-fifteen that morning, he said, the Japanese radar system picked up some approaching enemy aircraft, apparently bound for southern Honshu. Radio stations in various cities, including Hiroshima, were alerted and went off the air. By eight o'clock the radar operators had fixed the number of planes at no more than three, and their superiors concluded that the Americans were just doing a little reconnaissance. Accordingly, the alert was lifted and broadcasting resumed. Sixteen minutes later, the Hiroshima station went off the air again, and the Japanese Broadcasting Corporation's headquarters in Tokyo attempted to reach it by telephone to find out what was wrong, but got no response. Other means of communicating with Hiroshima were equally useless. The telegraph line had gone dead a little north of the city; the military in Tokyo tried repeatedly to get in touch with the Army's wireless station at Hiroshima but had no more luck than the civilians. Presently, railroad telegraphers at whistle stops a few miles out of Hiroshima began sending Tokyo frantic, incoherent messages about a tremendous explosion nearby. The General Staff was unable to understand how such a thing could have happened, since presumably only three American planes had come over, and even if a few bombs had been dropped, there was no store of munitions or other explosives near Hiroshima capable of producing a big blast.

The major was ordered to take off in a plane and find out what had happened. He was still a hundred miles from Hiroshima when he saw a thick, billowing cloud of smoke rising in the distance. He flew over the city in dazed bewilderment; below him there seemed to be "one great magnesium flare." The smoke made it impossible for him to get anywhere near the Fifth Division's airstrip, so he flew on to the Kure naval-base field, thirty miles south, where he found that the Navy people were still in the dark about what had happened. Sailors, they said, had been sent to Hiroshima, but a mass of fires had prevented them from entering it. Victims of the explosion had staggered out of the flames, their clothing ablaze, and told disjointed stories of a wind of incredible velocity that had blown through the streets. The Navy placed two thousand sailors under the major's command, and ten hours after the explosion he managed to get them into the city. In the next few days they repaired the railroad line and restored communications. The major also arranged for medical units to come into the city. When Japan surrendered, the major said, he had decided to stay on in Hiroshima, as he thought he could be more useful there than back at headquarters. He then thanked the Americans for listening, bowed stiffly, and sat down.

Next, Professor Tsuzuki got up and, after formally going through the business of reidentifying himself to the Americans, mentioned the heavy casualties. Not all of them, he thought, could be attributed to the explosion itself, the fires, or the falling buildings; some, he believed, were the result of radiation burns as well as what he called "unknown factors." Many of Tsuzuki's observations ended in discreet questions. For instance, he said that many residents of the city had detected a peculiar odor after the bomb exploded and a great number of the deaths had resulted from respiratory trouble, which made him wonder whether, just possibly, poison gases had been released. General Farrell, alarmed at the implications of such a suggestion, authorized one of his scientists to give Tsuzuki enough of an idea about the bomb so that he could see for himself that gas was out of the question. Finally, Tsuzuki asked if Hiroshima was safe to live in. The Americans answered that they wouldn't know for certain until they'd checked up, but that if they hadn't thought so, they wouldn't have risked coming there to discuss the point. Tsuzuki, looking relieved, bowed and sat down.

After hearing from a couple more of the Japanese, the members of the mission, with Farrell snapping at their heels, put in an active morning. The sixty per cent of the city that was destroyed by the bomb was a circular area about two and a half miles in diameter. Standing at its approximate center, the scientists split it up into segments and then each began working his way toward the circumference along a different route, toting Geiger counters and Lauritzen electroscopes, instruments used for detecting radioactivity. Each was accompanied by an interpreter, a guide, and a policeman.

Morrison's route led him out toward a cemetery. A number of the pedestrians he encountered on the way appeared to have been burned only superficially, and in an odd way. "Their faces looked all red and sunburned, only unevenly so," he said. "One cheek might be burned but not the other, depending on which way they'd been facing when the bomb went off." The Hiroshimians showed no interest at seeing an Occidental walking their streets. Morrison, through his interpreter, talked with several of them. Each was convinced that the bomb had scored a direct hit on his home. One man said that the atomic bomb was more humane than fire bombs because it usually destroyed whole families instead of leaving some members alive. "I didn't dare ask him what had happened to *his* family," Morrison told me. Another native thought that the atomic bomb had made it possible for the Japanese to surrender with honor. A third, an architect, who was apparently capable of a detached attitude, said that the bomb had simplified this planet's future, though in what way he didn't explain. The most frequent question the townspeople asked the visitors was whether Hiroshima would be safe to live in if it were rebuilt. "The Japanese were very worried about that problem because their country doesn't have many good sites for cities," Morrison said. "Japan has a long range of mountains close to its west coast, with only occasionally a flat coastal plain like the one Hiroshima was built on. Nobody knew who would do the rebuilding, if there was any. Perhaps a whole new set of people from some other city."

On the way out to the cemetery, Morrison passed the wreckage of the castle which had been the Fifth Division's headquarters. The four thousand soldiers there had been killed. Morrison's guide lamented the destruction of the castle, part of which had been used as a military museum, where some souvenirs of an ancient victory had been preserved. The loss of these treasures distressed the guide. So did the fact that a tree planted by Hirohito's father had been burned black and leafless. Some water lilies in the moat of the castle had turned black, too, the guide added, but he was happy to say that they had begun to grow again. "I wanted to make sure of that," Morrison said, "and I asked him to show me the lilies. They were growing, all right." From a mound beside the moat, Morrison was able to get a good view of the city. "It was the magnitude of the damage that was so appalling," he said. "For a moment, I felt the same sense of shock I'd felt the day before, when I got my first glimpse of the place from the plane. Then I looked at the ruins of the castle, and I could see, here and there, a burned body, or maybe a hearthstone or a dish. Most of us who hadn't dropped out of this atom project during the last two or three years had developed our own private justifications for staying with it. I know I had done so. They helped me in Hiroshima."

The members of the mission met for lunch at the Police Prefecture, a practically undamaged concrete building a mile and a half from the center of the blast area. Morrison spent most of the afternoon at the Red Cross Hospital, an earthquake-proof building constructed only ten years ago. Like the Chichibu Department Store, the Hypothec Bank, the Post Office, and other earthquake-proof buildings in Hiroshima, it was pretty badly battered. Most of its interior partitions had been crumpled by the explosion, but its walls and some of its flooring were still in place and there were still patients quartered there. Its skylight roof had, of course, been smashed, and rain was pouring in. Electrical and plumbing fixtures were broken. Floor tiles, flipped from the neat patterns they had formed in cement, were scattered all around. Heavy pieces of X-ray equipment had been ripped from their foundations and the steel sashes of casement windows had been wrenched this way and that. Morrison noticed that the crisscross pattern of one of these window sashes had been burned into the canvas back of a nearby deck chair. "A little blurred, but a good enough image," he told me, cryptically. "It was worth remembering."

One of the patients Morrison saw in the hospital was a man who had lost the hair on the forepart of his head. As soon as the alert had sounded on the day of the bombing, this man had gone down into a strongly built air-raid shelter some six hundred yards from the point above which the bomb subsequently exploded. He stayed there after everyone else left on hearing the premature all-clear signal, because he had formerly lived in a city that had been repeatedly bombed and he had developed an extremely cautious attitude toward B-29s. When he heard the *Enola Gay* approaching Hiroshima that morning, he crept to the entrance of the shelter and took a peek up at the sky. At that instant the bomb exploded and the blast tumbled him over backward into the empty shelter. At first he thought he was unharmed, but two weeks later he began to feel weak and his hair started to fall out. "Superficial radiation burns," Morrison said. "He was going to recover."

A doctor in the hospital told Morrison that an average of thirty people a day in Hiroshima were still dying of radiation injuries; how many of those who had left the city were dying, he naturally couldn't say. The doctor also told Morrison about Miss Naka, who was one of the bomb's most prominent victims. "She was the country's best-known dancer, its Martha Graham," Morrison explained to me. She had come to Hiroshima from Tokyo to visit the city's provincial museum, where some ancient costumes she was thinking of having copied for a ballet were on exhibition. When the bomb went off, Miss Naka was on the first floor of the museum, a concrete structure which, being on the fringe of the blasted area, pulled through all right. She thought she hadn't been injured and somehow made her way to a railroad station a short distance north of Hiroshima, where she took a train for Tokyo. She felt nauseated when she arrived in the capital, twenty-four hours later, but assumed that was because of the horrifying things she had seen. Ten days afterward, blood started oozing through the pores of her hands and feet. She died four days after that. "Respiratory failure was put down as the direct cause," Morrison said.

The scientists left Hiroshima late that afternoon and were taken back to their honeymoon island, where they spent the evening doing a good deal of talking. The doctors, in particular, seemed to have a lot to say. "I never can understand what doctors are talking about," said Morrison, the nuclear physicist. Almost everyone in the party had brought along prized bits of fogged X-ray film, or pieces of copper and glass, which he had picked up in the ruins and planned to analyze when he got to a laboratory. Morrison stayed up most of the night making entries in a notebook. "I guess my colleagues did, too," he said. The next morning the mission returned to Hiroshima to thank the Japanese who had helped them and to say good-by. After the amenities, the scientists piled into a truck that was to take them to the airport. As the truck got under way, some children ran after it, and the Americans tossed them candy. General Farrell was feeling better about things. A plane was waiting at the airport to take the mission to Tokyo to meet the press that afternoon. At last, he and his men would be able to assure the world that Hiroshima was free of radioactivity.

"Between us, we'd found a fair amount of data with which to answer those Japanese broadcasts," Morrison told me. When I asked him if he couldn't give me at least some idea of what had been found, he looked at me with surprise. "But I've already mentioned a couple of significant things," he said. I replied that I wasn't sure what they were. He sighed, and then, in a tone that implied he felt he was telling me the story all over again, he said, "You remember about the water lilies in the castle moat?" I nodded. "Well," he continued, "they wouldn't have been growing if any radioactive elements had remained in the target area. Then, there were those two thousand Japanese sailors who went into the city ten hours after the explosion. None of them suffered burns. Circumstantially, one could argue that the place must have been safe by that time. Besides, we had our electroscopes and Geiger counters; naturally, if they'd picked up signs of radioactivity, we'd have issued a warning.

"The thing we most wanted to know, though, was how high up the bomb was when it exploded. I'm not at liberty to tell you the exact altitude at which it was designed to burst, but from previous calculations we knew that if it went off at the point we wanted it to, the gamma rays would have become harmless within a few seconds after the explosion. On the other hand, if it had exploded nearer the ground, radioactivity would have remained in Hiroshima for a long time. The New Mexican bomb, for instance, exploded only a hundred feet up and radioactivity is still present there. Of course, the reports from the instrument box dropped from the *Enola Gay* indicated that the bomb had burst where we'd planned it to, but there was always the possibility that something had gone wrong with the gadget. So what counted most of all was that pattern of the casement window I saw scorched on the deck chair, or, rather, some other patterns like it. Mine wasn't particularly good, but my colleagues found others that were better, including an exceptionally clear one in the Post Office. All we had to do was figure the position and size of those casement-pattern burns in relation to the casements themselves and apply a little trigonometry and we were able to calculate the altitude at which the bomb exploded to within fifty feet." Morrison smiled, and I almost expected him to address me as "my dear Watson." Instead, he said quietly, "The bomb had burst at precisely the spot we wanted it to, high over Hiroshima. There had been a minimum of radioactivity in the city. And, as I was saying, that was what we had all been wanting to know."

The excitement of knowing that an atomic weapon existed had not quite worn off when the first efforts were made to come to terms with its magical power. Well before the American monopoly of nuclear arms ended, in 1949, scientists in the United States and elsewhere, most of whom had kept silence throughout the war, were warning that nature played no favorites with her revelations and that an international system for controlling the atom had better be devised. The American government, responding, deposed the military as titular overseer of the young phenomenon and formulated control plans, though it continued to assemble bombs in Los Alamos. The impression seemed to take hold that the new energy could be used for not only military but civilian purposes; some people even considered its might prodigious enough to ensure a lasting peace.

CHAPTER 5 | OCTOBER, 1946

THE UNSCIENTIFIC LOBBY

JUST ABOUT THE last thing the Manhattan District's scientists thought they were doing in the days when they were creating the atomic bomb was that they were also creating careers for themselves as Washington lobbyists. The fact is, however, that since the first atomic bomb exploded—at Alamogordo, New Mexico, on July 16, 1945—dozens of nuclear physicists have taken up lobbying for a cause that may be bigger than any other in the history of organized buttonholing. Compared to the activities of this lobby, the special pleading on Capitol Hill about such matters as silver, tidelands oil, and the revival of prohibition seems unimportant indeed. The aim of the scientists' lobby can be expressed more simply than the objectives of most lobbyists; it is, and this time literally, to save the world. Specifically, they want to prevent the outbreak of an atomic war. This would seem to call for professional lobbyists of the highest calibre, but the members of the scientists' lobby are men who could hardly be more callow in the art of exerting pressure. Most of them, before the success of their experiments with fissionable material, had never been in Washington. Many had been so preoccupied with their investigations of nature that they had never even taken time to vote. Scientists cannot, like other lobbyists, offer congressmen contributions for their next campaign, because they haven't the money. Nor can they promise large blocks of votes, since the only votes they control are their own (if they remember to cast them). Furthermore, they don't *want* to lobby. It takes them away from their laboratories, involves them in dealings with people who don't even know what a betatron is, and frequently entails making radio-network broadcasts on evenings when they would prefer to be home working on a paper for the smaller audience that subscribes to the *Physical Review*. Despite all this, the scientists haven't done too badly. For one thing, their arguments undeniably helped Congress make up its mind to pass the McMahon bill instead of the May-Johnson bill and thus place control of the development of atomic energy in civilian rather than military hands. When President Truman appointed the five-man, all-civilian Atomic Energy Commission, headed by David Lilienthal, the scientists had reason to congratulate themselves.

The lobby operates under the name of the Federation of American Scientists, whose headquarters are the upper floor of a two-story brick building at 1749 L Street, N.W., in Washington. The premises look neither elaborate nor picturesquely impoverished. There are four unpretentious offices and a windowless rear room, which, according to a standing joke among the scientists, is "where we keep our smashed atoms." The walls of the suite are bare and the furniture might belong to a small, struggling real-estate firm. A single shelf holds the library, which consists of three books—the *Congressional Directory, American Men of Science,* and a copy of the Smyth Report. The Federation has two girls to do its clerical work, and they are helped out evenings by volunteers. The Federation also has a press agent, Michael Amrine, a young man who used to be a newspaper reporter and who, like all his associates, is new to his job.

The day-to-day administrative work is handled by two scientists, both of whom are devoting themselves full-time to the job. One of them is William Higinbotham, the Federation's executive secretary, a short, frail bachelor of thirty-six. He is a physicist who worked at Los Alamos during most of the war as a specialist in electronics. The other is the Federation's secretary and treasurer, Joseph H. Rush, a shy, earnest Texan who spent two years at Oak Ridge as a physicist in the X-10 building, a laboratory for plutonium research. He has brought his wife and two children to Washington. Neither of the men has any idea when he will return to his profession. Rush has remarked that he wouldn't be surprised if he were mixed up with the scientists' lobby for the rest of his life. He did not mean by this that he necessarily expected to be active for many years. He is only thirty-five and comes of long-lived stock, but there is always the possibility, he feels, that the lobby, along with everything and everybody else, will be violently put out of business in the future unless it succeeds.

The Federation, which was set up on November 1, 1945, and was originally called the Federation of Atomic Scientists, now has twenty-five hundred members, eighty per cent of them under thirty-five and more than half of them Ph.D.s. Each pays annual dues of two dollars. Higinbotham, who has been on the job for two years, has yet to receive a salary check; his expenses are paid, but in a fairly spasmodic fashion. The Federation has passed up a number of opportunities for increasing its treasury's contents. Metro-Goldwyn-Mayer offered to pay the Federation five thousand dollars for the use of its name as "technical adviser" in the billing of *The Beginning of the End,* a film about the atomic bomb. M-G-M declined to give them the right to cut whatever they might consider silly out of the picture, and the scientists turned down the offer. On another occasion, a radio producer wanted to put on a program dealing with atomic energy. He was willing to let the scientists prepare the scripts themselves; his sole stipulation, and a rather vague one, was that it must be announced that the show was being presented by "exclusive" arrangement with the Federation. The deal would have meant a thousand dollars a week to the lobby, but it didn't go through because the scientists were suspicious of the word "exclusive." Amrine, who is more worldly than most of his twenty-five hundred employers, pleaded that the word implied no infringement on the organization's independence, but Higinbotham told him, "We'll give anybody any information gratis, but we won't do it exclusively." "You're splitting hairs," Amrine protested. "We'll split hairs to the last micron," Higinbotham replied.

The Federation's membership could undoubtedly be larger, but the organization is not especially interested in numbers; it wants only to serve as a rallying center for all scientists, members and non-members, who feel as it does—that 1) the bomb is a revolutionary weapon, 2) there is no defense against it, 3) the principles of its manufacture are already known to scientists of other nations, who will in time independently contrive a bomb, and therefore 4) some means of internationally controlling its manufacture must be devised.

Not all the Federation's members think alike on the details of what to do about the bomb, and the actions of the membership are not restricted by the directorate. During the Congressional debate on the May-Johnson bill, a measure that was fought by the Federation with as much savagery as a group of scientists can muster, one member of the organization, for convoluted reasons, chose to testify in favor of the measure. The Federation has never spoken sharply to this maverick for taking an independent stand. It does object, however, when a member, experiencing his first intimations of social consciousness after years of concentrating on ions and ohms, makes a speech on a major political theme, such as world government, and forgets to say that he is not speaking for the Federation. The Federation makes a point of being non-political. "Once we've said there's got to be control," Higinbotham has said, "we've said about all we've got any business to say. Just because we know a little physics doesn't make us statesmen—although it would be a good thing if schools would teach physics in such a way that people would get to know something more about the subject than just the fulcrum and the lever and the refraction of light. The Federation would break up if we went in for politics. We've got too many different opinions in stock, and there are some of us who don't have any. To hell with politics. The question is: Are you pro- or anti-suicide?"

The scientists' anxiety about the future is not a recent one. In January, 1939, three years before General Groves got his job, a small group of physicists at Columbia began to get somewhere with the basic principles involved in setting up an atomic chain reaction. They immediately realized that they had cause for soul-searching. They debated among themselves the possible long-range results of passing the information along to the government, with the recommendation that it be made the basis for a federal project, and finally decided that they had to do so, especially since there was definite evidence that the German military had ordered physicists to experiment with uranium. From time to time, after the Manhattan District was under way, scientists working on it drafted memoranda pointing out the awful potentialities of their work. They would hand these to their superiors and possibly feel a certain mental relief. A poll of more than a hundred and fifty of the project's scientists at the University of Chicago, taken shortly before the destruction of Hiroshima, revealed that over half of them favored "preliminary demonstration [of the bomb] on a military objective" and that about a third of them wanted "preliminary demonstration on an uninhabited locality"; only a small number voted for either "all-out use" or "no use under any conditions." Seven scientists at the university organized a Committee on Social and Political Implications, under the chairmanship of Professor James Franck, a Nobel Prize winner, and reported to the Secretary of War that using the bomb against the enemy would be not merely a matter of military strategy but a fateful political event. The report was sent nearly two months before the Hiroshima mission and five weeks before the trial explosion of the first atomic bomb. A short while later, sixty-four other scientists at the university sent a memorandum directly to President Truman endorsing the Franck report. Considering subsequent developments, it now seems that some sections of the report struck a rather prophetic note. It was stated, for example, that "the military advantages and the saving of American lives achieved by the sudden use of atomic bombs against Japan may be outweighed by the ensuing loss of confidence and by a wave of horror and repulsion sweeping over the rest of the world and perhaps even dividing public opinion at home. From this point of view, a demonstration of the new weapon might best be made, before the eyes of representatives of all the United Nations, on the desert or a barren island. The best possible atmosphere for the achievement of an international agreement could be achieved if America could say to the world, 'You see what sort of a weapon we had but did not use? We are ready to renounce its use in the future if other nations join us in this renunciation and agree to the establishment of an efficient international control.' "

By the time the public learned about the existence of the Manhattan District, the scientists were in a mood to shout out their long-suppressed opinions. There was plenty of incentive. Congress was expressing the view that the atomic bomb was not a revolutionary weapon, that it would be easy to work up a defense against it, that other nations didn't have the secret, and that no international control was needed. The mind of the general public was equally confused, if not dazed. (A Gallup poll has shown that seventy-five per cent of the public also think the formula for making the bomb ought to be kept a secret and that seventy-five per cent also think it cannot be kept a secret.) So the scientists, who had had three years to think things over and therefore knew where they stood, went to Washington and set up the Federation.

The Federation's first headquarters was on the fourth floor of a walk-up near the Statler Hotel in Washington and, like its present one, did not compare favorably with that, say, of the National Association of Manufacturers, a few blocks away. The rooms were poorly heated. The scientists sat around in their overcoats, shivering and wondering how a person goes about lobbying atomic bombs out of existence. Not many of them could afford to give their full time to the work, so they adopted a rotation system for maintaining the lobby and a method of financing themselves. Several scientists in various parts of the country would put in for a two weeks' leave from their jobs; if their requests were granted, their colleagues would take up a collection to pay for their railroad fare and other expenses. When the two weeks were up, the scientists on duty were replaced by another transient group, similarly financed. Sometimes a scientist, just off a train, would clamber up to headquarters, look around in bewilderment, and hesitantly tell a stenographer, "I'm Dr. So-and-So, from Columbia. What do I do?" The stenographer would yell into the next room, "Oh, Mr. Higinbotham! Fellow from New York is here. Got anything for him to do?" Higinbotham would shout back, "Tell him to go over to the Unitarian Church tonight. They want a speech." It was all fairly casual. Once, Higinbotham, seeing a stranger in the outer office, asked, "You from Oak Ridge?" "I'm the electrician. I got a repair call for here," the man said. To keep track of what was being accomplished, Higinbotham bought a bookkeeper's ledger, in which each of the scientists was to enter, day by day, what he had done in the way of lobbying. After twelve hours of legging it around the capital, one of them might scribble some such report as: "Saw my congressman. Nice fellow. Anxious to find out about nucleonics."

The scientists quickly discovered, to their embarrassment, that "atom" was a magic word in Washington and that they, the only ones who fully understood its meaning, were looked upon as glamour boys. Some people, dimly conscious of the fact that they were up against a new kind of problem, regarded them as the men who knew all the answers. Others considered them heroes for having shortened the war with Japan. A group of physicists occupying a box during a forum on atomic energy in Constitution Hall learned, just in time to duck, of a plan to turn the auditorium's spotlight on them. For a while, the scientists were given a whirl by the capital's celebrity-conscious hostesses, but that didn't work out very successfully. At one large dinner party, a lady who had been placed next to Dr. Leo Szilard, one of the pioneers in the development of atomic energy, heard her hostess, across the table, discussing the atomic bomb and cattily whispered to Dr. Szilard, "In our set, you're a *bore* if you talk about the bomb." At another gathering, a young matron, assuming that, because of the literary inclinations of the hostess, everybody present was an author, asked Dr. John Simpson, of the University of Chicago, what he had written. " 'Reduction of the Natural Insensitive Time of Geiger-Muller Counters,' " Simpson replied.

The green lobbyists gradually began to accomplish things. People who knew their way around the capital and understood what the scientists were trying to do came to see them. Raymond Swing, Richard Lee Strout of the *Christian Science Monitor,* and Alfred Friendly of the Washington *Post* gave publicity to their campaign and introduced them to legislators. Another of their allies was a brooding, high-strung Washington lawyer, who, although he has a profound dislike of scientists in general, has worked as hard for the Federation as anyone. "Those wonderful scientists!" he said bitterly to a friend the other afternoon. "First they make the damn bomb, and then they come here yelling, 'Control! Control!' " "But," his friend said, "the scientists don't like making weapons any more than an infantryman likes a slit trench. There was a war on." "Sure, sure," the lawyer said. "The scientists stand for virtue and I'm on their side, but I wish I could wave a wand and swap the last ten centuries of medical advances for the undoing of the invention of the bomb. What if we don't get control and a war breaks out in twenty-five years? What's going to happen to you and me and my five-year-old boy? What's the human race going to look like for generations afterward?"

A more cheerful champion of the lobby is Father Edward A. Conway, a Jesuit priest who is secretary of the Catholic Association for International Peace, a Washington organization. On his own initiative, he has raised considerable sums of money for the Federation. He sometimes quotes an invocation from the Litany of the Saints which he believes is especially applicable to the atom bomb; it begins, *"A flagello terrae motus, Liberamos, Domine."* He does not think it unnatural that a man of the cloth should be working closely with men of science. He considers their invention modern and materialistic to a frightful degree, but he interprets their determination to control it as a sign that they are finally being stirred by the age-old desire for peace.

"They have added a new argument for the abolition of war," Father Conway said not long ago. "The moralists have argued against it for centuries, but their words have fallen on deaf ears. In the past, scientists have simply discovered the secrets of nature and then washed their hands of them. Now they have discovered something so horrible that they realize they must act. By a different approach, they have come to the same conclusion as we—that the world must change in such a way that there will be no more war. We welcome the graphic, concrete evidence they provide. I recognize worthy allies when I see them."

The amateur lobbyists, coached by these and other new friends, had to be persuaded to forget the traditional distaste of scientists for anything resembling personal publicity. When Dr. Szilard was asked to write an article for *Collier's,* setting forth the Federation's aims, he exclaimed, "I have seen a copy of that magazine! It had monkeys on the cover!" The scientists' principal handicap, however, was their intransigent attitude, an attitude which had an occupational origin. They were accustomed to objectivity. An experiment worked or it didn't, data were correct or incorrect; there was no middle ground. They found it difficult to adjust themselves to the give-and-take way of getting things done in Washington, and they were unable to understand why everybody couldn't see at once how right they were. "Remember," Strout, the *Monitor* man, told them, "the average politician is a baby kisser, a cracker-barrel fellow. You men may know how to play with oscilloscope tubes, but he's better at small talk. We have a system in this country whereby the most intelligent people don't necessarily come to Congress, and even if some of them do, they don't inevitably become chairmen of committees. Russia and the cost of living are big enough problems. Now you fellows come along with the biggest, most complicated problem of all. I'm not so sure Congress—or, for that matter, man—is civilized enough to solve it. So be patient, will you?" Father Conway feels that the scientists' refusal to compromise is of great importance. "People," he says, "will grow more jittery as time passes. Others may be moved to console and lull them, but the scientists never will. We need such implacable realists."

The Federation's friends arranged quite a number of meetings, usually in someone's home, at which a few members and two or three congressmen could get together informally, and the scientists soon realized the value of Strout's counsel of patience. A Southern congressman, upon being introduced to two of the physicists, said, "My fellow-Americans, I have *always* been a friend of atomic energy." "Why don't you fellows go back to your lab and get up a bigger bomb instead of hanging around Washington?" another legislator asked. One evening, after a long and pleasant meal with a senator from the Middle West, three scientists went to work on him, trying to make him realize what would happen to the world in a war fought with atomic energy. The senator sat silent and comfortable in a Morris chair while the three men piled up the ghastly details. "I'm sure," he said genially, when they had finished, "that you boys will find some way to solve the problem." A few nights later, a chemist, discussing the same problem with an elderly congressman, pointed out that, for all anybody knew, the civilized world might be living out its last twenty-five years. "Young man," the congressman said, "that is not a very good argument to use with a man of my age. I am nearly eighty, and twenty-five years from now seems a long time off to me."

One evening, Rush, the Federation's treasurer, gave a lecture on the bomb at a meeting of a group of Republican congressmen in the Army and Navy Club. When he finished, he announced that he would be glad to answer any questions. "Dr. Rush," one of the congressmen began, "do you really believe the bomb is as dangerous as—" At that instant, a car outside in the street backfired violently. Everybody jumped and then smiled in embarrassment. "That fellow never did finish asking his question," Rush said.

The Federation's desire to see atomic energy in civilian hands arose from its conviction that no army, the American or any other, could be expected to work out a system for international supervision of nuclear weapons, and that military men almost certainly would not do much toward the development of peaceful uses for the newly released force. They felt that an army, being an agency for waging war, would naturally and properly concentrate on the improvement of atomic weapons. In America's case, this would have made other nations skeptical of its proposals to set up an international control system. The Federation further contended that scientific progress required freedom of research—freedom for scientists to exchange ideas, to study the results of their colleagues' experiments, and to consult one another.

They had, they said, been hampered by the Army's insistence on "compartmentalization of information," which meant that each scientist was supposed to know only enough to perform a specific job. This system, the Federation held, made for duplication, waste of time, and even physical danger. There was the "critical size" case. U-235 becomes so radioactive if more than a certain amount of it—the critical size—accumulates in one pile that it can kill people in the vicinity and that it also soon becomes useless. Yet there was a time when only a few men working on the project, at Los Alamos and the University of Chicago, knew what that critical size was. Meanwhile, Oak Ridge was producing and storing the stuff. A Los Alamos scientist, visiting Oak Ridge on some unrelated errand, inadvertently discovered that the whole installation was heading for trouble. Possibly violating Army rules, he let his colleagues in on the secret. As for duplication of effort, the scientists cite the time a large group of physicists at the University of California worked for two months on a problem that had already been solved elsewhere. Members of the atom lobby insisted that they were fully aware of the importance of security; scientists, they pointed out, were working on the bomb before there was any District, and kept it a secret for three years. "No general," Dr. Harold Urey, a Nobel Prize winner, has said, "ever invented a weapon, and that goes for the bow and arrow."

These were among the points the Federation people made in testifying against the military control bill at sessions of the Senate and House Special Committees on Atomic Energy. The legislators knew no more about nuclear physics than the scientists did about politics, but both groups tried to adopt a sympathetic attitude toward the other's specialty. There was naturally some irritation on both sides, however. The scientists felt that they were being put in the position of Galileo when he was called upon to account to the Pope for saying that the earth rotated. The legislators, in turn, weren't sure just what the lobbyists' game was. The scientists clearly had no profit motive, but neither did they sound like damn-fool idealists. They seemed to be in favor of self-preservation, a proposition so utterly banal as to arouse suspicion. Then, too, these people who had helped finish off Japan were so unimpressive; many of them were very young and most of them were disturbingly informal. One congressman told a colleague that he was willing to bet that none of them had ever met a payroll.

There were moments when the scientists were inclined to feel that more order was to be found in nature than in Congress. They were startled, for example, when, after a European scientist with a consonant-laden name had been called to the stand at one of the hearings, Senator Hickenlooper of Iowa inquired, "Aren't there any scientists with good, plain names?" They were surprised, too, to find that the nation's representatives were not averse to plugs. A Colorado legislator, eager to publicize lead, one of the important natural resources of his state, asked a testifying physicist what material provided proper protection against radioactivity. The physicist shrugged and said he supposed thick concrete would do. Well, then, the Coloradan pursued, what about those tanks that had been sent into the desert at Alamogordo after the explosion of the trial bomb? How had their drivers been protected against radioactivity? "With lead linings," said the physicist, and the congressman beamed.

The scientists had not anticipated that that doughty American character, the Western prospector, would be brought into the atomic-energy controversy, but he was. During a debate on the Senate floor, Senator O'Mahoney of Wyoming, apparently fearing that Manhattan District employees with "inside information" would stake out claims to uranium deposits to the disadvantage of other prospectors in his state, arose and, addressing the Senate chairman, declared, "Mr. President, I will say . . . that in the history of the development of the West, many a claim jumper paid for taking advantage of inside information by dangling at the end of a rope or standing before a pistol in the hands of an outraged principal."

The Federation's activities are not restricted to Washington. It carries on a nationwide educational campaign, in an effort to make the public understand the problems that have been created by the bomb. The scientists have learned that it is not easy to sell people on the idea of longevity. An experiment conducted by Federation members in conjunction with the University of Kansas indicated that a person of rather more than average intelligence must concentrate for six hours on the fundamentals of the atomic problem in order to understand them sufficiently to be able to pass them along to someone else. It might take a lot less than six hours, the scientists feel, if people only knew modern physics. "Oh," Higinbotham said the other day, "if we could just tell a congressman or anyone else, 'You realize, old man, that the change in the binding energy between initial and final configuration amounts to .1 per cent of the mass of each atom, which, according to Einstein's MC^2, gives 10^{-3} times 235, the uranium mass number, times 1.6 times 10^{-24} grams per mass unit times 10^{21}.' The congressman would figure a moment and then he'd say, 'Hmm, let's see—that equals four times 10^{-4} ergs, or two hundred million electron volts, per atom. My God! That's 10^8 orders of magnitude greater than chemical energy!' "

Spreading the news of the change in the binding energy is being done in a variety of ways. Mass meetings are held in auditoriums, and they are likely to be well attended if some good-looking film star, co-operating with the Federation, shares the speakers' platform with the lugubrious scientists. Copies of a short play called *Pilot Lights of the Apocalypse,* by Dr. Louis Ridenour, a University of Pennsylvania physicist, are being sent to anyone who wants them, and the sketch is occasionally presented, usually in university towns by casts of faculty members. (The action takes place some years after all the industrial nations have mastered the production and use of atomic power; several jittery countries, mistaking a widespread earthquake for an atomic-bomb attack, resort to push buttons to destroy one another in round-robin fashion.) Then, too, on the sixteenth of every month, the mayors of American cities whose population is approximately that of either Nagasaki or Hiroshima are likely to get off to a depressing start because their morning mail includes an envelope from the Federation containing a piece of fused, glass-like sand from the Alamogordo desert, a photograph of the damage done at Nagasaki, or some such reminder, as well as a letter that, if it were mailed November 16, 1946, might read, "This morning, at 5:30 A.M., it was exactly sixteen months since the first atomic bomb explosion at Alamogordo, N.M., plunged mankind without warning into the Atomic Age. . . . Sixteen months are gone. The bomb will not wait sixteen years."

In the course of their educational campaign, the scientists have found that only one tactic is dependable—the preaching of doom. "We have turned ourselves into twenty-five hundred Jeremiahs," Dr. Albert Cahn, of the University of Chicago, has often remarked. "It doesn't matter who it is. You have to go way back to the beginning every time and explain what a menace atomic energy is. You have to shake them by the shoulders." Any deviations from this method, the scientists have found, are met with yawns. A few months ago, three of the physicists were invited to address a group of fifty radio executives, announcers, and writers who were gathered at the Waldorf to discuss how their industry could help make the public more conscious of the dangers of atomic energy. Since the scientists would be educating men who had themselves chosen to be educators, they decided not to use a dramatic approach. Instead, in a straightforward manner, they spoke dispassionately, if polysyllabically, of the uses, already realized and potential, to which atomic energy can be put and of its possible effects upon military strategy. When they had finished, one of their listeners, a man who has had years of experience in public relations, took them aside and told them in a friendly way, "Gentlemen, you talked over our heads. You didn't talk low enough."

Looking back over its brief existence, the Federation of American Scientists feels that its most important accomplishment so far was helping to bring about the passage of the McMahon bill. They know, however, that this is a victory of only limited importance. The Federation's main concern is now to back up those who are working for an effective system for international control. One way of doing this is by familiarizing people with the principles of the Acheson-Lilienthal Report. The achievement of international control might be brought about much sooner, the Federation suspects, if there were Federations in the Soviet Union and other countries as well as here.

Federation members feel that, despite their efforts, the country as a whole—or, for that matter, the world—has not yet really begun to grasp what lies ahead if no control is set up. Many people have made a mental adjustment to the idea of the atomic bomb and its threat of sudden, terrible death by simply refusing to think about it. If a control system is set up, the scientists agree, these people will have saved a lot of wear on their nerves. However, for each day without such a system, more people will become frightened. "Without control," Rush predicts, "the tension will mount and mount until at last one day, nobody knows when, the news will be announced that another country also has atomic bombs. That may not mean the end of the world, but when that day comes, I rather imagine you'll get a pretty good picture of how people will behave just before the world *does* come to an end."

CHAPTER 6 | AUGUST, 1946

SEVEN MEN ON A PROBLEM

THE ACHESON-LILIENTHAL Report, whose principles the Federation sought to familiarize the public with, was devised by a group of seven men who made a strong bid for an endurance record of a very special sort when they spent two months, last winter, talking about nothing but atomic energy and how to control it. Five of the men comprised the Board of Consultants that was appointed in January, 1946, by a State Department committee headed by former Under Secretary of State Dean Acheson; the sixth man was secretary to the board and the seventh was a representative of the State Department.

At the time the board was appointed, the United Nations Assembly was considering a proposal that an international atomic-energy commission be formed, but no action had been taken. The State Department, however, presumed, rightly, that the problem was so important that the Assembly would not long delay approval of the idea. Accordingly, it decided to institute an American study of the project for worldwide atomic control, so that when an international commission was set up and ready to consider the matter, the American representative on it would have a sound course of procedure to offer the representatives of other nations. It was to make this study that the Board of Consultants was appointed, and the result of the study is the Acheson-Lilienthal Report. The study was a peculiar one, because the consultants had little idea of where to start and were even more uncertain about where they might be going. All they knew, these seven men of whose deliberations most people in the world were not even aware, was that they were supposed to produce, out of their collective minds, a way for the nations of the world to get along together without the dread of being blown up at any moment. To be sure, the board had certain incontrovertible facts at its disposal—technical ones established by the Manhattan District, for example—but essentially it was concerned with an era still in the future and about which no one, not even General Groves, knew much. The board counted its accomplishments not in terms of statistical tables, as many government boards do, but in terms of new concepts or new ideas. These did not come easy. The consultants talked atomic energy in offices, in Pullman compartments, and aloft in an Army plane. Sometimes they deliberated for as long as eighteen hours in a day. They ate and slept and wrangled late at night in places that weren't home to any of them, and then, as soon as they rose in the morning, they would meet again at the breakfast table and resume their marathon discussion. Despite this constant living with a baffling and elusive problem, the seven men not only evolved the idea of the International Atomic Development Authority, which Bernard Baruch, as the American delegate to the United Nations Atomic Energy Commission, later passed on to that body, but were even able to include in their report as positive and heartening a statement as this: "We have concluded our deliberations on this most difficult problem not in a spirit of hopelessness and despair, but with a measure of confidence."

The report's recommendations were unanimously agreed to by the consultants, and this surprised them, because their backgrounds are so varied that irreconcilable differences seemed almost inevitable. One of the five members was Chester Barnard, the president of the New Jersey Bell Telephone Company, a bald, cautious man who, at fifty-nine, was the oldest of them all. Another was Harry Winne, a vice-president of the General Electric Corporation. Then there was Dr. J. Robert Oppenheimer, the distinguished physicist who directed the Manhattan District's work at Los Alamos. The fourth member was a first-class chemist by the name of Charles Thomas, who, being a vice-president of the huge Monsanto Chemical Company, is, like Barnard and Winne, a businessman; like Oppenheimer, he had done some work for the Manhattan District, but at Oak Ridge. The board's chairman was David Lilienthal, who, as director of the Tennessee Valley Authority, is condemned as a radical by his enemies and praised as an advanced social planner by his admirers. The other men in the group were Carroll Wilson, who was secretary of the board, and Herbert S. Marks, a government lawyer of high repute and then assistant to Under Secretary Acheson. Although not officially members of the board, both Wilson and Marks took as much part in the two months' cross-country *Klatsch* as any of the other men.

In Washington, I looked up Marks, a short, black-haired, and congenial man, in his office at the State Department and learned from him, in a general way, how the report was put together. The first of the group's dozens of meetings was held on January 23, 1946, in Washington, on the top floor of the American Trucking Associations Building, in what had been the headquarters of the Office of Scientific Research and Development. "An impressive, oak-paneled room," Marks said. "Not really the best spot for us to get started in. We felt pretentious enough as it was. We'd just come from the State Department, where Mr. Acheson had given us a pep talk on how important it was to make some headway with the atomic problem, and here we were sitting around a table, presumably about to solve it. In a way, we felt sort of silly, but on the other hand we realized that somebody somewhere had to tackle it and we seemed to have been picked." Marks told me that he sensed a definite attitude of reserve at that first meeting. "I'm sure that Winne and Lilienthal didn't think of each other as kindred spirits right off," he said. "As for what the others thought of Oppenheimer, a theoretical physicist who picked up Sanskrit at the age of thirty—undoubtedly a queer duck." The board didn't keep minutes nor did it ever indulge in a discussion of what was procedural or substantive. The men received no salaries for the work they had undertaken. "They'd all temporarily quit their regular jobs," Marks went on, "although they called Winne an unemployed executive because a General Electric strike was on at the time. Maybe the strike could be considered labor's contribution to the Acheson-Lilienthal Report."

The board quickly came to a somewhat novel decision—to get the facts about atomic energy and not just argue over points of view—and to that end the non-scientific members were given an informal course in nuclear physics by Professor Oppenheimer, obviously an experienced hand. "We had a blackboard on that top floor," Marks said, "and Oppie, with chalk and pointer, would lecture away to us about U-235 and U-238 and U-239, and something called 'denaturing,' and the characteristics of this and that, and why uranium and thorium ores are the only raw materials out of which atomic products can be made." "Are they?" I asked. Marks replied, in a deliberately flat tone, as though he were reciting from the catechism: "Only in reactions of very light nuclei, and in reactions of the very heaviest, has there ever been, to the best of our knowledge, any large-scale release of atomic energy." He smiled. "That's one of the things I'll never forget, Oppie repeated it so often," he said. "Anyway, only the heaviest nuclei will maintain a chain reaction and of the elements containing the heaviest nuclei, uranium and thorium are the only ones of practical significance." Sometimes, Marks told me, after a lecture that was supposed to make this point abundantly clear, one of Oppenheimer's lay students would discourage the Professor by asking some such question as "Since this is all a matter of turning mass into energy, why can't clay be used just as well as uranium and thorium?" The Professor would smile gamely and repeat a good part of the lecture he had just finished.

Most of the time, however, the consultants discussed what to do about atomic energy. "Our ideas were the same ideas the public was talking over," Marks said. "Just because we'd been appointed by the State Department didn't make us any more ingenious than the well-known man in the street." Among the possibilities which the board considered in the course of its gropings, Marks mentioned these: Let's keep the secret. Let's give away the secret. Is there a secret? Let's discuss only peaceful uses with other countries. Let's concentrate on the destructive uses. Let's outlaw the bomb and other atomic weapons.

A suggestion frequently considered at those early sessions was to let nature take its course—that is, to do nothing for the moment but watch international developments. "I think that at first we were subconsciously inclined to shy away from specific ideas as much as possible," Marks said. "The problem was too vast. We needed a little time to get the feel of it." Lilienthal always let out a yelp when someone advanced the watch-and-wait proposal. "He had a newspaper clipping," Marks said, "that he'd wave at us. It was the text of the joint declaration by Attlee, Truman and Mackenzie King in November, 1945, in favor of international control. Dave would hold this up in the air and tell us, 'Gentlemen, maybe if you were President of the United States you might have decided differently, but the man who *is* President has committed us to international control, so let's quit considering something our government is opposed to.' "

During the first week or so, the members were in session eighteen hours a day. "Discussions and lectures, lectures and discussions," Marks said. "We'd send out for sandwiches, and we smoked too much." The conference room got to be quite a mess, but none of the men in it would have become aware of it if it hadn't been for a cleaning woman who persistently tried to get in and was just as persistently shooed away. After a week of frustration, she became vociferous in her demands that she be allowed to do her duty, and one of the men told her that important work was in progress in the room and that it contained secret papers. The cleaning woman was not impressed. "Important?" she said scornfully. "Secret? Why, *I've* cleaned up after Roosevelt and Churchill!"

At the end of ten days of Oppenheimer lectures, the consultants came to New York to listen, in an office in the Woolworth Building, to the reports of several scientists who had been appointed by the Army to a unit called the Technical Committee on Inspection and Control. These scientists had worked for the Manhattan District on various phases of nuclear research, and the Army, temporarily abandoning its policy of "compartmentalization of information," had recently brought them together to pool their knowledge in an effort to determine whether control of atomic energy could be achieved solely by inspecting plants engaged in developing it.

At that time, this method of control was widely regarded as a likely way out. This didn't surprise Marks. "After Hiroshima," he told me, "the public wanted to believe that some form of control was possible, and it simply adopted the first reasonable-sounding notion that was circulated." The Technical Committee's scientists, too, judging by their reports, seemed confident that plant inspection would do the trick. Lilienthal's group, however, came away with the impression that while plant inspection was all right, it was hardly enough to guarantee safety. "The more we listened," Marks said, "the more convinced we became that something might go wrong with the system at least part of the time, and that that, in the case of atomic weapons, would be too often."

The consultants had a variety of reasons for being skeptical about the effectiveness of plant inspection. To begin with, many of the steps involved in developing atomic energy for peaceful purposes are the same as those required to make atomic explosives. Thus, Marks pointed out to me, although an international group of inspectors might systematically check on a nation's atomic plants, the possibility of quickly converting those plants to the production of bombs would remain—"even," as Marks gently put it, "if that nation promised not to make any bombs."

Furthermore, Marks went on, the inspectors might not fully understand what they were inspecting. The members of the Technical Committee apparently assumed that the atom-splitting factories of the future would be like those of the Manhattan District, whereas in such a new and incredibly complex field, it is very likely that the factories will differ radically, in both design and operation. Then, too, said Marks, a couple of what he called human factors were worth considering. Inspectors working in countries in which they were strangers might easily be given the run-around or, in conscientiously trying to do a good job, they might cause international incidents by poking into places where they had no right to be and violating the privacy of citizens who had nothing to do with atomic energy. Moreover, some inspectors might not be particularly interested in doing a good job and might feel not the least insulted if they were offered bribes by representatives of the country in which they happened to be. Still another difficulty was that a large number of inspectors would be needed. According to the Technical Committee, Marks said, it would take three hundred inspectors to keep tabs on just one of the diffusion plants at Oak Ridge. "The inspectors would have to be scientists who knew their field so well that no one could pull a fast one on them," he said. "You can't find men of that calibre wholesale, and when you do find the right man, you've got to give him more of an incentive than that of merely becoming a cop." Little as the consultants thought of the inspection idea as the whole answer, the New York trip did yield one positive result. "We discovered," Marks said, "that we'd learned enough physics from Oppie to know what the Technical Committee was talking about."

Back once more in the Trucking Associations Building, the consultants were subjected to further education. This time it was talks on geology. Their instructors, experts working with the Army, were so dry and matter-of-fact that Marks found their delivery almost as remarkable as the information they supplied. "They droned on and on unemphatically," he said. "I wondered if they knew how important the things they were saying were. They told us, in their precise way, where the earth's crust happened to be embedded with uranium and thorium —of the deposits in Colorado, in Africa, Czechoslovakia, and the Arctic. We heard about 'igneous situations' and 'asphalts of low concentration' that contain bomb ores. I got the willies listening to them. So did the others. Here was this stuff lying about in widely scattered regions of the world, exposed to the same pressures and rivalries that have developed over oil, which is a valuable commodity, too, but hardly in the same class with uranium. I could easily imagine interested powers buying up bush-league parliaments or engineering rebellions in strategic areas in the name of 'freedom.' In short, the old-fashioned imperialist methods would be applied to something that was more revolutionary than most premiers would ever comprehend."

Gradually, though, as the discussions and lectures went on, the board's problem began to seem less staggering. "We could see boundaries to it at last," Marks said. "First, we had learned that atomic energy can be produced from only two ores. Next, the geologists had been of the opinion that rich deposits of the necessary ores were to be found only in certain specific but infrequent types of geological formations." It became clear to the board that if atomic resources were to be controlled, certain well-defined areas of the world would have to be watched intently but that vast portions of it could be disregarded. Lilienthal had stopped waving his clipping; ever since the geology lessons the men had been thinking internationally and they were beginning to reach conclusions. Plant inspection, they had decided, was not the whole answer to the problem; every step in the production of atomic energy would have to be under some sort of supervision. The consultants were also unanimous in the belief that no effective system of control could rely on good faith alone, since there was no way of telling what was going on in a man's mind while he was digging pitchblende, or processing it, or using it for a chain reaction. "You just couldn't afford to hope to guess right every time about people's motives," Marks said.

The consultants were about to try to work out a feasible plan when a fortunate misunderstanding arose between Lilienthal and Winne. One day, Lilienthal, in the course of opening a meeting with a chairmanlike preamble, told the board, "We must never forget the destructive force of atomic weapons." Winne seemed annoyed at the remark. "If all we're interested in," he said sharply, "is the destructive side of atomic energy, then this isn't the job for me." He subsided when it was quickly pointed out to him that Lilienthal hadn't said that the destructive force of the atom was their *only* concern, but his reaction to the remark prompted Oppenheimer to air an idea which Marks said he imagined the man had been brooding over in New Mexico for the past three years. Oppenheimer told his colleagues that the beneficial aspects of atomic energy were of interest not only to State Department consultants but to a great many scientists who had long been itching to get on with this phase of nuclear research. He said that encouraging scientists to go ahead and look for possible constructive uses for atomic energy—a cure for cancer, a source of power for industry, and so on—was the best and perhaps the only way to induce them to further explore the possibilities of atomic weapons.

"More research for atomic weapons?" I asked. "What for?"

Oppenheimer's involved but sound point, Marks replied, was that if some system of international control were figured out, the scientists co-operating with it would be expected to know more about atomic weapons than anyone else, including, say, an unprincipled scientist who might prefer to play along with some would-be world conqueror. Oppenheimer's idea was that the results of controlled research on nuclear weapons would be shared by scientists of many countries. Only one, maybe two, bombs would be in existence (not enough for any country to win a war with), and only scientists working for the international-control system would have access to them. "Oppie's plan," Marks said, "would set scientists up as social policemen, but in a way that would make it possible for them to do the job with enthusiasm and also to use their maximum intelligence, which, for scientists, happens to be an attraction. Nice thinker. Anyway, his idea is in the plan we finally came up with."

Once the points raised by Lilienthal and Winne had been intricately straightened out by Oppenheimer in this way, the committee went on with its attempt to evolve a plan. Naturally, Marks said, there were a good many false starts before they hit on the course that was finally adopted, but, as it happened, it wasn't very long in coming. "Charlie Thomas was the one who mentioned it first," Marks said, "but somebody else would have if *he* hadn't. After the things we'd learned and talked about, it was logical." What Thomas proposed was the internationalization of all thorium and uranium mines, and this idea eventually came to exert considerable influence in shaping the Baruch concept of an International Atomic Development Authority, which has occupied so much of the attention of the United Nations Atomic Energy Commission.

"Only something as drastic as the atomic bomb," Marks said, "could have got Thomas to suggest that the mines be internationalized. Don't forget that he's the vice-president of a hundred-and-twenty-million-dollar firm. Charlie hemmed and hawed plenty before he finally began with, 'Now, I'm just a chemist and I'm thinking out loud, but if we had an international corporation—I like that word—which would control the mines, and not have any individual nation in charge . . .' " Oppenheimer, who had been thinking about atomic energy longer than the others, was immediately in favor of the idea, but some of his colleagues had reservations. Lilienthal, for instance, thought it might lead to overcentralization. "Dave hates setups that are too big with the same passion that Brandeis, whom he idolized, did," Marks said. He added that he thought the two strictly businessmen on the board—Winne and Barnard—feared that if they agreed to the idea, they might be doing future industrialists out of the chance to participate in the potentially great commercial development of the future—the exploitation of the uses of atomic energy. "Luckily," Marks went on, "uranium and thorium have had a limited commercial value in the past so far as the vested interests are concerned—just some radium and pottery dye have been coming out of them, a bit of photographic material, and stuff to make gas mantles." The broad fear shared by Winne, Barnard, Thomas, and Lilienthal was that by recommending an international monopoly they might be helping to create a Frankensteinian bureaucracy which, once it got going, would threaten the country's civil liberties as well as its economic system. "But the stakes," Marks said, "were too high for those men not to overcome the fear eventually. They knew that we would have to pay a price for security."

It took the consultants some time to accept Thomas's unappetizing suggestion. Debates on the subject were prolonged and wearing. One morning a consultant might wake up and feel favorable toward the idea, but by afternoon he'd be opposed to it. Lilienthal, a conscientious chairman, was determined to hold the board together. Painstakingly, he explained to the men, "We don't all have to agree. Our report's just going to be a letter to a guy named Fred or something, in which we try to tell him a couple of things we've found out about atomic energy. So we'll just begin by saying, 'Dear Fred . . .' " The consultants, however, became increasingly edgy and Fred had to wait a long time for his letter. Lilienthal called a recess of five days, but when the consultants reconvened, their nerves were still just as taut. The chairman tried another idea. He told the men that it would probably do them all good to get out into the field and that he was going to arrange for them to inspect the Manhattan District's plants at Oak Ridge and Los Alamos. "It was just a matter of psychology," Marks said. "Sometimes you know you're right, but it takes a little time to believe it."

The therapeutic tour got off to a good start. The consultants began their trip by train, and en route to the station they bought a half-dozen bottles of whisky. Most of it was drunk that night on the way to Knoxville, and the atmosphere grew friendlier. The next day, when the train pulled into Knoxville, some of the consultants were quite hung over, a condition which was not relieved by the energetic reception the Army had prepared for them. Four Army sedans, with two-way radios and manned by chauffeurs and radio operators, were on hand to transport them to Oak Ridge, eighteen miles away. During the half-hour trip, the radio operators kept in constant touch with the station at Oak Ridge, reporting every detail of the journey's progress.

At Oak Ridge, the party was taken on a de-luxe tour of the reservation, which meant traveling over much of its fifty-nine thousand acres and visiting its four plants. This excursion was not especially interesting to the scientific members of the board. Thomas, who had visited Oak Ridge many times, begged off, saying that he ought to check up on some matters in the laboratories there, but Oppenheimer, although he, too, was well acquainted with the factories, dutifully tagged along with the laymen. Marks found the visit enlightening. He was amazed by the vastness and complexity of the plants and by the extraordinary nature of the machinery, which included pipes twisted into fantastic shapes, hundreds of electric bulbs blinking red and green and clicking all the while, and scores of dial meters, huge and mysterious. In one of the factories, the consultants were asked to strip down to their underwear and put on specially treated overalls, elbow-length gloves, high boots, and oxygen masks.

In the course of the visit, Marks was curiously stirred by a remark made by a colonel who was conducting the men through one of the plants. When the party reached a point from which a considerable quantity of weird machinery could be seen, the colonel made a sweeping gesture and announced proudly, "No other country on God's earth could turn out that equipment. We've got nothing to worry about." "A nice fellow," Marks said to me, "but it never occurred to him that maybe no other country would *want* to make machinery that complicated, that some other country might make simpler equipment that could do the same work." Marks shook his head slowly. "First," he said, "the complexity of the plants struck me, and then this colonel came along praising that complexity and made me realize that things might become much more simplified in the future. Sounds paradoxical, but it wasn't. It's just that the field's so young that big changes are bound to occur. I knew for certain then that our board had done the right thing in deciding that no phase of atomic production should be left uncontrolled."

The men spent a pleasant evening at Lilienthal's Tennessee home in the T.V.A. town of Norris, a few miles from Oak Ridge, and then, early the following morning, took off by plane for Los Alamos. "The plane of the Army's atom king himself, General Groves," Marks told me amiably. The flight started out uneventfully. Oppenheimer went to sleep, Thomas read, Winne wrote in a notebook, Lilienthal sat musing, and Barnard, making his first flight, grimly abstained from looking out the window. Then, three hours out of Knoxville, Lilienthal suddenly sprang up. He woke Oppenheimer up, told Winne to put away his notebook, called to Thomas, and bustled about enough to make Barnard forget about the plane's altitude. Lilienthal then led his four co-members into a small room in the plane that General Groves was accustomed to use for conferences while flying. Marks and Wilson weren't called in on this huddle, but Lilienthal explained to Marks later what had struck him. "Dave told me," Marks said, "that he'd finally figured out how denatured materials tied in with our work. Of course, Oppenheimer, and Thomas, too, for that matter, had told us about denaturants back in Washington, but it evidently took a little time for us nonscientists to digest it."

Marks gave me a few pointers about denaturing. Both U-235 and plutonium, the end products of thorium and uranium, can be denatured; that is, so treated as to lessen their effectiveness for the manufacture of atomic weapons for quite a period of time. The process doesn't impair the elements' usefulness for biological and chemical research and other peaceful applications of atomic energy. "Dave likes to compare denaturants to the cut alcohol bootleggers used to peddle back in prohibition days," Marks said with a smile. "A drink of straight alcohol would blow your top off, but cut, it would just give you a lift."

During the aerial conclave, Lilienthal said that denaturing would help curb the mushrooming of an international bureaucracy, the sore point over which the board had all but broken up in Washington. Strict supervision would be exercised over materials that had not been denatured, but more moderate controls would be adequate for those that had been. "In effect," Marks said, "if a man was engaged in safe activities, he would be subject to limited supervision. But if, no matter on what good excuse, he was working along dangerous lines, he would have to be watched twenty-four hours a day."

I asked Marks whether the denaturants couldn't be removed from the atomic elements, and he replied that they could. For this reason, he was convinced that a system of control which relied solely on denaturing would be as risky as one which relied solely on plant inspection, but he pointed out that denaturing was only one of the safeguards which the board was proposing. He went on to say, though, that the removal of denaturants is so involved an operation that if anyone undertook the task, it would be difficult for the most casual inspector not to notice that something was up. "Supposing," he said, "denatured material had been allocated to a plant which is located in Ruritania, and the Ruritanian Pooh-Bah decides to welsh on the Atomic Development Authority by removing the denaturants. The Authority's representatives, made up of people of many nationalities, are on the watch for just such a move and try to check on the plant. So the Pooh-Bah sends soldiers to get the Authority people out of the way and seize the factory. Assuming that the Pooh-Bah has the scientists to work for him, it will still take him in the neighborhood of a year to turn out a bomb. While he's at it, the member countries of the Authority, having received no satisfactory answer to what's become of their inspectors, go to war with Ruritania. Since the Authority scientists would have seen to it that there weren't enough atom bombs in the world to win a war, the attack on Ruritania would have to be along conventional lines. Naturally, the atomic plant would be the first target for the attacking planes."

Soon after the group landed at Los Alamos, Lilienthal knew that his efforts to restore friendly feelings were producing results. The day they arrived happened to be Thomas's birthday, and without any prodding from their chairman, the consultants decided to throw a party at Fuller Lodge, the local hotel. During the party, Barnard, the most reserved member of the board, started calling his colleagues by their first names. "The last man to unbend," Marks said. On the following day, the group began an inspection of the Los Alamos reservation. The New Mexican plants were interesting enough to

Marks, but he found the town of Los Alamos even more so. "It had the same feel to it as a college town," he said. "Wherever you looked, you saw someone you felt you could sit down and discuss some serious matter intelligently with."

One of the Los Alamos scientists showed the group through his laboratory. He was a young, quiet-spoken physicist who, three months later, suffered fatal radioactive burns in the same laboratory. To Marks, he appeared quite unlike the colonel who had conducted the consultants through the plant at Oak Ridge. "He didn't seem particularly proud of atomic bombs—America's or any other country's," Marks said. "He just explained things to us. Behind him were the same dials and the red and green bulbs going on and off with the funny clicking sounds. It was not a noisy place and we could hear him easily as he went on talking to us. After a while, the whole business began to seem outlandish to me—I mean the idea of this shy physicist standing there and telling us about the facts of death in this horrible factory that had been built in the beautiful mesa country." Marks hesitated a moment. "I could see then," he said, "that Oppie had been right when he told us that these scientific men would have to be given constructive things to do or they wouldn't be much good."

Many people would regard the last place the consultants saw as the most important spot in the world today—a vault used to store some of the so-called end product of nuclear fission, the stuff out of which the bomb is made. It is, Marks told me, one of the most carefully guarded and least-frequented vaults ever built. He said that he couldn't tell me where it is and that even if he were permitted to tell me much about it, he wouldn't really be able to think of a great deal to say. "It wasn't a large place," he said, "and it wasn't a spectacular one. I looked around me and there were the same materials, colors, textures, and fabrics you might see in any warehouse. I saw the receptacles that contained the labor of God knows how many men, the cargoes of thousands of freight cars, the mental triumphs of gifted scientists born in a dozen countries. The receptacles were small, and I thought to myself, hell, I could walk out of here with one of them in my pocket. Not that I could have. Too many soldiers outside and inside the vault were watching us closely—tough troops who looked as though they kept their rifles cleaned. And supposing I had got away with one, what could I, an ordinary layman, have done with it? In a way, the same was true of so much of the whole Manhattan District. It bore no relation to the industrial or social life of the country; it was a separate state, with its own airplanes and its own factories and its thousands of secrets. It had a peculiar sovereignty, one that could bring about the end, peacefully or violently, of all other sovereignties." The consultants were solemn when they left the vault. "We'd always assumed," Marks said, "that there were places where the stuff was kept, but now, having seen one with our own eyes, we were shocked."

The board returned to Washington and buckled down to writing its report. None of the men, according to Marks, pretended to believe that the report would answer all the questions. "Judging by the newspapers," he said, "they certainly weren't mistaken on that score." The members did believe, however, that the points they were making would have to become part of whatever United Nations control system was eventually agreed upon if that system were to succeed. The men worked smoothly, and there were no longer disagreements among them. Winne, possibly the most conservative of the board's members, was now so enthusiastic about the plan that he wrote of it, as part of the official report, "It may seem too radical, too advanced, too much beyond human experience. All these terms apply with peculiar fitness to the atomic bomb."

The report runs to thirty-four thousand words, but Marks said he could summarize it briefly for me. It calls for the internationalizing of all thorium and uranium deposits capable of producing enough ore to make them of any consequence and also of all production plants. Thus the only stuff from which atomic energy can be extracted would be under international supervision from the moment it was dug out of the earth. The mining of the raw materials, the refining of them, and the manufacture of atomic materials would all be done by the international Authority. Denaturing, too, would be a responsibility of the Authority. The denatured materials would be licensed by the Authority to governments for peaceful uses. Under this arrangement, plant inspection, instead of being the only precautionary measure against atomic war, would fall into place as one of a series of interlocking safeguards, and far fewer scientists would be needed to make the plan work than the Technical Committee's proposal had called for, because the Authority would always know just where its ores were, and in what quantities, and to what purposes they were being put.

The consultants, Marks said, tried to formulate a plan which would stand a chance of immediately eliminating the day-to-day possibility of sudden and simultaneous death to large masses of people in all parts of the world. Then, they sought to create deterrents to any nation's plans to wage atomic war. Finally, by eliminating the possibility of a surprise military atomic attack, they hoped to eliminate also the secrecy surrounding the atom, so that it could be openly studied with the purpose of directing its powers to beneficial ends.

The consultants spent three weeks drawing up their report, setting down the results of their grappling with the future. They found themselves in a state of mutual understanding of a sort that none of them would have believed possible at their first meeting. After their assignment was completed, they all felt a letdown. "Back to the dull present," Marks said. "Back to our same old jobs. Even Winne had to go to work. The General Electric strike was over."

CHAPTER 7 | JANUARY, 1948

THE CENTER OF REALITY

THROUGHOUT THE SEVEN weeks of tempestuous debate in Congress that preceded David Lilienthal's nomination as the first chairman of the United States Atomic Energy Commission, Lilienthal's opponents and supporters were able to agree on only one point—that the new agency is, in the words of one Congressional witness, "possibly the most important federal bureau in the history of the republic." The Commission, which will presumably exist as long as the country remains interested in atomic energy, has been in operation only a relatively short time, so it is obviously much too early to tell whether it will live up to this impressive characterization, but Lilienthal and the four other commissioners, as well as the bureau's managerial aides, scientists, lawyers, and other employees, certainly talk as though their organization had a substantial future. Without any self-consciousness, they refer to themselves as "pioneers" or mention the fact that they have turned down or given up better salaries because of their agency's "historic mission." They point out that the Commission, unlike the Manhattan District, is not an emergency project dedicated to the production of a single weapon. It has been given the power by Congress to devise and put into effect a long-range program for the development and employment of the country's atomic resources. Among the Commission's responsibilities, in addition to the turning out and storing of material for nuclear weapons, is the regulation of the peaceful uses of this revolutionary force. The organizing of research is also in its hands. So is the disposition of uranium and thorium after they have been mined, the operating of the huge plants where fissionable materials are made, the task of classifying and declassifying information, and the many other jobs, some of them still to be determined, necessary to the exploration of a novel and portentous field. All in all, the Atomic Energy Commission has a permanent air.

Some idea of the length of the career that lies ahead of the Commission can be gathered from the fact that the task of merely assuming possession of the properties that, by act of Congress, it is to manage went on during the entire first year of its existence. Legally, the domain of the Manhattan District passed neatly from the Army into the jurisdiction of the new bureau at midnight on December 31, 1946; the only person who appeared to have taken that date seriously was a Washington newspaper editor, who assigned a photographer to shoot a picture that evening of General Groves handing over The Secret to Mr. Lilienthal. Actually, the Commissioners—Lilienthal; W. W. Waymack, a newspaper publisher; Sumner Pike, an industrialist; Lewis Strauss, a financier; and Dr. Robert Bacher, a physicist —were so thoroughly aware that the transfer would be a complicated affair that they began to tackle it immediately upon being named by the President—in November, 1946, five months before their nominations were confirmed by the Senate. "Taking over Muscle Shoals on behalf of the T.V.A.," Lilienthal told me, "was quite a headache, but then at least I was handed an inventory by the Army Engineers, who certified it to be accurate. Here there was no such thing. This time the Army had been busy helping win a tough war, and had been unable to keep tabs. 'Take,' the Army simply told us. 'Take the world's most precious possession, which every nation covets, take everything we own.' " The Commission was wary of this offhand generosity, because someday Congress or another governmental body might call upon it to account for assets it knew nothing about. "The entire matter was most irregular," Sumner Pike told me. "Like a bank trying to check on someone who has never had an account." After a debate among themselves, the commissioners decided that, despite the risks, they would have to move in at once. Some of the reasons for the decision were technical. Costly experiments would be total losses if they were suspended, piles could not be turned off suddenly. Personnel could not be expected to stand by idle and unpaid while the Army laboriously compiled an inventory. Even more important, the Manhattan District, having fulfilled its assigned mission, had lacked the authority to push further explorations into the matter of releasing and controlling nuclear energy as vigorously as it might have liked.

Working fast, the commissioners and some of their aides took a trip around the country, by air and rail, to get acquainted with their realm. They did not have time for more than a brief inspection, but that was enough to show them that they were, in an official sense, a quite wealthy body. At Oak Ridge, they were escorted through the vast plants to which they had fallen heir and were briefed by experts on the functions of queer-looking pumps, pipes, spectrometers, and other equipment. When Lilienthal, bewildered by the bizarre apparatus, spotted a familiar object screwed to a pillar, he asked his scientific escort, "Is that *really* a pencil sharpener?" At Los Alamos, they learned how many atomic bombs the United States had. At Hanford, they discovered that its stockpile of plutonium had been considerably increased since V-J Day. At research centers such as the Argonne National Laboratory in Chicago, they listened to theoretical physicists describe their immediate scientific problems. At the end of their trip, the commissioners and their aides knew the rate at which fissionable materials were being produced, and they also had some idea of which production methods were becoming obsolete, which were still promising, and what new ones were being developed. They had investigated the living conditions of the sixty-five thousand inhabitants in the three towns—Los Alamos, Oak Ridge, and Hanford—they owned, and had been brought up to date on the safety devices, such as plastic masks, with which project employees were protecting themselves against beta rays. They had assembled the facts on many complex, confidential international arrangements for acquiring additional uranium and thorium. They had learned that the Department of the Interior's Geological Survey was scouting around to see what raw atomic-energy materials American soil contains. "Prospectors have been racing to stake out their claims," Commissioner Pike told me. "One of them has already dubbed himself the Uranium King. Atomic energy may be the modern thing, but it's in one of the country's oldest prospecting areas—the Colorado Plateau, which takes in part of Colorado, New Mexico, Utah, and Arizona—that Americans are searching for uranium. It's about twenty-five to thirty thousand square miles of grim, lonely country, no more than one per cent of it arable. It's got a fair number of wolves, elk, and mountain lions. It's the same terrain in which gold, silver, and lead have been found, and now they're looking for rock that's the yellow of gaslight. Men over sixty are doing a good deal of the looking—old birds who go out for months at a stretch, alone or in pairs, with a burro or two."

During their tour the commissioners also learned that they had inherited several large fleets of Army vehicles, some long leases on various tracts of land, and innumerable contracts with manufacturers of nuclear machinery. Among the most complicated assets they acquired were millions of documents in the District files. Some of them contained secret formulas and technological data. Some of them were receipts for shipments of U-235, and others were abstruse papers on scientific topics. Many belonged in waste baskets.

One of the Commission's chief difficulties is recruiting qualified men for key jobs. "We haven't been stymied on posts of medium importance," Fletcher C. Waller, the Commission's assistant general manager, told me, "but getting the top-flight managerial fellows is something else again. That type of man is doing all right for himself as an executive in some large corporation or as the head of a private research foundation. Then we come along and ask him to give up a forty-thousand-dollar job for one that pays less than half as well. Our salaries, except for scientific and technical people, are limited by Congress. No matter how keen he is about our work, he takes a long look at his family and the financial adjustment he'd have to make. Also, when he recalls how rough-and-tumble the political situation can get here, he probably wonders how long he'll have a job." When I talked with Waller, the bureau was still desperately seeking several men to direct engineering and medical research, and he didn't think there were half a dozen in the country of the right calibre. It was only quite recently that the Commission succeeded in coaxing the man it wanted—John C. Franklin, former vice-president of T.W.A.—to take over the management of the establishment at Oak Ridge. "What a job he got!" Waller exclaimed. "He has to administer nine hundred million dollars' worth of plants and experimental laboratories. He has to see to it that production contracts are fulfilled. He has to be mayor of a small city. He has to handle delicate relations with the state and county, since Oak Ridge, being a federal reservation, is autonomous. He has to run a trash-collecting system and a fire department, and keep an eye on our badge setup, and take care of a lot of other headaches. And for all that he gets what might be considered a darn modest salary."

Usually, Waller said, advisory panels of important people in related fields recommend to the Commission the names of several men they think are qualified for a specific job. Waller then talks to these men, and frequently has them meet one or two of the commissioners, who appeal to the candidates' patriotism, point out the opportunities in this unprecedented industry, promise them a good deal of independence in the job being offered, and turn on the charm. When someone of exceptional ability is persuaded to join up, according to Waller, it is regarded by the Commission as a wonderful break. "Before you know it," he said, "the new man goes out and tries to talk fellows like himself into coming on the payroll, and they listen to him as they never listen to us."

The recruiting of scientists, on the other hand, has not, I was told by men on the Commission, been as hard as was expected, even though there is a shortage of physicists, chemists, and certain other specialists, owing principally to the fact that the war interfered with the scholastic careers of a great many young men. After Hiroshima, a lot of the scientists who had helped contrive the bomb resigned their posts, reputedly because of moral repugnance to their homicidal feat. Lately, however, many of them have returned. Commissioner Bacher, who during the war was head of the Theoretical Physics Division at Los Alamos, thinks that morality had nothing to do with either the exodus or the return. "First of all," he pointed out to me, "quite a number of scientists never left. They were doing well for themselves, or felt an obligation to keep things going, or had no strong ties outside. I did hear some of my colleagues talk of their moral qualms, but I think that other reasons for leaving weighed more heavily. After the fighting, everybody, whether a lady welder in a shipyard or a cost analyst for a wartime government agency, wanted to go back to his old job and home and grocery store. Why not scientists? In addition, the scientists wanted to do fundamental research in their universities. There wasn't any such research in connection with the bomb. You know, we haven't really found out anything new about the atomic nucleus in the last ten years. Well, they've got the return to their old jobs out of their systems. Furthermore, they know that civilians are now in charge of this project and that we're providing elaborate facilities for basic research, all of which tends to make the idea of coming back less unattractive. Then, a number of them are disillusioned by the way international relations are going, and some can't find housing. A kind of geographical nostalgia has brought some of my colleagues back. They would rather live in the Southwest, on top of a mountain, than in the close air of Columbia or the University of Chicago."

A high-ranking Army officer who does liaison work with the Commission was somewhat less analytical than Dr. Bacher. "Listen," he told me, "don't give that conscience angle a second thought. These boys are playing around with fissionable materials. Right? Well, fissionable materials are good for either peace or war. It's like gasoline. You can pour it into a Sherman tank or a sight-seeing bus."

For all its organizational distractions, the Commission is not neglecting its paramount job of stepping up the country's output of plutonium and U-235, the radioactive elements from which nuclear products are made. These materials are mostly going into stockpiles for atomic weapons; some are being utilized in the form of radioactive isotopes. These isotopes, which, as most people know, are used in medical, industrial, and agricultural research, represent that salutary aspect of atomic energy that everyone at least occasionally dares hope may bring us nearer our brave new world. So far, the Commission has made shipments of a hundred types of isotopes to about three hundred and fifty hospitals, industrial users, and educational organizations. Since each user is required to file his research findings with the Commission, a store of benevolent knowledge is rapidly being accumulated. The isotopes are made in the Oak Ridge National Laboratories and distributed by the Isotope Sales Division, which, despite its enterprising title, has no salesmen. It does, however, have a gaudy blue catalogue, whose language is as brisk and businesslike as that of any volume put out by a mail-order house. It states, "A deposit of $125 will be required on returnable containers used to ship gamma ray emitters. A refund will be made upon return of container, express prepaid, in good condition." And "Charges for irradiations for periods in excess of one month will be determined by taking the monthly rate times the number of months, plus fractions of months computed to the nearest one-fourth month." Looking through the catalogue, one discovers that Europium 155 is selling at $31 a unit and Scandium 46 at $33. Antimony 122, an isotope with a half life of 2.8 days, a gamma radiation of 0.8 Mev, a target material of 0.20 grams, and an estimated content of 50 millicuries, looks like a real buy at $12 a unit.

These isotopes could not very directly help any nation win a war, but they are nevertheless sold with discrimination, because they are highly radioactive. Every buyer must fill out the Commission's request form, giving his scientific background and indicating in detail how he intends to use his purchase. He must also list what instruments he has for monitoring radioactivity and give the qualifications of the men who are to handle the equipment. He must explain how he plans to dispose of surplus and waste material. The Commission's Isotopes Division itself is a model of caution. Using an impressive assortment of instruments, technicians constantly check to see whether radioactive particles are floating in the air, inspect bench tops and other flat surfaces, and examine their shoes, clothing, and skin for possible contamination. Long tongs are generally employed for the actual handling of isotopes. Nearly all the isotopes emit radiations of such strength that they are kept in lead containers. Isotopes suspended in liquids are put in bottles and, to prevent breakage and escaping radioactivity in transit, the bottles are enclosed in stainless-steel containers, which, in turn, are placed inside thick lead cases. Solid isotopes are shipped in similarly encased aluminum cans the size of a man's index finger. "Short-lived," or unstable, isotopes are shipped to their destinations by plane; the rest go by ordinary freight cars. Before being shipped, the packages are inspected to make sure that their surfaces are free from dangerous particles that somebody might come in contact with while handling them en route.

Heartening as it is to know that isotopes are being put to good use, the chilling fact remains that they are merely a by-product and that practically all the Commission's fissionable materials are allocated to nuclear weapons. To put it bluntly, more and better bombs are being made. How many is a secret, but the people involved look back almost indulgently on those summer days of 1945 when America's atomic arsenal consisted of two bombs. Refinements for increasing the destructiveness of the bombs have been devised. The town of Los Alamos, the atomic-weapon center, is being enlarged and made more livable, to keep personnel happy and to attract more physicists, chemists, metallurgists, and other experts. Intimate liaison is being maintained between the military and the civilian Commission. Also, Army and Navy doctors are busily investigating the likely effects of atomic weapons upon human beings.

Most of the Commission's officials are unenthusiastic about the idea of letting the public in on such macabre information because, as one man put it, "people will get worried." It is an illogical queasiness, since the law that created the Commission specifies that the production of arms is to be its main consideration. The bureau people with whom I talked regret this situation, but they feel that as long as "other countries"—Washington's tactful name for Russia—are opposed to international control of atomic energy, there is no alternative. "I don't mean to sound smug," one official said to me, "but I honestly believe that right as well as might is on our side." Mr. Lilienthal, being in a position of great authority, is less inhibited than his colleagues about discussing our armament policy. "We are not making weapons to exert pressure on other countries," he told me. "International affairs being what they are, we are making weapons—period. It isn't unreasonable to believe that that may prevent war. The atom is the center of reality at the council tables of chancelleries all over the world. They know what we are doing. No nation in the world can make decisions these days without thinking of the atom." Lilienthal says that it would be much easier to recruit personnel if he could talk freely and didn't always have to think of security. He did disclose to me one argument he uses to persuade people to join his organization. "I point out to them," Lilienthal said, "that during a war no one hesitates to make sacrifices but that such sacrifices would be unnecessary if the man got busy now. I tell him, 'The time to help is now, when your son is ten, not when he is twenty and going off to a military camp.' Yes, those of us who work here are a grim but hopeful group of people."

Because international affairs are, as Mr. Lilienthal puts it, what they are, the Commission maintains a full-scale security system. Security details are on duty wherever Commission plants are operating. Manufacturers of equipment for the Commission are obliged to have guards, on whom the Commission keeps a close check. (The manufacturers, incidentally, are still not told the precise function of their particular products.) People suspected of being spies are gumshoed by F.B.I. operatives who have been assigned to the Commission. The Commission's own security force is staffed largely by men who performed similar services for the Manhattan District. The Commission's security watch, in fact, is as strict as the District's was, but, according to one security official whom I talked to, there is now a psychological handicap in keeping the vigil. "During the war, the public was on its toes," he said. "People knew about a definite enemy and could understand why security in general was necessary, whether it concerned a mysterious project called the Manhattan District or troopship sailings or new types of airplanes. Not only did they discipline themselves, but they kept on the lookout for suspicious characters. Today, in what is supposedly peacetime, there is a letdown. We have to keep reminding people that atomic energy is nothing to be casual about."

When the war ended, this official went on, many facts that had been treated as secrets became common knowledge. While the war was on, a man wasn't even allowed to admit he was employed by the Manhattan District, let alone talk about the location of Oak Ridge or the names of nuclear scientists and companies, such as General Electric and the Monsanto Chemical Corporation, involved in the work. The security man said that he wasn't necessarily criticizing the releasing of such information, but he pointed out that the difficulties in maintaining security have been greatly increased. There are some classified topics that are so clearly legitimate shoptalk for scientists that it would be absurd to try to prevent men outside the program from discussing them. "Take the chemistry and metallurgy of plutonium," the security man told me. "That stuff would fill volumes, but it still hasn't been declassified. Does it follow that scientists outside the program wouldn't or shouldn't speculate about the stuff? It would be like telling a lawyer he couldn't discuss the doctrine of *res ipsa loquitur.*" Furthermore, some Manhattan District workers, when they went home after the war, may have taken mementos with them—photographs, perhaps, or diaries containing details of their war effort. Although this was probably done innocently, the security officer cannot help brooding over the possibility that some of these mementos ought to be classified. In addition, he pointed out, people remember things. "Supposing I quit tomorrow," he said. "I wouldn't take any papers, but the secrets I've come into possession of! And my memory is excellent! Anyway, it is probably only a question of time before either the control of atomic energy will be internationalized or other nations will discover for themselves the secrets that are now only American property. When either of those things happens," the security man remarked, "we'll be in a perfect position to look back on today and say, 'What fools we were to get ourselves into such a stew!' But until it *does* happen, we'd be fools if we *didn't* get into a stew."

The atmosphere in which the Commission necessarily works is such that not long ago two of its security men found themselves interrogating a mentally unbalanced woman. "We feel sheepish about it, but the same thing could happen all over again," Joseph Volpe, Jr., Associate General Counsel of the Commission, who works closely with the security staff, said to me. "You simply can't take any chances. You just don't know where leaks are liable to come from." The woman had phoned Lilienthal at his home a little after midnight and said that she had vital news. "Can it wait until morning?" Lilienthal asked. "No," she answered, and gave him the name of the hotel in Washington where she was staying. Lilienthal called Volpe, who phoned the woman and was informed that she wouldn't be able to talk to him until a certain man had arrived. At two-fifteen that morning, Volpe called again, and learned that the certain man had turned up but that she was not yet ready to talk; she would let Volpe know as soon as she was. At six, Volpe sent two men around to the hotel with orders to stand by. At seven-thirty, the woman still had not phoned back, so Volpe ordered the men to investigate. It turned out that a relative of the woman had found her unconscious in her room at 5 A.M. and had her taken to a hospital. She was now in the psychopathic ward. The doctor in charge said that he would let them talk to her but didn't know why they would care to. The operatives felt the same way, but they went ahead. The interrogation amounted to a single question and the answer. One of them asked the woman what she wanted Mr. Lilienthal to know, and she replied that it had been important the night before but that now it was out of date.

As though it didn't have problems enough, the Commission has also concerned itself with the abstract matter of freedom. It is interested in preserving liberty of action not only for itself but for the thousands of men and women whose lives are affected by its decisions. The Commission is, after all, a monopoly. Furthermore, it is a government monopoly, and its power, having been established by Congress, cannot easily be disputed. Public-health and military considerations, in the government's opinion, were so pressing that the Commission could have no other status. "If," Mr. Lilienthal remarked to me, "we wanted to—and we don't—we could establish a complete overlordship with regard to anything that is at all related to atomic energy." Occasionally, the power-shy Commission officials worry over whether they are being unwittingly dictatorial. They are reluctant to throw their weight around, for practical as well as ideological reasons. "You get a better day's work out of a man," a Commission attorney told me, "if he thinks he's as much his own boss as he ought to be." "Take Los Alamos, Oak Ridge, and Hanford," Commissioner Waymack said to me. " 'Uncle Sam towns,' we call them—one-industry towns that can be closed down tomorrow if the Commission so rules. We've got no democratic process in any of them. The residents don't pay any community taxes and they don't have any form of self-government. They live on federal reservations, so they can't buy land or own their own houses. Naturally, we don't want to be dictators, and we also don't want to let the heavy hand of paternalism fall on them, either. How do you make sense of these towns in an authentic American way?"

The problem of freedom also comes up in connection with the rights of inventors of devices for the production and use of fissionable materials. Such rights are secondary to the rights of the Commission. According to law, patents for such equipment are the property of the government and must be sold to the Commission. "The inventor cannot stand on his traditional right of selling his brain child to the highest bidder," Waymack told me. "Because of security, we can't possibly let the inventor show it around to anybody. He may not like our price, but unless he wants to go to jail, he can't offer it to another country. Of course, we do our very best to play ball with the man, but fairness, you know, isn't foolproof."

Dealing with the Commission's physicists, chemists, biochemists, and other scientists is another problem in freedom. One of the bureau's touchiest concerns is the disposition of papers that are the results of a scientist's experimenting and thinking. These papers are his means of gaining recognition in his field. If his findings are published in some such journal as the *Physical Review* or read before a meeting of scientists, his chances of getting a better job or more equipment for his experiments are definitely enhanced. Nowadays, most scientific documents on atomic energy cannot be published, and, because of that, their authors' reputations may fail to thrive. Many papers written eight years ago, when the government began looking into atomic energy, have still not been released. To cope with this situation, the Commission has set up a Declassification Service to review such articles and determine which can be made public. So far, not quite two thousand papers have been released, and around half that number have been restricted. "When we do our reviewing," Dr. Harold A. Fidler, Chief of the Declassification Service, explained to me, "we ask ourselves, 'Whom will the release of this information help more, ourselves or a foreign nation?' Obviously, we're not going to let out a treatise on the gadgetry of the bomb or diagrams of our piles. But anything that's given out may help some outsider. It's not just a single secret that's at stake but a fantastically complex jigsaw puzzle of secrets. How can you tell precisely what details the other fellow is looking for? Also, how can you tell that scientists in other parts of the world haven't already found out for themselves what is in the paper you're considering? If they have and you hold up the paper, you're simply depriving your own scientists of knowledge they could use." In general, Fidler said, tracts on basic research stand a better chance of being passed than those dealing with the application of knowledge. However, he added, plenty of so-called "know-how" articles have been approved for publication. "For instance, we've released papers on certain instruments that detect radiation," he said. "No doubt they help a potential enemy to a degree, but we're vitally interested in protecting our own scientists against radioactivity. All the secrets in the world won't help you much if your scientists are dead."

In theory, at least, both the Commission's and the scientists' interests are safeguarded in the reviewing process. If a physicist at, say, the Argonne National Laboratory has a tract he hopes to read at the American Physical Society's next convention, he takes it to Dr. Walter H. Zinn, the laboratory's director. Dr. Zinn looks it over to see whether the scientist is justified in claiming credit for the work; he also notes down the date of submission, to prevent argument in case another scientist, somewhere else in the country, comes up with the same data. The director then makes a recommendation as to whether the document should be declassified or not and turns it over to a reviewer, selected by the Declassification Service, who is a specialist in the branch of science touched on in the article. If the reviewer returns a negative report, the Commission permits the author to appeal the decision to a board of four Senior Responsible Reviewers, all of whom are outstanding scientists. When a paper is passed, it goes on to the Declassification Service offices in Washington, where it is prepared for dissemination.

Members of trade unions—electrical, chemical, construction, and others—employed by the Commission are also bound by its decisions. The past of every employee of every company operating under contract to the Commission is investigated by the F.B.I., and if it is not considered satisfactory, no amount of argument by either the union or the contractor can prevail. If a union and a contractor hit a bargaining snag, the Commission does not permit outsiders to arbitrate, on the ground that the discussion of grievances would inevitably lead to the disclosure of secrets. To date, federal mediators, who have been investigated by the F.B.I. and cleared by the Commission for access to secret data, have been attempting to bring all disputants into agreement. One argument at Oak Ridge required over three hundred hours of lively bargaining to reach a settlement. Strikes and lockouts can, under the Taft-Hartley Act, be halted by federal injunction, a step which was actually taken in a dispute at Oak Ridge between the Council of Atomic Trades and the Carbide and Carbon Chemicals Corporation. The main reason for invoking this provision, of course, would be to prevent any stoppage of the work that is under way, but the element of physical safety could also be involved. "Lord, if the personnel in certain plants abruptly dropped their work and started picketing, they'd be in an unthinkable jam," one official said. "The plant wouldn't explode, but intense radioactivity would raise hell with it. I don't think the picket line would last long."

The public, largely unaware of either the Commission's powers or its soul-searching abstention from their abuse, often likes to tell the monopoly where to get off. Hardly a day passes without the arrival, in the mail, of a complaint. A West Coast stevedore has urged the Commission to go out of business because he is fed up with flinging around crates that he believes are full of atomic bombs. Another citizen has told the Commission that its name is incredibly dull. Inquiries for "atom-stoppers"—defenses against the bomb—are especially frequent. A Cleveland iceman has denounced the Commission because it has not forced the clothing industry to impregnate garments with lead, "since I understand that the damage is done after the bomb goes off." One memorable correspondent, an Alaskan miner's wife, has supplied the Commission with a series of lengthy and incomprehensible letters in which she discussed some allegorically scientific theories. Her sixth letter was terse. "I am a busy housewife, the mother of seven," she wrote. "If you do not send me a stenographer, I will not send you any more letters. It's the least the government can do. When the girl comes to Fairbanks, there is a small airplane that leaves every three days for where we live . . ."

CHAPTER 8 | SEPTEMBER, 1947

A SUNNY SPOT

ON LONG ISLAND, forty miles east of Lake Success, the present home of the United Nations, there is a spot where the subject of atomic energy seems a little less ominous. There, on the six-thousand-acre tract that Camp Upton once occupied, the Brookhaven National Laboratory, the first American research center to concern itself with the peaceful uses of atomic energy, has come into being. The laboratory won't be completed for several years, but part of it is already in operation; scientists are working there, many Long Islanders earn their living there, and the place has perhaps made plausible the notion that the American soldier fought for the benefits of nuclear fission as well as for a piece of Mom's blueberry pie. I received permission from the people in charge to go out to Brookhaven to see how the project was coming along and to talk with some of the scientists who are trying to prove, against heavy odds, that atomic energy has its attractive side. I had visited Upton on several occasions during the war, so I was familiar with the surroundings. The Army's barracks and most of its other buildings are still standing, but the pair of M.P.s who throughout the war guarded what is now the administrative headquarters are missing. Instead, I found an alert executive secretary named Mrs. Kuper waiting at the entrance for me. "Hurry, hurry," she said. "I think the director isn't busy. He won't be free again today." She led me rapidly to his office.

The director, Dr. Philip Morse, a man of forty with genial gray eyes, was wearing a striking red-and-green plaid shirt, without a tie, and had a pipe in his mouth. He came to Brookhaven from the Massachusetts Institute of Technology, where he was a physics professor. During the war, as a civilian expert, he headed the Navy's anti-submarine research. He discussed the new project in a relaxed manner and with great enthusiasm. The money to set up and support Brookhaven (twenty-five million dollars was spent the first year) comes, he said, from the United States Atomic Energy Commission, but the establishment is operated almost autonomously by nine Eastern universities—Columbia, Cornell, Harvard, Rochester, Johns Hopkins, Pennsylvania, Princeton, Yale, and M.I.T.—that have formed a group called Associated Universities, Inc. "The government supplies the money, the universities the brain power," Dr. Morse explained, "and the public is supposed to get the benefits. Ordinarily, universities are about as competitive as business rivals, but the peculiar nature of nuclear research has forced them to get together. For instance, take a nuclear pile. That's where we fellows generate our power—our kind of furnace, you might say. It's a source of neutrons. A pile is, literally, a pile of blocks of graphite, in which pieces of uranium are embedded, like raisins in a loaf of bread. It's as big—well, as big as a *very* large room. You need all kinds of experts to run it—men who know about insulation, electronics men, metallurgists, electrical engineers, and whatnot." The equipment for nuclear research is too expensive for any one college to buy, and a pile costs about ten million dollars. Scientists got into the habit of working in big-scale collaboration during the war and now, Dr. Morse said, they are able to take a communal establishment like Brookhaven in their stride.

During the winter of 1946, Dr. Morse told me, a number of atomic scientists from various northeastern universities met at Columbia and decided that they would have to have a common workshop, with all the necessary equipment, and a common nuclear pile if they were to go on with their work. The Manhattan District, which was then in charge of the country's atomic-energy affairs, agreed to help them. The District, being part of the Army, recommended that the scientists pick one of a number of available Army camps as a site. Brookhaven won for several reasons. To begin with, it is not too far away from any of the nine universities. "Besides, we inherited twenty miles of pavement, a swimming pool, outdoor bowling alleys, and other recreational facilities," Dr. Morse said. "Also, Upton had plenty of electricity, and it had just been painted. We've got three hundred buildings. When we receive a shipment of graphite for our pile, we don't have to worry where to store it. All we had to do was hang several dozen blackboards on our walls. We can't talk without chalk in our hands."

It is over a year now since Brookhaven got under way. Eight hundred people, most of them construction workers, are on the payroll. Ninety scientists are already at work, and in the near future there will be twice as many. Ultimately, the laboratory will have a permanent scientific staff of two hundred, plus a visiting staff of at least two hundred, all to be drawn from the universities in the association and from other scientific institutions in the Northeast. "There will be a variety of specialists," Dr. Morse said. "We'll have physicists, animal and plant biologists, medical researchers, geneticists, geologists, meteorologists, and biochemists. I don't mean to sound like a booster, but this will be quite a place. Half the American Physical Society's membership is concentrated in this region. Incidentally, any scientist in this area who's technically competent can use the laboratory, whether he's from one of the nine schools or not. For instance, a Brooklyn Polytechnic physicist is spending his sabbatical here right now." The place will not begin to bloom, he said, until the pile produces neutrons, which ought to be in another half year.

Summer, I gathered, is to be the high point of the year at Brookhaven. Meetings of scientists will be held in the auditoriums left over from Upton's Army days. Seminars will be conducted by such eminent men as Harold Urey, Leo Szilard, and Enrico Fermi. Students working for their doctorates will be assigned by their universities to Brookhaven to get data for their theses. "I like the idea of their being around," Dr. Morse said. "They're eager beavers. They keep us graybeards on our toes." I remarked that graybeards seem to be exactly what you don't find among nuclear scientists. "We do make up a pretty young bunch," Dr. Morse conceded. "Somebody once said we were sort of like musical prodigies, but that's not really so." The reason nuclear physicists are so young is that nuclear physics is young. It was only in the early nineteen-thirties that such monumental discoveries as the neutron, the process for creating artificial radioactivity, and the principles of the cyclotron took place. "The field," he said, "was clearly headed for big things, and young students made a beeline for it, like the kids who wouldn't be anything but air pilots. The older men already involved in research of long standing in other, equally significant fields stayed put. I probably would have myself, in their place. Why should a man who's been studying the structure of molecules for thirty years suddenly go over to nuclear reactions?"

A number of scientists are unwilling to work at Brookhaven because they doubt that research can be freely conducted under government sponsorship. "Research is a highly creative business, like painting or writing," Dr. Morse said. "A nice balance is involved. We have to be let alone, but the government has to account to the public." There are several "little things," as he put it, that may prevent the atmosphere at Brookhaven from becoming over-governmental. He pointed to his plaid shirt, which, he said, happens to be his favorite bit of haberdashery. "Not long ago," he told me, "I assembled everyone on the site and told them they could dress any way they pleased. The place will eventually look more like a university than an Army post. Scientists work better in that kind of setting." During the war, scientists had to spend half their time filling out justification forms explaining why they needed a particular piece of equipment or a particular man to assist them. To hold down the amount of red tape at Brookhaven, Dr. Morse is hiring a few extra secretaries and administrators. Some of the administrators are ex-Army men who did similar work at Oak Ridge and Los Alamos. Dr. Morse is determined to let Brookhaven scientists travel as much as their work requires. "A man's scientific health depends in large part on visiting around," he explained. "If he hears that Professor So-and-So, out at the University of California, has got such-and-such a result in his cyclotron, he has to hotfoot it out there and find out what it is or run the risk of going stale. For some reason, spending money for travel has always been intensely annoying to federal accountants. They'd rather let us hire five thousand dollars' worth of clerical assistants than spend two hundred dollars on travel."

The scientists at Brookhaven cannot, of course, be free to do and say exactly what they like. According to the rules laid down by Congress, about twenty-five per cent of the work at Brookhaven falls into the category of material that must be "classified," or kept secret. For example, none of the scientists now working on the pile is free to talk. All personnel has to be investigated by the F.B.I., and the laboratory maintains its own police force, which, among other things, checks the credentials of every person who enters the Brookhaven grounds. Only American citizens are permitted to join the staff. Dr. Morse doesn't wish the necessary security measures to become oppressive. "I don't want badges all over the place," he said. "Only the people who work in restricted areas will have them. Also, we don't have a military-security officer, as the Manhattan District did during the war. Instead, we have a committee of scientists, who pass on what ought to be classified. They've got a much better idea than our military censors had of what constitutes a scientific secret."

The scientists at Brookhaven are straightening out several misconceptions about the laboratory that are held by residents of nearby Long Island towns. The scientists are constantly making speeches before women's clubs, Chambers of Commerce, Rotary clubs, and Elks' clubs. "The organizations won't take administrators as speakers," Dr. Morse said. "They want real, live, genuine scientists. They're curious to see if they look like other human beings." Most of the Long Islanders' misapprehensions, Dr. Morse thinks, are a result of the fact that many people are unable to associate atomic energy with anything but terrible destruction. Laymen still call Brookhaven "the atom-bomb plant." A seventeen-year-old boy recently applied for a job because, he said, "my mother wants me to be trained for the next war." One Long Island man moved his family to the Dakota Bad Lands to get away from the threat he thought Brookhaven implied. The scientists assure their audiences that no atomic weapons are being made at Brookhaven and that discovering peaceful uses of atomic power is the purpose of all their endeavor, but many of their listeners consider this a dodge to mislead them. The learned lecturers are often asked if the pile is absolutely safe. The answer they give is that it is safe precisely because it is so extremely dangerous that fantastic precautions are taken to make it safe. "We want to live, too," Dr. Morse said. "We'll work with periscopes from behind a concrete wall that's five to six feet thick." The chemists and physicists devote most of their talks to telling the club members how atomic energy may bring about great medical progress, but when the question periods come around, all anyone wants to know is whether there is any chance that the pile will blow up.

"Well?" I asked.

"None," Dr. Morse replied wearily.

Long Islanders who are worried about the safety of their source of livelihood—oysters, ducks, and clams—to say nothing of themselves, are told that any radioactive gases that escape from the pile will be so diluted that they will not affect the normal degree of radiation on Long Island. One evening, a scientist who was attempting to make this point to a group of oystermen informed them that the amount of radiation in the Rockies was five times as great as on Long Island and yet was harmless. "Ain't no oysters in the Rockies," one of the listeners observed. A rumor spread that the operations at Brookhaven would produce a lot of static on radios in the vicinity. The New York *Daily News* printed a scare story to the effect that Brookhaven had "the largest federal fire department in the country." "I don't know how large the other fire departments are," Dr. Morse said, "but ours is the same size Upton's was before we took over." People have blamed purely imaginary illnesses on Brookhaven. A New Yorker week-ending with his brother in Sayville, sixteen miles from Brookhaven, suddenly put his hand to his head and declared that he would never come again, because the laboratory's poisonous gases made him sick. A warehouse worker on the premises had to handle a crate marked "Uranium Glass," a type of glass long antedating the atomic bomb. "It's less radioactive than that painted dial on your wristwatch," Dr. Morse commented to me. But the man had seen the terrible word, his fellow-workers jokingly told him he was a dead duck, and, nauseated and trembling, he reported to the infirmary. Airline pilots whose routes take them near the laboratory have asked their companies to inquire whether they are courting sterility. One woman wrote in to ask if radiation would induce pregnancy. Religious people have sent Dr. Morse letters in which they accused him of being "the tool of the Devil" for daring to tamper with God's elements. "Dr. Faustus," he remarked, sighing. All these fears manifested themselves during the spring of 1947, when there was nothing radioactive anywhere on the site, he said. Then he corrected himself. "I beg your pardon. In May, one of our physicists did send away to the Kix Cereal Company for an Atom Bomb Ring. They give it to children who save Kix box tops. It has just enough radioactivity in it to keep making little sparks. Rather cute."

Determined to protect itself against popular suspicions, the laboratory is undertaking an ecological survey. Ecology is the branch of biology that treats of the relations between organisms and environment. The study will take four years. After that, the laboratory will be able to reply with scientific evidence to charges that radioactivity is harming the surrounding area and population. "About seventy-five years ago," Dr. Morse said, "the herring off the coast of Norway suddenly disappeared, and that industry went *kaput*. The herring returned just as suddenly fifteen years later. Nobody ever found out what had happened." Something might go wrong with Long Island flounders, clams, ducks, or oysters, and Brookhaven would undoubtedly be blamed. A great variety of information, little of it directly related to radioactivity, will be turned up by the survey. For example, by the time it is finished, Dr. Morse expects that the laboratory will know where all the island's marine life gets its food. Long Island will also become meteorologically better acquainted with itself, because Brookhaven, to check whether its activities have any effect on the surrounding atmosphere, will set up a weather station. In addition, an investigation of the island's water sources is to be made. "Someday, somebody who lives three miles away may complain that he's getting dizzy spells because of his drinking water," Dr. Morse said. "Well, our survey may show that the soil three miles from here has a chemical that could account for such vertigo." He shook his head. "It was a break for us that a blight that kills off ducks every few years broke out the winter of 1946, not the following one. We couldn't possibly take the rap for that. We hadn't moved into the place yet."

Dr. Morse was just saying that he sometimes even gives a little thought to matters relating solely to nuclear research when Mrs. Kuper came in. "The University of Rochester crowd has arrived," she announced. "After that, you have a budget meeting at lunch. After that, some Elks are coming to see you." She turned to me and said that Georges Peter, the laboratory's architect, was waiting outside in his car to take me on a tour of the grounds.

Mr. Peter, a slender man of about forty-five, with pale-blue eyes, invited me to get into his antiquated Ford sedan, and we started off. Some of the streets, I noticed, were named after universities in the association, and Mr. Peter told me that there is one for each of the nine schools. The Army had simply used numbers for all the streets but one, which it called Bell Avenue, after Major General J. Franklin Bell, a commandant of Upton. The scientists decided that the name would serve as a tribute to one of their own number, Alexander Graham Bell, and let it stand. We drove by one building that was larger than the administrative headquarters—the Research Staff Building (once a Red Cross recreation hall), where most of the scientists have their offices. We then passed a long, one-story wooden structure, now the Brookhaven cafeteria. "Business must be good there," Mr. Peter said. "The manager's nicknamed it the Golden Atom." About a mile down Cornell Avenue, we stopped before a good-sized building that had once been a gymnasium. "We're not allowed inside," Mr. Peter said, "but let's take a look through the window." We could see the red lines of a basketball court still painted on the floor. More than half the floor was covered by thick, black blocks of graphite, reaching almost as high as the frayed basketball nets. "A warehouse for our uranium pile," Mr. Peter told me. "Eventually, that graphite will be machined to extremely close tolerances. Could make quite a few pencils out of that stuff," he added. "So soft-looking, isn't it? Difficult to think of it as a protective wall against the deadliest kind of radioactivity."

We next drove down Johns Hopkins Avenue. Presently, though we were still on the laboratory grounds, the street became a country road. In a few minutes, we were riding up a steep hill that has been named Rutherford Hill, after the British physicist. At the summit, we stopped beside a rusty, sixty-foot steel tower that is used by forest rangers.

We climbed a spiral staircase to the small platform at the top. To the north and south, we could see a vague blue haze where the Atlantic and the Sound wash the island. "That's where Camp Upton used to be," Mr. Peter said, pointing to a tract of scrubby land a couple of hundred yards to the north. "The camp got moved between wars to this site. Nothing left there except some septic tanks." He turned around to face Brookhaven, whose buildings dot the landscape in neat clusters. A quarter of a mile to the northwest stood a rambling structure that was an officers' dance hall during the war. "Our weather station's going to be there," he said. Well beyond it was a green stretch of ground where the laboratory's animal farm will be. "It will take up about three hundred acres," Mr. Peter said. "There will be mice, dogs, farmyard animals, and monkeys. We'll be experimenting with radiation effects. As you can see, the farm will be some distance from the rest of the site. We don't want innocent bystanders exposed to the sight of radioactivated goats." Nearby, to the east, Mr. Peter showed me the spot where, it is expected, a sixty-inch cyclotron will be in operation in two years. "It will point directly at this hill," he said, "so that if anything goes wrong, the radiation will go smack into the ground and be absorbed." The atomic pile, which is at the top of Brookhaven's construction schedule, will also be near the hill. It will be housed in an odd-looking, Cubistic structure over a hundred feet square and about eighty feet high, and a short distance to one side will be a smokestack three hundred and fifty feet high.

I noticed a sprawling, junglelike collection of old buildings and piles of lumber a half mile to the southwest and asked about it. "That used to be the disciplinary barracks," my companion said. "They're coming down. They're a firetrap. What we'll have in their place is an open field."

Mr. Peter looked out over Brookhaven. "I feel that there is a charm to this place," he said. "There's more vegetation here than you'd expect to find in an Army camp. Heavy construction will detroy some of it, but I can see a campus of lawns and trees. Morse and I want to get the calm atmosphere of a university. That seems to be rather important. Just a few days ago, a scientist kicked because one of our cops was assigned to our main street, Brookhaven Avenue, to direct visitors to buildings. The scientist said that he'd had a bellyful of uniforms at Los Alamos during the war. We put the policeman to patrolling in a back street. The cop, who happens to be an awfully nice fellow, was a good sport about it." He paused for a moment. "Mess halls into animal farms, gyms into graphite warehouses—cyclotrons, piles. I've reconverted before, but there's an odd kind of extra pressure to this job. Maybe people ought not to know when they're having a hand in something that's historic."

After a hasty lunch at the Golden Atom with Mrs. Kuper and Mr. Peter, I went by myself over to the Research Staff Building to talk with some of the scientists. I walked slowly down a long corridor. In the small offices on either side, I could hear voices and the scratching of chalk on blackboards. I came across an announcement on a bulletin board that a colloquium was to be held in one of the auditoriums that afternoon, when Dr. Arthur Roberts would discuss "The Magnetic Moment of the Neutron." I finally stopped before an open door. In the room beyond it, a man of about forty-five was standing, all by himself, at a blackboard, upon which he had just finished writing "Insulated Rigid." When he saw me, he asked me in and we introduced ourselves. He turned out to be an M.I.T. physicist with the improbable name of Dr. Stanley Livingston. Like Dr. Morse, he did anti-submarine work during the war. "All the difference, being back in fundamental research," he said.

"Just where does it lead?" I asked.

"Probably to more fundamental research," he answered. "For a man of science, it's enough to say, 'We're learning more.' Once in a while, we get our emotions worked up and decide we're fond of a theory and analyze our data to prove it, but if we can't, we just go back to learning more about something or other. It's hard to explain." Dr. Livingston stopped for a moment, then said, "Supposing I tell you that fundamental research is like rolling a billiard ball up a mountain that's shrouded in fog? You roll it up easy and it comes rolling back to you. You roll it up very hard and it does the same. Then you roll it up medium and it disappears. What happened? Was it the speed's fault? Did you hit a hole? Or what?" He shook his head. "That doesn't really answer your question, though. Fifteen years ago, I had a lot to do with building the world's first cyclotron. I was a student then at the University of California, and helping build and run the machine was my Ph.D. project. I considered my cyclotron the purest form of science. We just wanted to bombard nuclei with it, in order to study physics. But ever since then I've been running into stories of the practical application the engineers and doctors have been putting the machine to. A couple of Sundays ago, my family and I became acquainted with a lady neighbor over in Bayport, where we found a house to live. She's a widow. She told us that her husband had died of leukemia, but that he had lived a year and a half longer than he would have if he hadn't been helped by some radioactive material that had been made in the M.I.T. cyclotron. Well, I was in charge of operating that cyclotron, but I wasn't operating it to extend her husband's life. I was just trying to find out something more about physics." Dr. Livingston broke in two a long piece of chalk he was holding. "Frankly," he said, "I'd hate it if a close friend of mine was depending on my making an all-night run with a cyclotron to turn out radioactive material to cure his disease. It would distort my sense of detachment. I'm interested in fundamental knowledge, but of course it pleases me to know, statistically, that cyclotrons have helped people."

Dr. Livingston abruptly switched the subject and began to talk with animation about a new machine that he and several of his assistants are designing, a refinement of the cyclotron, called a proton synchrotron. This kind of machine is still only a concept; none has ever been built before. It will take five years, Dr. Livingston thinks, to complete the first one. "It'll cost twenty-five million dollars," he told me, "and it won't work unless its crew has flashes of genius." He expects that the machine will accelerate particles to "the energy of billions of electronic volts," which is much beyond anything yet achieved. "I think we'll be able to create matter out of energy with it. And there's a negative proton that's never been observed, and if any machine can help us do that, it'll be the proton synchrotron."

"And it's impossible to foretell to what use this negative proton will be put?" I asked.

Dr. Livingston closed his eyes in pain, then patiently replied, "I don't really know. That's not my department."

A few doors down the corridor, I noticed the office of a double doctor—a man who holds both a Ph.D. and an M.D. degree. He is on leave from his chair at the Yale Medical School. He agreed to talk with me if I would agree not to name him. "We in medicine," he began cautiously, "are dealing with people, not theories. We don't like them to get their hopes up. It's not fair to us, either. We know so little about this new field." Brookhaven's pile and cyclotrons will be important to medical-research people because it will be a constant and plentiful supply of radioactive materials. "What are the effects," he asked, as though addressing a class of medical students, "of the terrific punch of one ten-thousandth of a second's radiation as compared to *x* minutes of Roentgen rays?" Radiation, he explained in partial answer to his own question, has already caused mutations in penicillin molds which have resulted in both a greater yield and a reduction in cost. The same will be true of streptomycin, which at present runs to a thousand dollars for enough for a brief series of shots. A great deal will also be learned about the effects of radiation on human beings when Brookhaven has its hospital in operation. The hospital, which will be the first of its kind—handling mostly radiation and cancer cases, and specializing in the use of isotopes—will have a hundred beds. "And in addition," the doctor added, "we'll be learning right along from the experiments on our animal farm." Having a hospital close to the Brookhaven pile will be an advantage, since medically useful isotopes, whose half-life may be as short as ten minutes, can be rushed to the hospital and used at once. No one can yet estimate the value of isotopes in investigating diseases against which the medical profession has made little headway. "They're chemical microscopes," the doctor said. "They have a sensitivity thousands of times greater than anything we've ever known. That's about all we know."

The doctor told me that one of his main interests is now geriatrics. "Geriatrics," he said, "is the opposite of pediatrics. It's the care of the old. It's a relatively new field and it's about time we looked into it. When older people contract a disease, we say it's because they're old, and we call their disease 'degenerative.' A highly fatalistic attitude. It reminds me of the way certain primitive peoples treat the older members of their tribes. They hit them over the head or throw them off a cliff, on the erroneous theory that they contribute nothing."

He hopes that between the effects of radiation and the tracing talents of isotopes the mysteries of geriatrics will be dispelled. Cancer, arteriosclerosis, diabetes, and anemia are among the diseases and conditions that, when they occur to older people, are often called "degenerative." "Take anemia," the doctor said. "We have a little cell—the red cell—that, when certain ions of potassium collect in it, causes anemia. But we don't know how potassium gets there. How do living cells concentrate those ions? Up to now, no one has been able to study the behavior of cells. With the help of radioactive tracers, we may be able to find out just how 'degenerative' anemia or any other disease is. We'll be able to tell if there is fundamental alteration or change of cellular environment." He stopped abruptly. " 'Change of cellular environment!' " he repeated. Then he laughed. "Why, come to think of it, that's exactly what we mean when we say we're sick!"

The next man I talked to was Dr. Norman Ramsey, a very friendly consultant in the Physics Section. His office is also in the Research Staff Building. He didn't care one way or the other about whether I named him. He told me that a few days before he had performed a little stunt that rather impressed him. He had given a talk on the principles of nuclear physics in one of the auditoriums to the laboratory's clerks, stenographers, watchmen, mechanics, and maintenance crew. He had done this on the dare of a friend, who doubted that anyone could make the subject interesting to an untutored audience. To his surprise, the lecture had gone over. "At least," he said, "this is what my skeptical friend and the stenographers told me." He had been asked to make the speech again, so that more of Brookhaven's non-technical employees could hear it. This reaction had revived his faith in a notion he has held since August, 1945. "I honestly believe," he said, "that anyone can understand enough physics to get rid of the idea that the world is confronted by some supernatural hocus-pocus. I've had the fear that scientists are tending to become a special class. We're so damn busy that it's not easy for us to go out and give lectures. We work even when we're not on the job. Physics is a highly sociable profession. We visit each other evenings, drink beer, and the beer leads to ideas. Sometimes an idea starts out as a joke—the person who spouts it doesn't believe in it, but his listeners do. Sooner or later, we'll have to get sociable with the public." Dr. Ramsey's interest in instructing the laity is only partly idealistic. "I want this laboratory to work," he told me. "I don't feel like a Frankenstein for what I did during the war, but I don't mind telling you that I sleep better nights now that I'm back in fundamental research. I'd be miserable if a hostile public spoiled things. All we're doing at present is telling them that the laboratory isn't endangering their lives, so they tolerate us. But if they get to know some physics, they may really want us."

Dr. Ramsey took out of a desk drawer a copy of the talk he had delivered to the Brookhaven employees and handed it to me to read. In an incredulous tone, he said, "It's the damnedest thing that these Long Island stenographers should have liked it. So did the Air Forces' 509th Composite Group. I gave the same talk to them. That was in August of '45, in the Marianas. The *Enola Gay* took off from there for Hiroshima, and the Air Force fellows wanted to know what had hit the Japanese city. As it happened, I was one of the five physicists who assembled the Nagasaki and Hiroshima bombs."

Dr. Ramsey and I walked out of his office into an anteroom, where a gentleman with a magnificent head of gray hair and a distressed look was waiting to see him. Dr. Ramsey introduced him to me as Mr. Eldon C. Shoup, and asked if he might be excused for a few minutes while he made a telephone call that couldn't wait. Mr. Shoup shrugged. He is the executive vice-president of Associated Universities and has a lot to do with Brookhaven's budget. Before coming there, he was merchandising manager for a paper manufacturing company, and during the war he did administrative work for one of the wartime federal agencies. "It's some job trying to watch the budget in a laboratory like this," he said. "With paper products, it's easy. You know where you stand. For instance, a little cost accounting, and you can figure out how much a hundred bolts of crepe paper will cost to make. But with electronics—why, you can't even tell what will happen to something as simple as an amplifier when you buy one for those scientists. You drop in to see how the amplifier is working and it's been turned into just a box. The fellow tells you, 'The time constant didn't respond fast enough, so I ripped it apart. This box is first-class. Thanks a lot.' " Sometimes, Mr. Shoup said, the scientists get the amount of money they want confused with the voltages they need. So far, he has had to revise his budget figures every three months. "Once," he remarked, "I decided to be strict with a physicist who had put in for a couple of million dollars' worth of equipment. 'Now,' I said to him, 'exactly what purpose is this equipment intended for?' 'Sir,' he told me, 'if I knew exactly what I was going to get out of my research, I wouldn't be asking for the equipment.' "

From the Research Staff Building, I went to call on Dr. Lyle Borst, one of the country's leading pile experts. His office is in a white wooden building a quarter of a mile away, off by itself. When I reached it, I found a grim, highly inhospitable special policeman sitting at a receptionist's desk. He looked me over and asked what I wanted. Then he picked up a phone, watching me all the while. In a few minutes, Dr. Borst, a slight, thin-faced man, appeared, wearing an overcoat. He eyed the cop and then said to me, "How about going outside and finding a place to talk there? That is, if it isn't too cold for you."

He told me, after we had found ourselves a bench on the lawn, that he was busy at the moment trying to figure out how to dispose of waste radioactive materials. "For the first time," he said, "man is creating something that cannot be destroyed—radioactive materials. Burning them or drowning them won't do it. You'd be banking on a chemical reaction. Here we are dealing with nuclear reactions." Most of the waste materials decompose pretty quickly, but he is concerned with those that don't. "For example," he said, "technetium—that's Element No. 43—is only half shot after fourteen thousand years, and radioactive carbon after five thousand years. The stuff mustn't ever be let loose. If their radiation gets into biological organisms, including human beings, it will destroy them." At present, the materials are not a danger; thick concrete tanks, sunk deep into the ground, will contain them safely as long as they are not disturbed. "But," he pointed out, "since we're thinking in terms of geological ages, how are you going to guarantee that some damn-fool archeologist won't go sticking his nose into the stuff ten thousand years from now?" The best thing, Dr. Borst thinks now, would be to remove these nuclear booby traps from the planet. "One notion we've been kicking around is to send the stuff by rocket to the moon. Half the time we can't tell if we're kidding, but we keep talking about it. If a big enough rocket were ever developed, the idea might not be implausible. I say get the stuff away from the earth. Isolate it. Use the moon as a graveyard. The lovers won't mind. The moon will look the same as ever." Dr. Borst then told me about another, more pedestrian precaution that he has been turning over in his mind. "I think," he said, "that warning notices in many different languages ought to be inscribed at such strategic spots as piles and storage tanks where these long-lived materials are kept. Then, if there is a war, the conquering invader may treat his booty with the proper respect. The invader would certainly know how to read. Yes, first he'll drop atomic bombs, then he'll have to be cilivized."

Before I left, Dr. Borst said that he hoped I hadn't minded the cop's fussiness. The building is restricted territory. "I'm in charge of the pile," he explained. "And the pile is top secret. I couldn't have you in my office." He said that every time something goes wrong at Lake Success, the security regulations for the pile scientists become tighter. The politicking of some of the United Nations delegates has dismayed him. He guessed that, working on a pile as he has been doing, he had a rather different attitude toward the world. "I see everything through a periscope," he said, smiling, "from behind a thick concrete wall—the Concrete Curtain." His hand swept the section of Brookhaven I had come from. "Those fellows are lucky. They're not confined completely to classified material. I'm thinking of changing my specialty. I've been in it since Oak Ridge was first planned, eight years ago. That's a long time to be quiet." His tone became mildly cheerful. "But perhaps I oughtn't to complain," he said. "I'll be among the first to know when international peace is a reality. The day it happens, I'll be told I can open my mouth."

CHAPTER 9 | JANUARY, 1947

SEARCH FOR A HIDEOUT

WHILE AMERICAN MILITARY men concede they still have a good deal to learn about atomic weapons, they are already agreed on at least one point—that if an effective system for the control of atomic energy is not put into operation, the United States will need underground sites for shelters, factories, and warehouses, as well as for installations from which crews of specialists can direct aerial missiles toward the enemy. The admirals and generals aren't given to saying much publicly about this matter, and have, indeed, issued only one official statement on it. That was a collaborative effort of the Army and Navy, put out a while ago by their joint Munitions Board, saying that in the course of an impending nationwide survey of suitable subterranean sites, considerable attention would be given to natural caves. "Among the characteristics [of caves] to be recorded," the announcement read, "are floor space, ceiling, humidity, overhead cover, soil and rock conditions, access approaches, and general interior conditions. Other factors which will be considered are concealment from aerial observation and proximity to transportation, communications, utilities, and housing facilities."

Shortly after the appearance of this announcement, I heard that civilian volunteers were helping out the authorities by exploring "wild caves," as caves that are not exploited commercially are known. Long before the Munitions Board became interested, these explorers, or speleologists (the word "speleology" comes from the Greek word *"spēlaion,"* meaning "cave"), had been poking around caves for reasons of either science or sport. Now, since the development of the atomic bomb, their peculiar researches have taken on an unexpected importance. It occurred to me that it might be enlightening to accompany a group of speleologists on one of their field trips, and after some investigations as to who could arrange this I called up William E. Davies, chairman of the Mapping Committee of the National Speleological Society, in Washington. I told him what I wanted. "You ever been in a wild cave?" he asked me. I said that I hadn't, and that the only cave I'd ever been in was one that used to be frequented by tourists, not far from the grotto at Lourdes. "Well," Davies replied, with what I took to be a speleologist's brusqueness, "there's nothing I can do to stop you. We're going down to West Virginia this weekend to look over Trout Cave. Bring along old clothes. Be down here Saturday morning."

I got to the capital a day early, because I wanted to dig up somebody who could elaborate a little on the official announcement. By late afternoon, after considerable heel-cooling in anterooms, I succeeded in having a talk with two officers who were familiar with the subject—one from the Army and one from the Navy, and both displaying enough rank to get a salute out of an enlisted man in peacetime. They didn't want to be identified in any way, so I will call them simply the Colonel and the Commander. The Commander, who did most of the talking, told me that he really didn't have much to say about the speleological activities of the armed forces, because the country's "back-to-the-caves movement," as he jocularly called it, was still in its infancy. The survey, he said, had so far been mostly a matter of compiling what was already known about caves and abandoned mines, a task on which the Bureau of Mines, Army engineers, geology professors, and members of the National Speleological Society were co-operating. As yet, almost all the field work was being done by the speleological volunteers. "This thing may be big," the Commander went on, warming to his subject, "bigger than the Manhattan District. People have got to be educated. They've got to become underground-conscious. I'd like to see industry start thinking about putting plants underground. We were mighty impressed with what we found in Germany. Those jet-plane factories in salt mines, I mean."

"Hell," the Colonel broke in, "the Army of Occupation is still out looking for some of those factories. Finds more all the time."

"After all," the Commander continued, "sunlight isn't so wonderful. You have to be near a window to benefit by it. With fluorescent fixtures, you get an even light all over the place. I was reading only the other day about a factory the Swedes put underground when they thought Hitler might bomb them. They found it was cheaper to run than the surface-type plant. No paint bills, no roof fixing, no window washing."

"Personally," the Colonel said, with a shrug, "I don't think there's enough uranium in the world to do all that damage they've been talking about. Aviators will always miss targets. The fellows who figure these things don't take into account how many bombs hit the wrong targets in the war. Uranium's going to be wasted the same way."

The Commander politely waited until he was sure the Colonel had finished, and then said, "It's that old American disease. We never act until we have an emergency on our hands. Mind you, it's not just civilians, either. Why in hell's my own crowd pulling back to Washington? They ought to stay aboard their ships, or if it's shore duty they want, they ought to pick themselves a berth outside the capital. It gives me the willies every time I think of how concentrated we are in this town. This is no time for getting concentrated. The country's got to disperse."

Shortly after seven the following morning, Davies picked me up at my hotel. I was sitting on a sofa in the lobby, drowsily trying to comprehend the morning paper, when he arrived and had me paged. He is an intelligent-looking, stocky, brown-haired man of thirty, who majored in geology at M.I.T. and Michigan State and is now a War Department civilian specialist, working as chief of research for the Army Map Service. He lives with his wife and small daughter across the Potomac in Arlington. "This cave hunting probably seems far-fetched to you," he said as we shook hands. "I certainly hope it turns out to be." We walked across the street to his car and started off on the five-hour drive to Franklin, West Virginia, the town nearest Trout Cave. Six other people, who were also driving down from Washington, were to join us there. An earlier group of speleologists, Davies told me as he picked his way through the capital's traffic, had already mapped part of Trout. Today's party, it was hoped, would go a long way toward completing the job. When the map was finished, it would be turned over to the armed forces.

Trout Cave, according to Davies, who had been in it on a couple of previous occasions, looked quite promising, but most of the caves that the Society had already fully mapped came nowhere near conforming to the specifications that the Munitions Board had laid down. "They've told us they want areas of fifty thousand square feet, with a slope to the floor of no more than five per cent," he said. "The minimum ceiling has to be eight feet and the minimum width ten. Not less than fifty feet for overhead coverage—from ceiling to ground surface, that is. Not so good. At least, I know I'd want more than fifty feet over *me* if an atomic bomb went off nearby. After all, blockbusters have been known to dig in thirty feet or more. That fifty-foot specification is probably a mistake. No doubt there'll be plenty of other boners. You have to remember that this underground-sites business is just in its first, formative stages."

So far, Davies said, the Munitions Board's survey was concerned simply with finding out how much ready-made underground space there is to help see the nation through an emergency. If it turns out that there's not enough, then presumably the authorities will want to start digging. As to where the digging ought to be done, all Davies knew was that big cities are not ideal spots. "It costs so darned much to dig a hole in them," he said. "Take a little hole, like the one for the Pennsylvania Station in New York—seven million dollars, and that was forty years ago. Probably cost more than twice as much now." Limestone, he said, is one of the softest kinds of rock, but of America's large cities, only Detroit and Chicago are built on that. Moreover, it would be pretty expensive to shore up the walls and ceilings of a shelter dug out of soft rock. Whether hard rock or soft rock provides the best protection against bombs is something of a question. I gathered; perhaps limestone, being porous, would absorb the impact of an explosion, riding with the blow, while a hard rock, like granite, might crack and collapse. "Up in New York," Davies told me, "they're sitting on gneiss and schist. Awfully old, hard rock."

We were driving through the rolling Virginia countryside near where the Battles of Bull Run were fought, and Davies broke off to point out a couple of historic landmarks. Then, returning to the subject of the day, he said that certain abandoned mines might serve the Munitions Board's purposes better than natural caves because many of their passageways are fairly level tunnels, with ceilings of adequate, fairly uniform height. Ordinarily, he went on, what chambers there are in coal and gold mines are not sufficiently large to be used without further excavation; silver mines, on the other hand, would probably not need enlargement. Davies, too, brought up the use to which the Germans had put their salt mines during the war. Salt mines, he said, made good wartime hideaways because they are extremely dry and can easily be enlarged. Unfortunately, he said, the United States has only a few salt mines—near Detroit and in upstate New York. Lead, limestone, and copper mines might make good, safe shelters, but there aren't many of the first two kinds, and copper mines are often so deep that water seepage is likely to cause trouble. Many iron-ore mines are of the open-pit variety and therefore useless. "All in all," Davies said, "the man-made caves in this country won't solve the Munitions Board's problem."

The Speleological Society, Davies went on, was founded in 1939 and has a membership of six hundred men and women. The majority of them burrow about in caves just for the fun of it and take only a passing interest in the scientific aspects of the thing. The speleologists refer to such members as "spelunkers." Two of the people we would meet in Franklin, Davies said, were spelunkers who had once been mountain climbers by avocation but had switched to caves because they thought it more exciting underground, where the hazards are the same but the setting is less prosaic. "It all begins," Davies continued, "when you find yourself in a hole somewhere in the side of a cliff. In a commercial cave that's been pepped up with colored lights and things, you take a quick look and leave. But in a dark cave, that old urge to come to grips with the unknown hits you. And when you have drops that may be two hundred feet to watch out for, you really feel as though you had the unknown right in your hands." "Is that the kind of cave Trout is?" I asked, in a tone that must have conveyed anxiety, for Davies laughed reassuringly as he replied, "Oh, Trout's a cinch. Why, a lot of it's dry, and it even has a horizontal mouth. Most caves are muddy and you have to squeeze down vertical holes. But you may find Trout dirty. The Confederates mined saltpeter there to make gunpowder during the Civil War, and the rocks are still covered with soot from the miners' flares. We'll need long, hot baths tonight."

We reached the Skyline Highway and started climbing the Blue Ridge range. "We're coming into limestone country," Davies said, and after that we rode along in silence for half an hour or so, admiring the mountain scenery. Then, as the highway began to run downgrade, Davies returned to speleology. "Some people will tell you that it isn't really a science in itself," he said, "but a part of a number of other sciences. Take me, for instance. I'm a geologist, and I can naturally learn more about the structure of the earth by studying its interior than I can by staying on its surface. Hydrologists have a better idea of the qualities of the water in the vicinity of a cave after they've studied moisture conditions inside it. Botanists make a study of the fungus plants that grow in caves and thrive without light; you drop a bread crumb in some caves and by the end of a month it's sprouted filaments two feet long. Archeologists are forever turning up old Indian dwellings in caves, and paleontologists sometimes find prehistoric skeletons right in the same place. We've had herpetologists join our parties, too, looking for cave-dwelling salamanders that have become blind through the ages, and entomologists have come along to collect semitransparent crickets. And this afternoon we're going to have a nuclear physicist with us—Joseph Rush. It's his first trip. He, too, has become curious about caves."

The scientists and sportsmen get along together fine on these trips, Davies said, and the spelunkers often pitch in to help their more purposeful comrades with such chores as taking temperature or humidity readings and testing the acidity of water with chemically treated paper. "You never can tell how those spelunkers will come in handy," Davies said. "Last year, in a cave, another fellow and I ran across a rare black stalactite on a ledge about six feet above our heads. We wanted it badly but couldn't figure out any way to get at it. My friend weighed a hundred and eighty and I weighed a hundred and sixty, so we couldn't very well lift each other. Just then, a young girl who was a member of our party came walking by. Nice and thin. Why, she was no harder to hoist up there than Katharine Hepburn, and she had that stalactite down in a minute."

We had crossed the West Virginia line and were driving fast on Highway 220, alongside a narrow creek. "That's the Potomac," Davies said. "It pinches out around here. Its headwaters are only a few miles away." Then he was back on his favorite subject again, wondering aloud if the armed forces' sudden interest in caves would make more people speleology-minded. He said he hoped so, because there was still a lot to be learned about caves. "I'd be glad to see them make a study of health conditions in caves," he went on. "No matter what cave you tackle in this region, you can count on a constant temperature of between fifty and fifty-six degrees inside, and nearly always on high humidity. I don't know if that's good or bad for a person, but I do know that I've never caught cold in a cave. Some pretty smart friends of mine think that dampness at a constant temperature might be good for consumptives, but others say that germs have a field day underground, because there's no sunlight. It would be nice to find out."

Davies said he hoped that, now the Army and Navy were pushing the hunt, more caves would speedily be discovered. It was his guess that for every known cave there are nine unknown ones. Electrical devices and other equipment that his Society cannot afford are needed to locate them. Up to now, caves have been discovered mostly by accident. "And that usually happens on a sharp winter's day," Davies said, "when the air from the cave hits the colder air outside. Hunters or kids out on a hike see the vapor coming out of the earth, go take a look, and there's your cave. Or sometimes a farmer will find the mouth of a cave right in one of his fields. Those vertical mouths make trouble. A farmer I know up in Cumberland, Maryland, told me that two of his horses fell into caves like that last summer while he was plowing. He has a neighbor who cusses something fierce because his crowbars disappear into the ground whenever he tries to build a fence. Up in my country, in Pennsylvania, I know of hundreds of sheep and cattle that have broken their legs that way. Why, I once heard of a farmer out in Kansas whose house suddenly went sinking into the ground. I don't know, people get off a ship and talk about how good it feels to have solid earth under them." Davies chuckled. "Why kid yourself?" he said. "The earth's hollow."

At twelve-thirty, we reached Franklin, population 613. We registered at the town's one hotel, where the lady desk clerk, who remembered Davies from other expeditions, told him that the rest of the party were eating in a restaurant across the street. We dumped our stuff in the lobby and joined them. They were just finishing their meal. Rush, the nuclear physicist, is a reticent, serious man of thirty-five, an alumnus of Texas A. and M., who was at Oak Ridge during the war. The group included a geographer—Dr. William Brierly, a tall, pipe-smoking man who is employed, like Davies, by the Army Map Service, and who holds a Ph.D. from Clark University, in Massachusetts. The two ex-mountain climbers, Johnny Meenehan and Jack Wilson, looked about Davies' age. Meenehan works in a photography shop in Washington and Wilson in the office of a lumber company there. The president of the Speleological Society, William Stephenson, a rather intense man of forty-three, was also at the table. During the week, he works in the Patent Office, for the Department of Commerce. "Hope you're not tired," he said to me with the solicitude of an Eagle Scout toward a Tenderfoot. "Too bad the cave couldn't come to us." The sixth member of the group was a girl Marine, absent from duty on a week-end pass, who was introduced to me as Dutch Schultz. (Her first name turned out to be Claire.) She is a spelunker—twenty, affable, and reminiscent of a recruiting poster. She comes from Brooklyn, a fact that, she later told me, she thought had something to do with her interest in caves. "It's so crowded in Brooklyn," she said. "I always feel so much better when I'm in a cave."

After Davies and I had had something to eat, we all went over to the hotel and changed to old clothes. When we reassembled in the lobby, Stephenson handed me a miner's brown helmet he had thoughtfully brought along for me. "Holds a carbide lamp and protects your head from the rocks," he said. Everyone else had a helmet, all brown except Meenehan's, which was red and had "ICE COLD BEER" stenciled on it in white—a souvenir, I surmised, of an earlier and possibly more lighthearted speleological junket.

We got into our cars and drove a few miles southwest of Franklin, still following Highway 220, which presently led into a narrow valley, lying between an almost perpendicular cliff about nine hundred feet high, to which clung a few boulders and scraggly trees, and a looming mountain so thickly covered with fir trees that, though the day was sunny, it had a dark and somber look. The road brought us directly below the cliff, where we pulled over into the grass and stopped beside a pasture in which a fine herd of Jerseys was grazing. Beyond them, at the foot of the mountain, were a low, white farmhouse and a barn. As we got out, I noticed a smell of mint in the air. It was a difficult setting in which to concentrate on atomic war. Stephenson pointed to what looked like a black dot on the face of the cliff, about a third of the way up. "That's it," he said to me. "That's Trout's mouth."

Meenehan and Wilson briskly opened their car trunk and pulled out a large clump of rope. "We've got four hundred feet," Meenehan said. "That ought to do it." Wilson took one end of the rope, trotted down the highway with it, and then, with the help of Meenehan and Dutch, shook the whole thing free of snarls. Meenehan tied the other end to his belt and began to climb the cliff, his red helmet bobbing up and up as he sprang from one toe hold to the next. He reached the mouth of the cave in about ten minutes and tied the rope to a gnarled and stunted tree near it. "O.K.!" he yelled down. One after another, at intervals of a minute or so, the members of the party grabbed the rope and started up. I rightly suspected that I would be the slowest, so I waited until last, and then spent most of the next half hour slipping, sliding, and falling to my knees.

When I finally managed to reach the entrance to the cave, I found the rest of the group waiting for me. "Good-sized mouth for a cave," Davies told me cheerfully as I lay on the ground gasping. "Has a width of twelve feet and a height of eleven."

Stephenson was apparently exhilarated by the climb. "I could build me a house here!" he exclaimed. "Rainy days, Trout would be my front yard, fair days—that." With a sweep of his arm, he indicated the mountain opposite us and the floor of the valley, with the now tiny cows grazing in it far below.

"Of course," Davies continued, seemingly not at all impressed by Stephenson's fair-weather front yard, "this entrance might need lead or reinforced-concrete gates to protect against flash effects. Otherwise, the blasts might penetrate pretty far in." He looked hopefully at Rush, but the nuclear physicist made no comment.

"Well," Brierly said, "it wouldn't take many guards to keep saboteurs out."

"No," Rush said, "but the guards would have to have Geiger counters as a precaution against any atomic time bombs a saboteur might try to sneak by them."

My companions began to light their carbide lamps and clip them to their helmets. The lamps threw only a pale light in the sunny entrance. Davies pulled out the map the first surveying party had made, studied it a moment, and said, "There won't be much for us to do in the first two chambers we come to. They've already been surveyed pretty thoroughly. Don't get lost," he warned me as I scrambled to my feet. "Stay close to us." We filed into the cave, and almost at once it broadened and the ceiling grew higher until it was perhaps some thirty feet above us. "This first chamber alone," Davies said, "takes care of that fifty-thousand-square-feet specification. It's four hundred and fifty feet by a hundred and ten." The carbide beams were now sharp and penetrating. Straggling along in loose formation, as though we were on our way to a picnic, we had proceeded only a hundred yards or so when I looked back, hoping for a final, reassuring glimpse of sunlight. I was too late; the mouth of the cave was out of sight, and so far as I was concerned, we were lost in the underground.

The walls began to converge, and soon we came to a hundred-foot passage only four feet wide. About forty feet from its entrance there was a pit some twenty feet long and fifteen feet deep. It was spanned by a log, perhaps six inches in diameter, which, I was told, had been put there by the Confederate miners. I was surprised and relieved that it showed no signs of rot. The walls were quite jagged, and we had to hold onto them to balance ourselves as we teetered across the log. When I reached the other side, my hands were scratched in a number of places and black from Confederate soot.

Brierly was the first across, and by the time the rest of us caught up with him, he was exclaiming, "Beautiful! Beautiful!" over a grayish object, about an inch long and shaped like a peg, that he had found. I asked him what he took it to be. "Alas! Poor Yorick!" he said. "He died two hundred and fifty million years ago, in Devonian times. Hail, noble brachiopod, first cousin of the clam!"

"Don't mind Bill," Davies said. "He's crazy about fossils."

The going became painfully slow. Finally, the corridor widened into another chamber, about as large as the first, whose floor was a jumble of massive boulders, ten or twelve feet high, like the bed of a river below a falls. "God, what a mess!" Meenehan grunted, as he clambered over one.

"I've seen whole precision-instrument factories that were smaller than this room," Stephenson said, and added, thoughtfully, "Perhaps convict labor could be used for cleaning up this debris." The boulders pleased Davies. "Usually," he said, "I'm a little leery of dry limestone caves like Trout. The wet ones are generally safer, because water cements limestone. But one look at stuff this size and anyone can see that Trout has already had the big collapse that most caves have at one time or another. Still," he added cautiously, "I'd keep an eye out for unstable ledges." He pointed to the ceiling, now some twenty feet high. "Good," he said. "Nice and arched. Ceilings are less secure when they're flat."

Rush spoke up. "Mr. Davies, isn't limestone a rather porous rock?" he asked.

"Darned right," Davies replied. He looked at Rush sharply. "I suppose you mean molecular activity," he said. "I suppose you're thinking that radioactive gas might seep through."

The physicist shrugged. "Of course, I don't *know,*" he said.

"And," said Davies, "who does? Maybe there ought to be a test bombing of caves."

"Well," Rush replied, "the bombs that have been used so far have exploded above the target. But for caves I suspect that there might be a type made that would penetrate two or three hundred feet before going off. It might shake the ceiling loose."

The other members of the party, leaning against the begrimed boulders, were silent. "It's weird," Davies said musingly, "to think of Trout being brought down around our ears by a bomb."

"Oh, let's get going," Wilson said. "We haven't even done any crawling yet."

At the far end of the chamber, we came upon a large colony of bats clinging, in clusters of a hundred or more, to the stony ceiling, which was only five or six feet over our heads. Brierly said that they were the same variety of brown bat that one sees flitting about in the twilight on summer evenings but that they were hibernating and therefore only about half as large. "Their pulse is way down to conserve their energy," he explained. "They stay close together like that for warmth." Our presence seemed to disturb the bats; they stirred uneasily and about twenty of them swelled up to normal size, detached themselves from their clusters, and began to fly around. One of them whizzed past me, and I ducked. Brierly smiled and assured me that there was nothing to worry about. "As you probably know, bats have a wonderful radar system," he said. "They emit a high-frequency sound, inaudible to us, that bounces back from any object they're approaching and warns them to change their course." Just then, one of the bats sideswiped Davies' helmet. "Maybe that one's radar isn't working so well today," Brierly said. "He's probably sleepy."

Twenty feet past the bat colony, Wilson got his chance to crawl. The walls abruptly closed in until they were little more than a foot apart, and the ceiling dropped to between two and three feet above the floor. One after another, on our sides, we wriggled into the tunnel. I had barely started to inch forward when the Army field jacket I was wearing caught on a protuberance and there was a sound of cloth ripping. Brierly, who was behind me, called out airily, "Don't worry. That's just a bit of jutting coral. You should really feel quite snug in here—we've got six hundred feet of solid rock over us." Just then, there was a faint roaring noise, which seemed to come from far behind us. "Don't move," Brierly said, not quite so airily. The noise ceased. "Loose rock falling somewhere," he muttered, "but not very much of it, praise be."

The tunnel was about seventy-five feet long, and it took at least twenty minutes for the lot of us to wriggle our way through it. When we emerged, we were in a third high-ceilinged chamber, where Davies said we were to start our mapping operations. He produced a compass, studied it briefly, and then consulted his map. "Trout runs in an almost straight northeasterly line," he said. "If they wanted to, the Army and Navy could knock out the walls of these chambers and turn the place into one big cavern, with maybe enough room for a fairly large factory. On the other hand, they may prefer it the way it is—that is, with several compartments that could be sealed off if something went wrong in one part of the cave."

Dutch and Brierly began to measure the chamber with a fifty-foot tape, and Meenehan took pictures of it from various points with a flash camera. Brierly reported that the distance between two stalactites at the chamber's narrowest point was twenty feet. Davies put away his compass and got out a hygrometer, with which he took a humidity reading. "Eighty," he said. "Pretty dry for a cave." I was surprised that the humidity was so high; my mouth had felt parched for some time and I had presumed that it was the result of being in a so-called dry cave. I asked Davies about it. "Blame that on the saltpeter in the dust," he replied. "It's an alkaline."

Brierly said that reminded him of something he'd been concerned about: How could Trout, if used as a shelter, be supplied with water? "The Potomac's not far from here," he said, "and it never runs dry. Do you suppose it could be pumped up?"

Rush, who had been listening quietly, spoke up. "You'd have to pump like the devil to swing that," he said. "And you'd need large filtering works. You couldn't pump it up direct."

"Oh," Brierly protested, "the headwaters of a river ought to be clean."

"Come, come, now," Davies told him pleasantly. "You know as well as I do that one man's drinking water may be another man's sewer."

Stephenson, Wilson, and Meenehan had gone on through another tunnel. When the rest of us joined them in a fourth chamber, which they were measuring, they said they had come across a side passage that they had a hunch might lead to a new series of chambers, and they wanted to investigate. Davies thought that was a good idea, and the three adventurers swiftly disappeared into a hole near one end of the chamber. While they were gone, we completed the measurements for them. This chamber was somewhat smaller than the others we had seen, but Davies, staring speculatively at a cluster of hibernating bats, said he thought that it might at least be a good place for storage. "We may need enormous stock piles," he said. "Take food, for instance. Any enemy that uses atomic weapons will have an easy time contaminating the contents of grain elevators and canneries."

"Fissionable material might be stored here," Rush said.

"Or valuable documents," Davies said. "Like the aerial photographs that we took during the war."

"Or the Declaration of Independence," Rush said.

"This might even make a good office for the President," Brierly said. "He won't be able to stay in the White House. He'll have to be in a safe place."

Three flickering lights appeared in one corner of the chamber, and we heard Stephenson, Meenehan, and Wilson calling to us. They made their way over boulders to where we were standing, and reported that the passage had turned out to be what speleologists call a "parallel," meaning that it was rather like a detour on a highway, and from their point of view more or less of a fizzle. All of us pushed on again, along a corridor at the far end of the chamber, and after a short distance we struck mud, the first visible moisture we had come upon. Davies' hygrometer showed that the humidity here was a hundred. I noticed a white fluff of fungus at my feet, a growth that in the woods I might have kicked up into the air. Here, in this setting, it seemed like a rare and beautiful flower. "I guess this is where the cave stops being good," Davies said. "Half a mile from the entrance. That's about far enough for today." Stephenson, however, didn't agree. He had discovered an opening at the base of one of the corridor's walls. It was three feet in diameter and rimmed with sharp coral teeth. "I'm going to have a look in here," he told Davies. Meenehan, Wilson, and Dutch volunteered to join him. "Here's where the fun begins," Stephenson said. With that, he stretched out on his back, put his head into the jagged hole, and kicked at the floor of the cave to push himself in.

Davies showed the rest of us an alternate route back, which led, by way of more bridged pits and boulder-strewn passages, to still another chamber that he wanted to measure. It turned out to be gratifyingly long (four hundred and fifty feet) but rather narrow (forty-five feet). We were about to go on to the cave's mouth when we heard Dutch hallooing behind us. We yelled back, and in a moment her lamp shone through the darkness from the other end of the chamber. The crawl with Stephenson and the others had got too tough, she said, after laboriously clambering over the rocks to us, and she had given up at the end of thirty feet. She thought it would be a good idea if we waited for them. "Not that I'm worried, you know," she said, "but there were a lot of loose ledges."

Dutch sat down on a boulder. "I either like a cave or I don't," she said, petulantly. "And I don't like Trout. It's dirty. Piercy's Mill, over near Petersburg, is a nice cave. It has a river and two ponds." Davies was thinking along different lines. Trout, he said, was fortunate in having a good deal of dry area; moveover, it was as nearly level as the Army and Navy required, and had the advantage of being right beside a highway. Brierly observed that, even so, it was a fairly difficult cave to reach, but Davies pointed out that it was in what would look to an enemy like a non-strategic area, not worth bombing.

"Don't count on concealment," Brierly said. "Railroad spurs would have to be built to bring in supplies, and trucks would have to be parked down on the highway. You'd have to have contact with the outside world."

"You'd still have the protection of the cliff over you," said Davies.

"But your railroad lines wouldn't," Brierly retorted. "Nor would the town of Franklin, if that's where your personnel were housed."

"Well," Davies said, smiling, "maybe the bomb will be a dud."

Rush cleared his throat. "It's conceivable that this cave could be used for storage, but I'm not so sure about anything else," he said.

"Not for shelter or industry?" Brierly asked. Rush hesitated, and Brierly went on, "I guess you're still thinking about the cave's porosity and the possibility that an atomic bomb could penetrate this kind of rock."

"Yes," Rush said slowly. "And then there's the matter of air. Mammals breathe, machines need fires. If you tried to start up a blast furnace in a crowded, poorly ventilated cave, some carbon monoxide would be bound to escape and the first thing you knew your workers would start to feel drowsy, fall asleep, and never wake up. Obviously, you've got to have big blowers to keep your cave habitable. A blast furnace, for example, eats up fifteen to twenty thousand tons of air a day. All right, you camouflage your blowers, but the enemy spots your railroad spur leading to the cave and drops an atomic bomb. And the blowers suck in some radioactive particles along with the air and then where are you?"

"A cave is such a nice place in the summertime," Dutch said. "It's so cool."

The discussion subsided and we waited in silence for the return of Stephenson and his companions. I felt very hungry. "What time is it?" I asked.

"Nine-fifty," Brierly answered.

"Well," Rush said, "we missed the nice country sunset."

I tried to picture how the pasture out alongside Highway 220 looked now. The morning paper had predicted clear and considerably colder weather for the night, and there was to be a new moon. When Stephenson, Meenehan, and Wilson finally showed up, they were muddy and appeared to be tired but cheerful. Meenehan had found a fossil for Brierly. "What a crawl!" Stephenson exclaimed. "When we finally got to the end of that tunnel, I pulled out one of our membership blanks and left it there. Anybody who can get back there belongs in the Society." Then the eight of us started out over the boulders toward the new moon and the clear and considerably colder weather of the outdoors.

CHAPTER 10 | OCTOBER, 1947

THUNDER WITHOUT RAIN

THE THIRTY-FIVE-MILE ride from the small New Mexican capital of Santa Fe to Los Alamos—the only place in the world, as far as is known, where atomic bombs are being made—is a wearying, not particularly attractive journey. The road winds too much, and, since it is under repair in a number of places, a series of bumpy gravel detours have to be negotiated. The road crosses the Rio Grande, but the stream, belying the song, is very muddy, not silvery. And the country alongside the highway, caught in fleeting glimpses between auto jolts, seems brown and drab and unyielding. It is only after attaining the mesa, seventy-five hundred feet high, on which the unique community is situated that it is possible to see in what a lovely, flourishing setting atomic bombs are being made. The mesa itself is quite unbrown, with yellow and ponderosa pines, newly sown lawns, and Russian olive trees; Western tanagers and chestnut-backed bluebirds wing in and out of this greenness. To the north and south are neighboring plateaus, bordered off from Los Alamos by deep, weirdly shaped canyons. (One of them has "DANGER" signs nailed to the trees at its edges because some surplus radioactive material was dumped into it a few years ago.) Towering to the west are the Jemez Mountains; to the east is the Sangre de Cristo range, which is distinguished by the twin Truchas Peaks, thirteen thousand feet above sea level and the highest points in New Mexico. While I was in Los Alamos, the year's first snow, falling distantly, descended on the peaks until finally they looked like lone stationary clouds in the intensely blue skies with which this region is covered for more than three hundred days of the year. Also, the aspen trees in the mountains, interspersed among endless pine and spruce expanses, had turned, and they appeared as so many pale-yellow snowbanks below the Truchas Peaks. "The air is so pure and dry," an old friend of mine, a physicist who moved here with his family from Chicago, told me, as we were having a late-afternoon drink the day I arrived. "It's been so good for the children. They do seem much stronger to you, don't they? Another thing, they're not as high-strung as they used to be in Chicago. I think the country has a lot to do with that. The mountains are soothing. They're so permanent. Nothing could ever disturb those mountains—nothing except maybe our bombs."

Like the setting, the town, or, as everyone calls it, the Hill, is in a flourishing state. A great variety of conveniences have been installed. More are under way. This tendency toward civic improvement is not surprising, since the community's collective I.Q. is quite possibly one of the highest in America. Of its eight thousand inhabitants, fourteen hundred are scientists and engineers with college educations. Government officials, comparably schooled, make up six hundred, and eight hundred other residents are highly skilled technicians. The child population comes to two thousand. Civil-service clerks, maintenance crewmen, and transient construction workers account for the rest. The first settlers of this atomic colony, the men who arrived late in 1942, could have qualified as Philosophers in a Platonic Republic. Then, seventy-five outstanding scientists, versed in natural phenomena, Palestrina and Bartók, painting, and fine cooking, surreptitiously invaded Los Alamos to see what could be done with a mesa. The only obstacle to their investiture was A. J. Connell, the operator of the Los Alamos Ranch School, an institution that was attended by forty-three wealthy boys who had been sent, mostly from the East, to become healthy and, if possible, wise. When an Army officer told the headmaster that the school, which Connell himself had founded thirty years before, had come to the end of its days, Connell replied, "You must be mistaken. The property is not for sale." He then listened to a longish dissertation on the government's condemnatory powers. The boys were, however, permitted to finish the school year. By the time they left, military police were on guard at the tableland's extremities. Connell retired to Santa Fe, where he died two years later.

The log structures and stone cottages that Connell built for the boys and masters are now the show places of the mesa. As some kind of testimonial, top officials and scientists have appropriated for themselves the limited number of dwellings left behind by the headmaster. Two of the larger buildings, the Big House and Fuller Lodge, are used as sleeping quarters for visitors as well as for a few permanent employees. Fuller Lodge, an efficiently managed three-story log building, with a big stone fireplace, large bedrooms, and handsome hickory furniture, is considered good enough to handle the glamour that occasionally comes to the mesa in the form of congressmen and senators. One of the dignitaries I met, a Pennsylvania congressman, was so favorably impressed with the accommodations at Fuller Lodge that he declared, "This place is better than any motel we've hit." The "we" included himself and his bride of a few weeks. They had decided to spend their honeymoon by taking a motor trip to the nation's various atomic installations, thus combining pleasure and Congressional business. During their sojourn at Los Alamos, the bride got in a few rubbers of bridge with the local lady card players and the groom, to qualify himself as an authority on nuclear energy, went up in a plane and buzzed the Alamogordo site where the first bomb was exploded in 1945. A member of the Joint Congressional Committee on Atomic Energy, an Ohio Senator, also breezed in, by plane, while I was at Los Alamos, but he didn't stay as long as some people there had hoped he would. He arrived at two-thirty in the afternoon and by five-thirty he had completed his field work and was off again.

Since the Los Alamos Scientific Laboratory, to use the establishment's official name, arrived more than four years ago, in 1943, the Ranch School's buildings have been surrounded by hundreds of others. In fact, the plateau, which measures only six miles by two, is as crowded as many cities, despite its location in one of the Union's least populated states. The heart of the community is, of course, the Technical Area, where the strategic laboratory is to be found. The Laboratory does not approach in size the immense factories at Oak Ridge, but it is, in fact, only a laboratory, not a production center of fissionable materials. The Tech Area, as it is popularly known, is bisected by Trinity Avenue ("Trinity" was the code word for the bomb test in 1945). On either side of the street are high, steel-wire fences and, at close intervals, huts for sentries whose duty is to keep out of the area, the most closely guarded in the country's entire atomic domain, unauthorized personnel. By looking through one fence, you can see a small pond on which the schoolboys used to canoe and boat. It reminded me of a swamp, but perhaps the cluster of research buildings which surrounds it makes it seem smaller and shallower than it is. The buildings are, for the most part, painted a ghastly green. They are wooden, two or three stories high, and remarkable only in that their plainness would never intimate to an outsider that they contain fabulously expensive equipment and rare materials. Another thing I could see by looking through the fence was that one of the Tech Area's boundaries was formed by a canyon—a precipitous canyon, with a base of jagged boulders.

The relics of the Ranch School have also been joined by prefabs and trailers, and barracks buildings that have been converted into relatively cozy two- and four-family apartment houses. Dormitories have been erected for single people. A neighborhood of Quonset huts, ingenious rookeries in which the families of electricians, construction workers, and maintenance men dwell in confusion, has sprung up at the east end of the mesa. The Hill's western part is regarded as something of a Park Avenue. This is the section in which "permanent" houses have been built. Scientists and government officials live in most of them. The houses have been done in the style of the Southwest—one story, very wide windows, adobe exteriors. Their similarity would infuriate Frank Lloyd Wright, but they have six comfortable rooms, and the lady of the house has no servant problem, because Spanish maids from Santa Fe and Indian maids from the pueblos in the Pojuaque Valley are both available and efficient. Cafeterias, self-help laundries, and an eighteen-hole golf course help make up Los Alamos. So does a barnlike movie house, which is sold out daily. The Hill has a radio station, KRS (the call letters stand for Kommunity Radio Service), which has been especially constructed—it has no antenna—so that its programs cannot be heard by anyone who does not live in Los Alamos. The purpose of this is to keep any potential enemy plane from being able to fly in on a beam; ack-ack emplacements have been prepared against the possibility of an enemy raid.

A handsome high school and primary school have been constructed, and pains have been taken to hire good teachers. An abnormally high percentage of the schoolgoing public is in the primary school, the explanation being that it was only recently that the majority of scientific fathers were in high school. In the main, the youngsters, for reasons of one sort or another, consider their town acceptable enough. The winner of a recent essay contest, sponsored, during Fire Prevention Week, by the high-school civics teacher, declared that fires should be prevented in Los Alamos because the whole world considered it a great community since it was the place where the atomic bomb was made. Most high-school students I talked with thought the town was fine, because the school's football team, the Los Alamos Atomic Bombers, hadn't been licked in two years. Over at the primary school, I learned from the kindergarten teacher, Miss June Labovitz, a young Minneapolis girl, that her small pupils have a fairly detached attitude toward the town. During the war, she said, they played at murdering Japs. After the Hiroshima raid, each child bragged, "My daddy made the atomic bomb!" For the next year or so, the children would carefully build their blocks high and then dash into them, screaming, "I'm an atomic bomb!" They no longer exhibit such antics. "Now," Miss Labovitz said, "they play the same as they would if they lived in Minneapolis. Oh, everything's different from what it used to be in the old days on the Hill. I don't even dare wear slacks to work any more."

Miss Labovitz's wards are not the only ones who have proved adjustable. The community appears to have got used to itself. "We are stabilized," Dr. Norris Bradbury, the director of the Laboratory, assured me. He said this sententiously, because, for a while, the Laboratory's vicissitudes—such as mass resignations right after the war—made it look as though the American entry in the great atomic race might be scratched. Now, the Laboratory has settled down to a steady routine of bomb-making and some basic research. Another person who is interested in stabilization is the Atomic Energy Commission's new field manager, the top official on the Hill. He is an alert, considerate individual by the name of Carroll L. Tyler, a retired Navy captain who comes from Maine. Like many sea dogs, he is outspoken in manner, but he seems to be outspoken in behalf of someone else rather than himself. When he began planning a Community Center—a big affair consisting of bowling alleys, a dance hall, a bank, and so on—he made it a point to ask residents what they wanted the center to include. He is building more housing, good-looking, permanent units, which he is putting in the forlorn eastern section, not in the more elegant western area. "Right now," he told me, "you'd think we had railroad tracks running through the town, with the eastern area on the wrong side." Since his arrival, a Letters to the Editor column, which contains all kinds of complaints, appears regularly in the Los Alamos *Times,* a weekly newspaper, that can be easily controlled by the field manager's office. The captain has also been trying to arouse the town's interest in self-government, but the community, whose product could conceivably rule the world, is reluctant to rule itself. "When I came here," he said, "I was told that there'd been an awful lot of squawking about people not having a say in the Hill's affairs. I agree with the squawk, but just try to get them to write themselves a constitution, just try to find more than a handful of residents who really give a damn. Sure, I'd have to hold on to veto powers for myself. I've got my orders and I can't let anything affect security or weapon production, but when those weren't affected—and they would rarely be—I can assure you I'd hate to use my veto. Maybe the people here didn't really mean their squawk. Maybe they just like to let George do it."

Perhaps the townspeople aren't straining themselves over the theoretically alluring objective of self-government because life on the mesa is, apart from a few inconveniences, an agreeable and orderly one. At seven fifty-five each morning, a shrill steam whistle pierces the plateau's stillness. By then, Father has pecked at his wife, hugged his brood, and dashed for the Tech Area. Five minutes later, the whistle blasts again, and Father, if he is punctual, starts his day's work with his cyclotron and radioactive materials. Mother spends the morning by getting the kids off to school, telling her Indian or Spanish maid what to do, and shopping at the Supermarket. If her husband doesn't work too far from the house, she stands a fair chance of lunching with him. Even if he doesn't show up, she can still look forward to her afternoon clubs—the

Garden Club, or the Parent Teachers Association, or the Ladies Auxiliary of the Veterans of Foreign Wars. Or she may be culture-conscious, in which case the Mesa Club is her dish. There she may see films on the Pueblo civilization, which once thrived in this region, or practice Christmas carols, or listen to a lecture by a member of the colony of artists who live between the Hill and Taos.

Shortly after five, the men are home and have the invariably beautiful twilights to watch with their family. Friends, a movie, or a little-theatre production can take care of the evening; the scientific set does a lot of record-listening. Week-ends people drive down to Santa Fe to shop and sit around the amiable bar at the Hotel La Fonda. The hunters go up into the mountains to keep the deer and the antelope from playing. The fishermen have the Rio Grande to investigate for trout; the more serious fishermen go up toward the Colorado border, two hours away, and tackle their sport all week-end, staying the night in crude cabin camps or on the ground in sleeping bags. A ski run is twenty minutes away. A number of the Hill's residents have become permanently fascinated by the pre-historic Indian ruins nearby, and inspect them whenever they have no steam whistles to hop to. The Hill itself is not without its events. Dorm Parties, gay affairs where it pays not to drink too much be-cause of the mesa's altitude, are frequently held. The Old Timers' Club throws square-dancing sessions at Fuller Lodge. The Civic Club, which has its own building, is jammed Saturday nights with happy bomb-makers doing the *Varsovienne,* a jolly Southwestern trot.

The serenity of life on the Hill, however, is not uninterrupted. Almost daily, explosions can be heard coming from nearby plateaus that have such names as North Mesa, South Mesa, and Two Mile Mesa. They usually mean that experiments are being carried on. When an especially loud bang goes off, someone, using the local pleasantry, will say, "Thunder." But it is thunder preceded by no lightning, accompanied by no clouds, and followed by no rain. At Sandia, near Albuquerque, the armed forces have a base whose purpose is to enable the military to grow better acquainted with nuclear arms. Possible exposure to radioactivity also does not make for serenity. All Tech Area employees are examined periodically;

some who work in special areas are given examinations so thorough that they have to be absent from their jobs for two days. The doctors look for something called Dickey bodies, make blood counts, and analyze urine. "You have to spot radiation exposure in its earliest phase," one of the Laboratory's doctors told me. "Otherwise, the burns knock out the bone marrow and that puts the patient in poor shape to fight infection."

When the Hill's fire engines go by, the residents trust that it is an ordinary fire, not one which involves radioactivity. A highly detailed system for evacuating Los Alamos in case of an accident that would cause a release of radioactive particles has been worked out. "The main point," Ralph Carlyle Smith, a Tech Area official, told me, "is to get out of the way of the wind. The wind here seems to come predominantly from the west, although it swirls a bit."

The hazards of fire and radioactivity have not, thanks to remarkably well-conceived safety precautions, interfered with the community's outward calm. Occasionally, however, the thought of the Hill's mission disconcerts its intellectuals. The bomb-making is not an inevitable topic of conversation in Los Alamos, but, once broached, it is discussed without hesitation, even volubly. The first reaction is almost invariably defensive. One point is usually made, and with strong conviction. As one electronics man stated it, "We're not just turning out weapons. We have what is probably the best-equipped lab in the world and we're carrying on plenty of basic research in it. Just like scientists elsewhere who claim they're doing peaceful research. Peaceful! How do they know their data won't be used militarily? How do we know our data won't be used for cancer? Science is ambiguous." It is only after this reaction that strained international affairs are offered as a justification for their work.

Personal reasons, of course, are also given. Some scientists confess to an absorption with "bomb physics." "You've no idea," one of this group informed me, "what interesting problems the weapon poses. We've still a long way to go, you know." Some know that they could never command jobs comparable to their present ones in a university where a Fermi or Oppenheimer was on the faculty. A number of the younger members of the scientific staff are pleased not to be earning a college instructor's miserable salary. Several find comfort in the thought that bombs can always be reconverted for peaceful uses. One fellow told me that the New Mexico climate had done wonders for his hay fever. A few are astonished at their power, which daily enables them to give orders to sizable groups of men, including Army and Navy brass. "They're big-time operators," a recently ordained Ph.D. explained, "but some of them aren't the physicists they used to be. Los Alamos is their Hollywood."

One of the Tech Area employees with whom I talked was Robert Davis, a young Californian who edits scientific treatises and who, incidentally, is a gifted painter. When I asked him what he thought about the Hill's production of weapons, he answered, "It doesn't matter any more. It does, of course, but not in the way it once might have. Now it is a detail. Right after the war, the disposition of the bomb could have been the setting for the arrangement of a durable peace. But the die seems to have been cast, mostly by powerful men. During the war, we used to have rabid political discussions here about what ought to be done eventually with the weapon, but now the reminiscences are only about big poker games and Dorm Parties. Even some of the men who swore that they would never set foot in Los Alamos again came back last summer for a brief bit as 'consultants.' Why not? The world situation is so lousy and in August it's so pretty and cool here. Inside the Tech Area, where people really know something about the bomb, you hear the same opinions you would expect from the man in the street, even if the street, in this case, happens to be a restricted one."

"What is to be done?" I asked.

Davis smiled.

"I'm painting like mad," he replied.

Dr. John Manley, a friendly, sensitive physicist of considerable reputation and influence, told me that he had gone through a long searching of himself before he had decided to settle down at Los Alamos. He had come to Los Alamos in April, 1943, quit in the fall of 1946 to teach at Washington University in St. Louis, and then returned at the start of 1947. The dates, he said, reflected the confusion through which he had passed. It was odd, he pointed out, that he should have remained a year longer than many of his colleagues, then decided to do what they had done, and, after only a few months away from New Mexico, come back. "The project," he explained, "almost fell apart after the war, but some of us had a purely intuitive feeling that the place ought to be kept alive. So I stayed on. But I don't find weapons delectable, and when Arthur Compton, the president of Washington University, offered me a post, I took it. University life has always appealed to me. You have summers off, you go to scientific meetings pretty much when you want to. I found St. Louis pleasant, but the newspaper stories went on being terrible, and after a while I asked myself, 'What am I doing?' Specifically, I was giving two courses and supervising the thesis work of five graduate students. I was also reading right-thinking magazines and sending occasional checks to right-thinking organizations. But it dawned on me that I wasn't being as effective as my training made possible, particularly in view of the fact that so few people at Los Alamos were really experienced. I went to Arthur Compton and told him that since I felt so deeply about the national and international situation, my job seemed sort of silly. I've often wondered," Manley continued, "if my friends thought my step was militaristic. Perhaps they might also wonder what I think of what they are doing. At least one of them knows. He is a wonderful physicist who is teaching at an Eastern university. His contribution to Los Alamos during the war was really significant. We've had long talks. He doesn't want to come back to Los Alamos. He says he must teach young people in order to ensure 'our national scientific strength.' This is very important, but, coming from a man of his special abilities, it is, in my opinion, sheer rationalization. He is straddling. He is not facing up to his social conscience." When I asked Dr. Manley if he felt relieved at being back, he said, "I am as relieved and as unrelieved as the international situation."

Another Los Alamos man with whom I talked was Dr. Marshall Holloway, the physicist who supervised the Bikini explosions. He wanted me to understand right off that the tests had appealed to him as a job, an interesting one, and that he hadn't gone out to the Pacific to conduct an experiment in public relations. He had, however, held a sneaking hope that when the newsreels of the bursts were shown, the public would be profoundly impressed. "The Hiroshima pictures just showed a flattened city," he explained. "The Bikini ones would show the process of the explosions." But the public, he said, had failed to be aroused. He wondered if anything short of an attack could do the arousing. "I used to have this fantasy," Holloway told me, "of setting up bleachers and grandstands on the outskirts of various cities all over the world and then having a kind of road company of us scientists explode a bomb for each of the assembled crowds to observe. After the reaction to the Bikini films, I don't even think this would work." Some people, he went on, thought that an international strike of scientists might bring about peace, but he wasn't very sanguine about that notion. "Even," he said, "if there weren't a single scientific scab, it wouldn't mean the end of wars. My neighbor, an electrician, would have to feel the same way I did. So would the politicians. So would the world's certified public accountants and piano salesmen. If they didn't, there'd be more wars. Maybe not streamlined ones, maybe they'd use just brass knuckles, but they'd have it out."

The least troubled scientist I met was Dr. Max Roy, one of the Laboratory's mainstays. Roy is an organic chemist who has taught at Brown. He is important enough in the workings of Los Alamos to rate one of Connell's comfortable log buildings. He is about forty and has an extremely engaging manner. "To be perfectly frank, people are no damn good," he began, in a conversation at his house. He then went on to speculate whether an atomic war would necessarily be as dangerous as has been widely printed. "I don't know what would happen in an atomic war," he said. "You don't know. As far as military casualties are concerned, wars have been getting less and less lethal. Also more costly and complicated, like life. We have civilized our warfare, shall we say? But human nature hasn't changed a bit. Why, millennial possibilities didn't even occur to me on V-J Day. I'd like international control, but why build your opinions on hopes?" The matter of man's memory came up next. He seemed to think it was about as long as a cat's. "At one time," he remarked, "I hoped the bomb would impress people, but, hell, even a number of scientists right here in Los Alamos sound unimpressed. Take the Johnstown flood, take any catastrophe. People are impressed at the moment, then they forget."

"Are you afraid of being killed by an atomic bomb?" I asked.

"Nothing I can do about it, so why worry?" Roy replied. "I stand as good a chance of getting killed driving down to Santa Fe. It's a terrible road."

It was possible, he thought, that life as we know it had already been lived on other planets. "Perhaps," he said, "people on those planets got to know too much and destroyed themselves. Perhaps that is our pattern." He walked with me to the door of his house, where he wished me a pleasant trip back to New York, and said, "Give my regards to Broadway, the country's best target."

The coming of the Laboratory has affected the life of the inhabitants in the Pojuaque Valley below the Hill. It has benefited a number of people financially, but, in general, the feeling is that it would be better if the Laboratory had never come and the little rich boys had never gone away. The Indians, for example, have once again found that the white man's ministrations are not necessarily a boon. I learned about them from Miss Edith Warner, a frail, elderly lady who migrated to the Southwest from Philadelphia twenty-five years ago and has since, through a train of odd circumstances, become a power in local Indian circles. I talked with her one evening in her adobe house, which was illuminated by flickering kerosene lamps. Standing a few feet from us was Attilano, her Indian male servant. Occasionally, Miss Warner would turn to him for corroboration of her facts, and each time he replied, "That is what they are saying in the pueblo." She told me that the Indians were making more money, but not enough to make up for what they had lost. "They cannot get wood, water, or greens for their dances," she said. "They used to go to certain canyons for that, but now they are shut off from those places by guards or by radioactive contamination." Their community life has also been upset. The women, she told me, had never done outside work in such numbers. Now, thanks to their earnings as domestics on the Hill, they made more money than their husbands, who, for the most part, are in the business of selling inferior corn and alfalfa. This, of course, had created an awkward situation. Some of the men, she said, had reconciled themselves by becoming lazy. The children's care had fallen off and the pottery-making, which had been the women's craft, had been neglected. "Whenever anything goes wrong," Miss Warner said, "whether it is of a personal nature or general, like the lack of water, they curse the Hill."

Miss Warner herself has not done too well. Her home has become unlivable because a new bridge, made necessary by the increased traffic brought about by the Laboratory, has been constructed a few feet from her house. Scientists, however, have personally built a new adobe house for her farther up the road. Their labor is probably one of gratitude, possibly of atonement. During the war, Miss Warner, surmising that the activity on the Hill had something to do with defeating the enemy and certain that the living conditions were rudimentary, decided to make a contribution to morale by having groups of eight scientists come to her home for dinner each day of the week except Sundays and Mondays. She made the meals festive and the atmosphere genteel, because she thought that the learned men missed nice things. Her hunch proved correct. The scientists came to look forward keenly to the congenial occasions in her adobe house. Then, when the bridge began to evict Miss Warner, the scientists came down on their Sundays to make mud floors and fireplaces and bricks under the supervision of Indians. "They enjoyed themselves," Attilano said. "They were very kind," Miss Warner told him. "The new house is too small," Attilano said.

A surprising number of the painters, composers, and writers who live in the Valley and near Taos have taken a mystical view of the Laboratory's location. They say that there is a spiritual affinity between the Indian ruins and nuclear weapons. Realistic explanations, such as the Hill's isolation, or that Oppenheimer, who spent much of his boyhood in this region, showed General Groves the site, fail to budge them. "Nothing," I heard a watercolorist say, "can explain why, with the whole country to choose from, they came to this particular spot. It is the ruins. It is their meaning." Most of the artists regard the project as an intrusion on their tranquillity. "I came out here fifteen years ago," a sculptor told me, "to get away from noisy civilization. Now, it's chased me to this remote region and looks down at me from the top of a mesa." Some social contact has sprung up between the scientists and the artists, but it is limited. One of its deterrents is that a dinner invitation from a scientist, returning hospitality, means that his guest has to run the gantlet of the Hill's suspicious border guard. "Those scientists are nice enough," Gus Baumann, a woodcut man who came to Santa Fe thirty years ago, told me, "but I'll be damned if I'll bother with that red tape. Besides, all I'd see is how the place has been changed, and I like my old memory of it too much."

Cady Wells, a successful painter who lives just a few miles below the Hill, recently placed his beautifully furnished ranch house on sale because of the Laboratory. A friend of his, Mrs. Dorothy McKibbin, a gentle, middle-aged lady who runs the Hill's small branch office in Santa Fe, tried to dissuade him. The two had corresponded during the war when Wells, an over-age volunteer, was in the Army for five years. When he was overseas, he heard that some construction was taking place on the Hill and frequently asked Mrs. McKibbin to tell him about it. When he was mustered out, he discovered for himself. Evenings he had been accustomed to stroll in the darkness on his terrace. Now, the lights shining in the Tech Area and the houses on the Hill made the evenings brighter. During the day he heard the "thunder," but it was the lights that chiefly reminded him of his new neighbors and their purpose. His first painting as a veteran was that of a tree with a bomb in its trunk. Other paintings followed and each had a similar motif, no matter how bucolic the subject.

Mrs. McKibbin, aware of what was eating at her friend, told him that the Hill and its people were not so bad. They went up to the Hill together and she introduced him to her favorite friends among the scientists. But it was no use. The evenings continued to be not dark enough; the motif persisted. He began to talk about selling his place. Mrs. McKibbin made him visit the Hill again. She had him invite scientists who knew painting to spend evenings with him in the relaxed setting of his home. He finally made up his mind about the house. When he did, Mrs. McKibbin was among the first to know. She said she was sorry to hear his decision.

"Dorothy, I've got to get away from atomic energy," he said.

"Where will you go?" Mrs. McKibbin asked.

Out West, in the beautiful state of New Mexico, the great weapons of the last war, the Nazis' V-2 rocket and the American atomic bomb, were arranging their peace more successfully than nations were. Indeed, at opposite ends of the state, the details of their forthcoming nuptials were diligently rehearsed. When, finally, the match was made, a new reality came into being—a missile that could go places, and do things when it got there.

CHAPTER 11 | MARCH, 1946

V-2S AMONG THE RATTLERS

TWO HUNDRED AND FIFTY miles to the south of the Los Alamos Scientific Laboratory is the White Sands Proving Ground, the U.S. government's first rocket center. Probably it is just so much *esprit de corps,* but some of the military personnel there seem to harbor an almost hostile envy of the nuclear laboratory. They feel that, owing to the inexplicable decisions of powerful men in Washington, greater secrecy is maintained at the atomic-bomb installation than at their own. They are convinced that the rival New Mexico project is enjoying a definite fiscal partiality. They believe that the government has made more of a fuss over the bomb than the rocket in the field of international diplomacy. They make the same charge against the United Nations. The press, they feel, has also played favorites. "We're a stepchild," a proud U.S. Navy commander stationed at White Sands told me. "As if atomic bombs are going to be any good without guided missiles taking them to their target! And not only that. We can tie up with bacteriological warfare; we can deliver those germs." As the final argument, the members of the sensitive clique point out that the spot where the first atomic bomb was tested, in 1945, is actually part of the White Sands range but that it might just as well not be. "They went and left the place radioactive," the same Navy man remarked.

There are also, by way of counterbalance, those whose outlook is anything but downtrodden—highly dedicated individuals who are enthusiastically shooting for the heavens. The great majority of the people there are understandably encouraged by what has been accomplished so far. The rocket firings, or launchings—or shoots, as they are most often called—are coming off with regularity. The White Sands post, which is controlled by the Army, has undergone a series of living and working improvements, and plans for its expansion have been made. Scientists and engineers attached to universities and industrial companies fly in from all over the country to carry on their investigation of the upper atmosphere. The Pentagon, according the guided missile formal recognition, sends its highest-ranking officials to inspect the place. New Mexico residents who live near the Proving Ground have become accustomed to the sight of whizzing flashes above the undulant desert waste. They are even a little pleased with the significance with which this remote region has been imbued. Alamogordo, a town of four thousand, which lies between the Proving Ground and the site of the first atomic explosion, considers that it has hit some kind of civic jackpot. Bright orange-and-white signs on its main street proclaim "ALAMOGORDO: HOME OF THE ATOMIC BOMB, CENTER OF ROCKET DEVELOPMENT!"

This emergence of White Sands as an American rocket center has been accidental. Originally, it was established as a temporary installation, a place whose life would last two, perhaps three years. That was back in the fall of 1944. The Germans had suddenly let loose with their V-1s and V-2s, and the U.S. Army, eager to retaliate in kind, wanted an American outpost where it could safely experiment with rockets. The Army did not happen to have much in the rocket line in those days, but it was just as well it started when it did, for it picked itself a wilderness that needed a little going over. Until the military's arrival, the terrain had shown itself to be excellent country for (a) Billy the Kid's stagecoach holdups and (b) rattlesnake-sunning. The range, which measures forty by ninety miles, has on its west border the Organ Mountains, a rugged, stony mass that derives its name from the fact that several of its peaks are closely bunched and are supposed to resemble organ pipes. The rest of the site is endless sand, relieved by endless sagebrush. The animal population of the desert and Organs, practically any member of which is good for a bounty, is composed mainly of mountain lions, coyotes, wildcats, and those rattlers. The human population, when the Army moved in, was about as friendly. Ranchers whose lands overlapped the installation's edges were afraid that their cattle's grazing area would be encroached upon, and adopted a sullen attitude. Las Cruces, the county seat, twenty-eight miles away, suspected that the influx of Army personnel and money would cause a phony boom, such as the one that befell Deming, its neighbor, during the first World War, when the Air Force trained there; Las Cruces is a prosperous, easygoing town that hasn't yet got over the fact that Billy the Kid slept there, and resents any threat of change. Both the installation and its work were military secrets, with the result that matters were aggravated, since the ranchers and townspeople, ignorant of any purpose, were able to indulge their worst fears. Also, a few Army officers, despite the efforts of their popular commander, Colonel Harold R. Turner, ingratiated themselves with the natives by getting proprietary about things they neither owned nor needed. "During a war," Colonel Turner told me, "there is always a shortage of diplomats." Water is scarce out here. Gas stations on Highway 70, five miles to the north, sell it at twenty-five cents per gallon. "Our first day, I felt like Moses," Colonel Turner recalled. "Plain nothing was in front of me, and I went around putting a stick here and a stick there, and ordering, 'Let there be water here and let there be water there.' " Good weather was one of the reasons for choosing White Sands, but sandstorms—during which everyone has to wear goggles—and winds that have knocked down buildings have hampered operations from time to time. The sunsets are pretty, but when they're finished, the coyotes take over with their howls.

Besides drilling wells, Turner and his command of a hundred and sixty-five men and officers, when they arrived, in 1944, built roads, set up camp with old structures they had scrounged from other Army posts, erected a power plant, and, most important of all, constructed rocket-firing facilities. They also had to impress the rattlesnakes, a battle that is still in progress. It is difficult to overemphasize the ubiquity of the diamondback around White Sands. Army doctors keep showing films to help the men know a rattler when they see one, but this is like telling a fellow where his fingers are. The damn things are all over the place. Bulldozer drivers, breaking ground, bang their wrenches on the machines to rustle out any snakes that might be loitering within them. G.I.s, absently policing the area, have inadvertently run their brooms over rattlers that were peacefully coiled in slumber. King snakes, which destroy rattlers, are regarded as welcome characters and encouraged to serve as sentries at various spots around the camp. One evening during my stay at White Sands, a Coca-Cola machine in an enlisted men's shack gave off an unusual whirr each time a nickel was dropped into it. A corporal, a Tennessee-mountain boy, finally got curious and played his flashlight on its dark rear, and made out a rattler. It was evidently being disturbed by the machine's rumble and shaking its rattles in protest. "To hell with him," the mountain boy said, shoving another nickel into the slot, "I'll git him in the mornin'."

At the outset, the hard work entailed in establishing the post seemed pointless. The Army did not move in until July 13th, 1945, when the Nazis' guided missiles, the original inspiration of the place, were no longer in business. There was, of course, the chance that the Japanese might come up with a similar weapon, but when they also surrendered, the men were really puzzled by their labor. Toward the end of August, however, big news reached the Proving Ground and everything suddenly made sense. The American Army in Germany, counting its captured assets, had 100 V-2s in its possession and was sending them on to New Mexico. It was clear, since by then both V Days had been celebrated, that the Army intended to pursue its project into peacetime and on a sustained basis. Shortly thereafter, three hundred freight-car loads of Nazi rocket parts arrived from Europe and were transported from Las Cruces over the highway to White Sands. Now that the station had rockets, experts who knew how to fire them were needed. Here again the Nazis helped out. Toward the end of the European war—before the Germans gave up—the Allies and Russia, independently, went on rather specialized liberating forays, the point of which was to round up Reich scientists, technicians, and engineers, presumably to help win the next war. The American undertaking was known as Operation Paperclip and it seems to have done rather well with its harvesting of rocketeers. Among its learned catches was Count Wernher von Braun, a handsome expert of only thirty-three, who was the active head of the Peenemünde Rocket Station, in northeast Germany, where the V-1s and the V-2s that were rained on British soil were developed. "The way I see it," Major James Hamill, a member of the Paperclip mission and the present custodian of the liberated scientists, told me, "it's just like a basketball game. It would have been like taking a bad shot at the basket if we hadn't picked up these men. You not only miss the hoop but you give the enemy a chance to get the ball on the rebound."

As a result of this curious legacy, the camp's scope was considerably broadened. The rocket-firing facilities had to be enlarged, because the Army had no missile that compared in size or power with the huge V-2s. Quarters had to be constructed for the Germans, who have since moved on to Fort Bliss, in El Paso. American scientists and engineers, a number of whom had been in England during the uncomfortable V-2 period, came to White Sands to study under Von Braun and his colleagues. In general, they have proved to be tractable instructors. They did their teaching diligently, telling all, and explaining the many documents stamped *"Geheim"* (Secret) that had fallen into American hands. "They are extremely intelligent," Herbert Karsch, the Proving Ground's technical director, informed me. "They are men of science, and they are willing to work for anyone just so long as they can work. On no occasion that I know of did they discuss politics or religion with us. A couple of times they forgot that I know a little German, and I caught them referring to us as *'Americanische Dummköpfe.'* I called them on that and they cut it out." It wasn't all work for the Germans during their stay at White Sands. They were taken on a trip to the Carlsbad Caverns. They visited El Paso, eighty miles away, and pronounced it cleaner and more modern than they had expected an American city to be. The Organ Mountains reminded them of the Bavarian Alps. In the winter, they skied in nearby mountains, a privilege that was especially gratifying to Helmut Schmidt, one of their number, who had been an Olympic ski champion. When the weather turned warm, they became *Wandervögel,* donning their *Lederhosen* and faring forth into the mountains for picnics and the singing of unpolitical, unreligious *Lieder.*

So well did the Peenemünde group carry out its assignment that some Americans in White Sands feel an uncertainty as to who organized which—the War Department the Germans, or vice versa. At any rate, by the end of six months the Americans themselves were able to shoot the V-2s. The Germans were then sent to Fort Bliss, which is where they are still continuing to occupy themselves in America's behalf. At present they are conducting, in collaboration with Americans, an ambitious, highly secret research project for the government. Occasionally, two or three of them are recalled to White Sands for consultation on some difficult problem. They live comfortably on the Bliss reservation with their families, which the government obligingly brought over. Von Braun, who delights Army officers with his grasp of American slang, was permitted to return briefly to the Reich in order to marry his fiancée, an eighteen-year-old girl. All of them have expressed a desire for citizenship, and their children are enrolled in El Paso schools. The members of the colony are permitted off the reservation and are to be encountered, like any other native Texans, in El Paso shops and night clubs. So sure are our officers that their wards are happy displaced persons that they are even allowed to go over the short bridge from El Paso onto the foreign soil of Juárez, where they could technically request asylum of the Mexican administration. This wandering from the fort is done in automobiles, several of them the latest models, which they have purchased with the money they arrived with, or with the income they have received from the United States. They were originally signed on for one year at a small wage and six dollars a day for expenses. Since the expiration of the contract, however, they have come into substantial raises. It is probably the first time that the kidnaper has also paid the ransom. The Army carefully shields them from inquisitive journalists, on the theory that those Americans who have not yet discovered that global, like nuclear, fission is a fact of life might misinterpret the treatment being accorded these workers for the wrong war effort. However, Americans of that sort need not feel that there is no justice. Last spring, when the men were out on one of their mountain-climbing picnics, a fellow by the name of Horn put his hand on a ledge of a rock and an American rattlesnake bit him.

At present, it is the V-2 that is the chief missile for the shooting that goes on here. It is fired more frequently than any other type of missile and, because of its enormous fuel load, goes higher. This ability to achieve altitude is of prime value to our research men, who are attempting to find out such matters as the currents, temperatures, and pressure patterns of the stratosphere, the ionosphere, the E Layer, and other sections of the upper atmosphere through which an effective guided missile must travel. Although the *Army Ordnance Journal* prints articles entitled "The Occupation of Mars?" rocket experimentation is so embryonic that the emphasis is on basic research rather than on application. This research is being conducted by scientists from universities such as Johns Hopkins, Harvard, Princeton, and Michigan, and from large industrial companies, particularly General Electric, Douglas Aircraft, and Bell Laboratories. They come with instruments, such as spectrographs, cameras, and special thermometers, and fit them into the rockets. When the rockets reach the summit of their climb, the instruments begin to record information. Frequently, the data brought down in one V-2 take from six months to a year for the research men to analyze when they return to their home laboratories. The cost of a single shoot usually runs in the neighborhood of a hundred thousand dollars. The ultimate use of this work need not necessarily result in weapons. As in all science, the research can lead to peaceful as well as lethal application. Thus, depending on how the human race plays its cards, the guided missile may make possible faster bomb deliveries or faster mail deliveries.

Besides the research, a program of educating personnel in the mechanics and principles of guided missiles is under way. At Fort Bliss, in a building apart from that used by the Germans, the Army maintains a rocket school, where a nine-months course is being taught officers who have engineering degrees. The make-up of the student body is international. In addition to Americans, the class includes officers from Canada, Britain, Turkey, Chile, Denmark, France, India, Ecuador, Argentina, the Philippines, China, Mexico, Iran, and Guatemala—all countries, it would appear, that are at the moment considered to be likely allies of the United States. At White Sands itself, a new Army unit, the First Guided Missile Battalion, has been activated. Its members gain practical experience by assisting in planning shoots. repairing missile parts, fueling the rockets, and handling instruments that are necessary to the launching. Many of these men, it is hoped, will be able to instruct new recruits. The Navy, faced with the special problems of firing missiles at sea, has set up at the Proving Ground its own installation. The Air Force is also interested in the post's activities.

The supply of V-2s on hand should, at the rate they are being fired, last the United States another couple of years. Copies could be made, but American experts, having been given a start, are confident that they can develop an improved rocket of their own before they run out of V-2s. In conversations among themselves, they now describe the German product as "crude." Tests of experimental American models, which have such names as Little Joe and the Wac Corporal, are being made. These shoots are highly restricted affairs. They are nearly always held on a Thursday. The reason for this is an arrangement the government has worked out with the ranchers, dude ranchers, and filling-station owners whose properties border on the Proving Ground. This agreement provides that firings may take place on Mondays, Tuesdays, Thursdays, and Fridays. It generally takes two days to prepare a missile for launching and frequently something goes wrong, so the Proving Ground likes to allow itself a little leeway. Nobody works over the week end, so Mondays and Tuesdays are out. Since Wednesdays are prohibited, Thursday is generally the day. The co-signers of the agreement are paid for their cooperation, and part of their emolument includes expenses for spending the day in town. By now, however, they are so used to the shoots that they rarely avail themselves of this. So far, only one injury has been suffered. "A cow," a White Sands sergeant told me. "She was trespassing."

The V-2 shoots are also held on Thursdays, but they are anything but classified. In fact, they are gala occasions. The Russians captured more of these missiles than the United States did, and there is no need for secrecy. Everybody in the district knows the exact time of the launching, and hours before this moment is reached Highway 70 is clogged with motorists trying to find themselves good vantage points. A section of the road is blocked off for safety's sake, and beforehand Army Stinson L-5s, small liaison planes, swoop low over it to see if any driver, possibly quite uninterested in rockets, is stuck there with a flat or no gas; if there is, a towing vehicle is dispatched by the Army. Shoot Day has a festive air in camp. The place is blinding with brass from the

Pentagon, West Point, and Annapolis, and, apparently, all the Mexican generals, retired and active, are on hand. Southwestern state and municipal officials attend. Students at the international rocket school, getting credit for a field trip, arrive from Fort Bliss in special buses, from which they emerge resplendent in the uniforms of their various armies. Buses loaded with Boy Scout troops, collegiate R.O.T.C. men, National Guardsmen, and delegations from Chambers of Commerce and civic clubs also pull in. The affair even has a family flavor. The wives of White Sands personnel have a standing invitation to see the shoots, and they prove their interest in their husbands' work by driving in from their homes in Las Cruces and Alamogordo. The mothers among them come with babies in their arms, and rambunctious six-year-old boys, veterans of other launchings, scamper all over the place loudly imitating the impending rocket's roar. The Proving Ground's command, acting the gracious host, arranges a sightseeing tour for its several hundred guests. This includes a look at the assembly hanger and at the White Sands Proving Ground Museum, where a V-2 is on display, and a quick visit to the launching site, seven miles away from camp headquarters. After that, they are treated to forty-five minutes of movies dealing with guided missiles, a large part of the footage being taken up by captured German films that show the Peenemünde station in action during the war. It is all quite pleasant and gay, and everyone seems to have a good time. The people watch the spectacular climax of their party from the camp area, and when the missile shoots aloft, trailing flame and noise, and rapidly accelerating, "ooh"s and "aah"s go up from the crowd. The little boys see how pale their imitations were, and their elders say that the sight has any Fourth of July fireworks trimmed all hollow and that they would never have missed the experience for the world. Then the visitors leave, their autos causing desert dust to swirl and hover above the resuscitated Army structures. Later on, at the end of the day, the Proving Ground personnel, for whom the rocket's launching was a sweat and a strain, also leave, heading for bars and double features in Las Cruces and El Paso to celebrate the expenditure of another V-2.

There is no longer any question that the thriving installation is here to stay. Billy the Kid would never recognize his old haunt. Every day, a stream of stenographers, clerks, and maintenance men commute in Army vehicles from Las Cruces and Alamogordo. The post has a paved road of its own. The ranchers have become friendly. A chance meeting between a cowman and a soldier is likely to wind up with the uniformed man coming back to the ranch house for coffee and beef. Las Cruces is no longer scared of a phony boom. "It's a nice thing to be able to sit on my terrace and watch a rocket go up," Mayor Sam Klein told me.

An outdoor basketball court has been constructed. Bingo nights are frequently held on the post. So are parties, during which sitters are hired to keep an eye on the children who are cached in the camp dispensary. Both the enlisted men and the officers have their own clubs. Name bands play for the enlisted men at their dances. The dancing in the Officers' Club is done in the Rocket Room, an imposing affair whose pine walls are adorned with stag heads. This club is equipped with a dozen slot machines. It takes a long time to go broke on them, because, for purposes of morale, they are charitably rigged. On the porch are two ping-pong tables, and above them are fluorescent fixtures. At night, when Douglas engineers play ballistics experts under the brilliant blue illumination, the desert air is so soft and still that the balls are never wafted.

Also there is a church. It is a regulation Army-model chapel. Its assembly and paint job were completed during my visit to White Sands, and I went around to see the chaplain the day that happened. He is a young man in his thirties by the name of Raymond L. Kasper. During the war, he saw considerable service as a chaplain in European combat areas. He is friendly but his manner is blessed with a complete lack of ecclesiastical gladness. I found him in his baptistry, where he was yanking open a crate of tapers. His chapel's career, he told me, would begin the next day with a wedding. The stained glass he had drawn from the Army had an attractive pattern. He had negotiated himself an excellent small organ, which was in tune. He had hopes for the camp. A couple of weeks ago, engineers had struck a rich source of water that would double the post's supply. Housing units for seventy-odd families were to be constructed within a few months. He pointed through the window to the empty spot, a half mile away, where the dwellings would be. From outside, the shouts of G.I.s playing on the basketball court reached us. The noise probably reminded Kasper that more recreational facilities were in the works. He thought they would relieve the monotony of the post. It was odd, he said, but some boys from city streets had told him that the desert had brought them a serenity they had not expected. Several fellows from wooded country didn't like, it was true, being able to stare across the flat terrain at a landmark that was fifty miles away, and a soldier who had done a long trick on a Pacific isle was on the verge of a crackup. Kasper quoted him as saying, "I never went rock-happy there, but this place is just as lonely, and it's in my own country, in peacetime."

Kasper, during my interview with him, never mentioned the last war. He did not mention the V-2s, whose flights would take them high over his new church, or the Nazis or the works of Peenemünde. Nor did he say anything about any next war. He was concerned with individuals only, and their pursuit of their troubled or untroubled existence. Kasper apparently had faith that the good will of these individuals would take care of things. He pointed again to the housing site. Then his hand abruptly swept the sandy, flowerless stretches to either side of it, and he said sharply, "There is nothing here but room for growth."

WHAT'S UP THERE?

THE ONE HUNDRED V-2s that have made the White Sands Proving Ground an extremely significant installation were captured by the United States Army at Nordhausen, an industrial town in central Germany that has since passed into the hands of Russian occupation authorities. This war booty is now being used by American scientists and engineers for discovering what the conditions are in the upper atmosphere. The reconversion has been brought about simply by firing the V-2s as high as possible (the record is a hundred and fourteen miles) in the direction of the desert instead of at London and by packing them with scientific instruments rather than explosives. The experimenting at White Sands, which the government is supporting with an enormous outlay of money, is being conducted in an intensely realistic way, but there are at least two dreams in the background of this work. One of them, an ancient aspiration that dates back to early Chinese science, envisions the exploring of other planets and includes such fantastic possibilities as space ships and trips to the moon. The other dream belongs to the world's admirals and generals, who, impressed by the deadly achievements of the Nazis' Peenemünde Rocket Station, are curious about the possibilities of so-called push-button warfare, which, as now visualized, would depend upon guided missiles. For the moment, however, all that is being attempted is a series of experiments that will help the United States get on more familiar terms with the mysterious region that lies high above the earth. The dreams can wait.

The Nordhausen prize is being administered by the V-2 Upper Atmosphere Panel, which was organized by the owner of the rockets, the Army's Office of the Chief of Ordnance. The Panel is composed of scientists, who represent research outfits, such as universities and industrial companies, that are co-operating with the military. This group decides which experiments are worth expending rockets for, and assigns the missiles to the specific research organizations that want to send their instruments aloft. The Panel also sees to it that the resulting data are circulated among the right American experts. Once an assignment has been made, the organization can count on the White Sands Proving Ground's permanent personnel, which is both military and civilian, to take care of the actual launching. These launchings, which are complicated and hazardous, are held every few weeks. I was invited by the Army to attend one of them—the twenty-seventh, to be precise. This particular V-2 was dedicated, as it happened, to an experiment of the General Electric Company, and soon after arriving at the desert post I went around to see Dr. Charles F. Green, a consulting engineer for that company. Dr. Green, an amiable man in his fifties, was sitting in his office, a small room inside the hangar where each V-2 is assembled before being towed off to the launching site. No. 27, as the missile was straightforwardly called, had been taken away a few minutes earlier, and Dr. Green and I were the only occupants of the cavernous, drafty hangar. "Don't worry," Dr. Green assured me, guessing what was on my mind, "you won't miss the firing. It'll take until the middle of tomorrow before the rigging job is completed." He thought that I might have a better idea of what the launching entailed if, after we were through talking, I had a look at the interior of a rocket that was on display in the museum maintained by the Proving Ground. Dr. Green said that the captured *Vergeltungswaffe Zwei,* or Retaliation Weapon Two, or V-2, had proved to be extremely valuable for researchers, despite the fact that they were in rundown condition. "During the war," he said, "the Germans used their rockets only three days after final assembly, and here we are using three-year-olds." Still, he pointed out, the V-2s were hitting altitudes that were five times the record ascent for a sounding balloon. Eventually, he thought, a better rocket would be produced, but the Germans had been years ahead of everyone else with their V-2. "Why not?" he asked. "They were betting on the rocket while we were betting on the atomic bomb."

Thanks to the V-2s, he continued, more had been learned about the upper atmosphere in the past two years than in the previous twenty. However, we still have a long way to go. "Right now," he said, "we know as much about upstairs as a fish does about land." According to Dr. Green, we live at the bottom of an ocean—an ocean of air, which constitutes about one one-thousandth of our planet's thickness. "If you took a globe a foot in diameter," he said, "and swabbed a coat of paint over it, the coat would amount to the region we're investigating." The fish, he went on, knows what a fisherman looks like but can't explain him. In the same way, scientists have made various observations without knowing their causes. The temperatures above us, for example, can't be fully accounted for. "At the earth's surface," Dr. Green said, "the temperature is about seventy degrees. You'd expect that the higher the rocket goes, the colder it would get, and when it reaches an area called the troposphere, from fifteen to thirty-five kilometers up, the temperature is around minus sixty-seven to minus one hundred thirty, but at forty kilometers it's seventy degrees, the same as the earth's surface. At eighty kilometers—that's in the stratosphere—it's minus a hundred and fifty degrees. At a hundred and twenty-five kilometers, in the lower part of the ionosphere, it gets up to plus one hundred fifty, which is hotter than it ever is here in the desert at White Sands. Two hundred kilometers is the top altitude for which temperatures are known. There it's really hot—one thousand degrees."

The scientists were also curious, Dr. Green said, about the high-energy cosmic rays that exist above the atmosphere. Information about the rays would mean a great deal to nuclear physicists. Astrophysicists wanted to probe further into solar phenomena in order to know more about the universe in general and the sun in particular. The composition and density of atmospheric gases are something else the researchers are after. So is the behavior of molecules in the high altitudes. Up there, I learned, the distance between molecules is three hundred and seventy inches; on the earth's surface it is only about one millionth of an inch. "This increase in molecule separation," Dr. Green said, "causes the laws of air resistance, as we know them, to cease operating. If you let a parachute loose upstairs, like as not the umbrella and the rip cord will be floating alongside each other." Dr. Green added that he could reel off a lot of other scientific objectives but that the entire research program could be put, quite succinctly, in the form of a single question—"What's up there?"

General Electric's interest in the next day's shoot had to do with what is called "heat transfer." It seems that the friction created by the V-2's supersonic speed of up to thirty-six hundred miles per hour produces an intense heat inside the rocket, and the researchers were attempting to discover how much of this heat the missile's interior could stand before it became damaged. Previous experiments, Dr. Green told me, had shown that the rocket was sometimes subjected to a temperature of a hundred and eighty degrees. It would be immediately useful to learn about the effects of heat, so that the delicate instruments inside the experimental rockets could be adequately protected. Less immediately, such information might serve to increase the safety of airplanes. "If a supersonic plane is developed," Dr. Green said, "the more we know about heat transfer, the more we'll know how much refrigeration the plane will need in order to protect its occupants." To get this data, special thermometers were going to be placed inside No. 27. The thermometers took up so little space, Dr. Green said, that three other research groups were going to be able to share the rocket with General Electric. The Naval Research Laboratory was putting aboard a spectrograph, an instrument that enables us to find out more about the spectral characteristics of light in the high altitudes. The University of Michigan was contributing an air-sample bottle to the cargo. This bottle would open up at a given height, suck in a sample of the atmosphere, and then seal itself. "A very important piece of equipment," Dr. Green said, "but we've had tough luck with it so far." Harvard would be sending along something that took up even less room than the thermometers. "A packet of seeds," Dr. Green said. "Professor Fred Whipple is eager to find out the effects of cosmic radiation on the growth of seeds. Perhaps bigger and better crops will result. He's been sending up very pure breeds of corn, wheat, and cotton seeds and then planting them. Too early yet for results." On one occasion, Professor Whipple had a colony of fruit flies carried by a V-2, the idea being to see what the genetic effects of cosmic radiation would be. "They're the only living things that have been up a hundred miles," Dr. Green told me. "Wish they could talk."

Like most men of research, Dr. Green was reluctant to discuss the possible applications of the White Sands data. Military uses, as I expected, were absolutely secret, although military men have made no bones about their dream weapon—an atomic bomb transported by a guided missile. Dr. Green did, however, speculate on one general possibility from which a number of other possibilities could flow. This was the idea of an orbital satellite—a missile that would revolve indefinitely around the earth at a height of a hundred miles or, for that matter, at a higher altitude. At the height of a hundred miles, the G.E. expert remarked, the satellite would circle the world in one hour and thirty-three minutes. He felt reasonably sure that such a satellite could become a reality in perhaps ten years if the government cared to spend the great sums necessary for its manufacture and maintenance. Equipped with the right instruments, Dr. Green said, a satellite of this sort would undoubtedly improve weather forecasting. "People rap the weatherman," he said, "but there are certain unaccountable winds, which he can't be blamed for. With our satellite, we'd have a constant check on cloud movements and pressure patterns. We could predict accurately for the next few months. Hot summers ahead or cold winters—it's all in the upper atmosphere." Or, he continued, one might use the satellite to photograph bleak polar regions that no one had ever seen or mapped. Communications could be improved. The satellite's instruments, for example, might shed considerable light on the causes of radio static. "Those sunspots have something to do with that," Dr. Green said. "Maybe we'd even discover what they have to do with Wall Street cycles." Dr. Green also informed me that the radio spectrum was pretty well used up, and that more channels were needed for both broadcasting and short-wave messages. A satellite, he said, could serve as a repeater, or relay, station for transmitting programs or messages. The satellites could also be used as relay stations for television, which, as everyone knows, depends on height for the range of its programs. Only four such stations would be needed to telecast a program around the world; at present it takes that many to get a program from Schenectady to New York.

Dr. Green abruptly ended his speculations. "Pretty soon I'll start talking about trips to the moon," he said, "and then you won't believe anything I tell you. Anyway, if you went to the moon, you'd only be faced with the problem of getting back. The return trip would be different." He paused briefly, looking thoughtful. "It would be easier to get back," he said finally. "The earth's gravitational pull would be working for you."

Taking Dr. Green's advice, I went over to the Proving Ground's museum, which is housed, not far from the hangar, in a long, khaki-colored Army van. The museum's arrangement is simple; a stripped V-2, resting on steel supports, has the place of honor in the center of the room; against the walls are rocket parts, some of them in glass cases. Only one other person, a young Army captain, was in the room when I arrived. He was inspecting a glass-enclosed object with the engrossment of an art lover at the Metropolitan Museum of Art. When he saw me, he pointed at it and exclaimed, "What a beautiful thing! Every couple of weeks I come over to see it." I joined him and looked at what struck me as the insides of a fairly large, tubeless radio set. A printed card in the case identified it in English as a mixer computer and in German as a *Mischgerat*. "That's the rocket's brains," the captain said. "It makes corrections, gyroscopically, way up high. If the missile's pitchings and rollings make it deviate from its course, leave it to the mixer computer. Why, you could call it the V-2's G-2!" I must have seemed unresponsive, for he asked, "Are you an engineer?" We introduced ourselves. He was Captain Edward Detchmendy, a member of the Proving Ground's roster and a confirmed rocket buff. He showed me two more of his favorite gadgets in the exhibition, and then turned his attention to the V-2. "Simplicity itself," he said, indicating a formidable mess of motors, pipes, wires, and tanks. The rocket's length, he hold me, was forty-six feet, but, probably because its exposed innards were distracting, it did not seem that long. Detchmendy tried to explain its construction to me. There were four main sections. At the tail was the propulsion section, and at the front was the warhead. Next to the warhead was the gyroscopic equipment that Detchmendy admired so much. After that came a series of fuel tanks, which took up fully half the rocket. This was to be expected, I was told, since fuel accounts for nineteen thousand of the twenty-seven thousand pounds that the V-2 weighs at takeoff. Three types of fuel are used. The tank nearest the gyroscopic section is for ethyl alcohol, and the next one for liquid oxygen. "That liquid oxygen makes up over half the fuel load," Detchmendy said. "You see, the rocket's enclosed and can't get oxygen from the air. In fact, there isn't much air up where it goes." The fuel tank nearest the rear is filled with hydrogen peroxide. "The very same stuff that ladies use to bleach their hair," Detchmendy said. The rocket, he continued, has to burn up its enormous fuel load in one minute in order to get its speed. In two seconds flat, he said, the rocket has gained ninety per cent of its power. In four seconds, it raises itself vertically. By the end of the minute, the missile is twenty miles up. A good V-2 would continue to soar for three more minutes, at which point it would be about five times that high. "What would happen to a human passenger?" I asked impersonally. "You'd die," Detchmendy replied. "You'd suffocate or burn. Also, the rate of acceleration would make trouble for you. You know how you jerk back in a car that starts too sudden? A V-2 picks up a hundred and eighty-two feet a second, and if you were inside it, your eyeballs and intestines would really go way the hell back. I'm sure you'd find yourself some way of dying."

He told me that my question hadn't surprised him. The Proving Ground, he explained, had received letters from nearly a hundred individuals who wanted to book passage for one of the shoots. A couple of soldiers had put in for reassignment as "rocket riders." One person had volunteered in order "to get away from it all." Another had said that a study of the various methods of suicide had led him to believe that a rocket flight was the most "beautiful." A note of not too long ago had stated, "I am 5′11″, 190 pounds, strong, healthy, and want to do what I can for my country." Philatelists, of course, keep sending in stamped envelopes, and occasionally their requests that the envelopes be put aboard a rocket are heeded. "We just pick up the envelopes at the impact point, and mail them back," Detchmendy said. "A little screwy, but safe."

Detchmendy, after a last, affectionate look at his *Mischgerat,* told me that he had to report to the launching site, seven miles away, and offered me a lift in his jeep, which I accepted. "Well," Detchmendy said as we rode along on the camp's one paved road, "this is where the shooting takes place." On both sides of the road were miles and miles of sagebrush and dunes. Only to the west could I see where the sandy expanse stopped. There the high, very rocky Organ Mountains, one of the Proving Ground's boundaries, looked down on the flat terrain. "If the rocket misbehaves," Detchmendy said, "and shoots over the Organs, we say, 'She went over the left-field fence.' Over our east border, and she's over the right-field fence. We prefer for her to fall inside the ball park." My eye was suddenly attracted by a moving patch of white. It was the V-2, about a mile ahead, being slowly raised by a special truck from a horizontal position to a vertical one, like an ack-ack gun being brought into position. The missile was painted white and its pointed warhead had been silvered, so that its flight could be followed more easily. "Up goes No. 27," Detchmendy said. "Once they get her straight up, she'll be planted on a portable launching platform."

We drove right up to where the rocket was and got out of the jeep. About a hundred civilians and Army men, dressed in fatigues and dungarees, were gathered around it. Despite the fact that it was now dedicated to the cause of science, the missile, standing, miraculously balanced, against the background of desert waste, and with the faces of the men turned up toward its towering, gleaming warhead in a kind of worshipful attitude, seemed oddly ominous. Then a crane, which was about sixty feet tall, moved toward No. 27. The crane, which straddled the rocket, had platforms at various levels, on which the Proving Ground's crew stood in order to prepare No. 27 for its flight. When the missile was finally within the crane's steel embrace, a swarm of G.I.s climbed up ladders to the various platforms, where they began opening doors to the V-2's compartments, so that the instrument specialists could later insert their equipment. A team of surveyors on the ground were making sure that the missile was absolutely vertical. If it were off the vertical by even a single degree, Detchmendy explained, its angle of elevation at takeoff might be disastrously affected. "Might as well have a look at the blockhouse," he said. "They won't let you in it tomorrow."

The blockhouse is headquarters for the shoots. It is a white, squat concrete structure one hundred-odd feet to the west of the launching platform. Its exterior, except for antennae on its roof, is that of a rather rambling pillbox. Its interior, which is always pleasantly cool, because of the thickness of the concrete, consists almost entirely of instrumentation—consoles, apparatus with tiny running lights, fire extinguishers, equipment that pulsates with small, steady clicks. Detchmendy led me to the blockhouse's three windows, which, for protective purposes, are narrow slits containing sheets of thick, laminated glass. I peered through one slit and could make out only the fins at the bottom of No. 27. "At takeoff time," Detchmendy told me, "technicians stand at each of these slits to see how things are going with the missile, but by the time the fuel's been ignited there isn't much that they can see, except a big flame shooting out of the rocket's tail." The others in the blockhouse would be occupied with the instrumentation. "Only twenty people will be in here tomorrow," he informed me. "You can see that for yourself by counting the oxygen bottles and masks hanging on the wall. They'd never let more people in here than the number of oxygen bottles, because the rocket might keel over onto the blockhouse and cut off our exit. The concrete's ten feet thick along the walls and twenty-six feet thick on the room, so the blockhouse could probably stand up, but toxic gases from the V-2 might seep in, and we'd need the bottles while we were trying to escape into the air outside." A strapping fellow who was hustling by called out to Detchmendy, "Hi, Detch! We're sticking salts into her this time. Going to get a tomato-red flame out of her." Detchmendy explained that it had been decided to mix certain salts with the V-2's fuels in order to make the rocket's flame especially red, thus making it easier for observers to follow the course. Field crews, stationed at desert and mountain posts scattered across the Army's range, would keep in communication with the blockhouse, would keep track of the rocket's course with telescopes, cameras, radar, and other equipment, and would phone in reports to the blockhouse. The crews could also, since the missile was radio-controlled, blow it up while it was in flight. "They do that," Detchmendy said, "if the V-2 is off course and possibly headed in the direction of populated communities. The rocket explodes and comes down in a shower of shrapnel."

We walked toward the door, where a sturdy, desperate-looking lieutenant who was entering the blockhouse nearly collided with us. "Hi," Detchmendy said. "Why aren't you rotting out on the desert?" Then Detchmendy introduced him to me as the Desert Rat, adding that his formal name was Lieutenant James Kincannon. Lieutenant Kincannon is the post's Recovery Officer, a job that calls for him to go out and find the missile's scientific instruments wherever the point of impact may be. Detchmendy gave me a brief account of Kincannon's work, to which the Lieutenant listened with no sign of self-consciousness, pride, or, for that matter, interest. After every shoot, Kincannon's search takes him bumping over the desert dunes in his jeep with one or two jeeploads of interested scientists tagging closely behind him. A pair of Army photographers also follow him, their purpose being to provide the Recovery Officer with documentary evidence that his job has been well done, by taking pictures of the scientists holding their recovered instruments. Sometimes the instruments, smashed or unsmashed, are found in the desert, sometimes in the Organ Mountains; sometimes the valuable data go unretrieved. "The dunes do a beautiful job of concealing," Detchmendy said. "You can be within twenty feet of the rocket without knowing it. Once Jim, here, looked for a missile for thirty days, and couldn't find it until a rancher from nearby the Proving Ground was riding his horse and the horse's shoes stamped on metal." Kincannon finally opened his mouth. "You game to go along with me on an impact hunt?" he asked me. I nodded blankly. "Well," he said, "meet me outside the blockhouse right after the shoot. Don't be late. Look for the Monstrosity—that's the name of my jeep. Can't help spotting it. It'll be kind of loaded. I carry ten gallons of water for the vehicle, five for passengers. Also four quarts of canned oil. Tools for the vehicle and rocket extricators will be in it. It has two-way radio-communication equipment, a bedroll, and binoculars. I carry a first-aid kit and a snake-bite kit with serum. I always have my forty-five for snakes and mountain lions, and also for coyotes. And don't bring a pillow, the way *some* people have. That's sissy stuff." Kincannon abruptly proceeded into the blockhouse, and Detchmendy said to me, "Take along a pillow."

When we emerged from the blockhouse, I noticed that there were no longer any G.I.s on the crane. A group of eight civilians had taken over. "The instrument boys," Detchmendy said. They were on the crane's third platform, fifty feet up, which was on a level with the warhead. Most of them were shouting orders to enlisted men below, who were tenderly hoisting equipment; one of the experts had his face stuck inside the warhead itself, where he was yanking furiously at something with a wrench. Detchmendy said that he had to get back to the blockhouse, but before he left me he cupped his hands and yelled, "Hey, Pappy! Pappy White!" A short, red-headed man of about forty looked down at us from the third platform. "Take care of this guy!" Detchmendy shouted up. White said

O.K., and I started up the steel ladder of the crane. When I reached the platform, I learned that the men were busy with a variety of significant chores. Besides checking the cabling that would keep the ground personnel in touch with the rocket, they were giving their instruments a final inspection. After that, they were going to fit the instruments into the rocket in a way that would ensure their not being broken and their ability to record data. For this shoot, I was told, the instruments would be safer than usual, because No. 27 had been assembled in such a way that as it descended toward the earth it would break up into three separate parts—the warhead, the body, and the tail. The impact upon striking the earth would consequently be so much less severe than usual that the rocket would not even dig a crater. Arranging the instruments was practically as important as the flight itself, and would take the rest of the afternoon and all night to complete. All the men on the platform were G.E. experts with the exception of one, a meteorologist, a curly-headed, baby-faced fellow named Sturgeon. He was the air-bottle man from the University of Michigan. Sturgeon smiled miserably when White told me that he had been nicknamed, inevitably, Virgin, because he had come to White Sands for four shoots but had yet to be successful with his air bottle. Once the missile had not gone up high enough, twice it had failed to rise, and on Sturgeon's last attempt the shoot had been canceled, because of a bad accident at the launching site. Alongside Sturgeon was his bottle, which was made of steel and was thirty-two inches long and eight inches in diameter. It was shaped like a fire extinguisher except for a long nozzle, which, I was told, would protrude from No. 27 during its flight, in order to suck in the atmospheric sample. The bottle was painted bright yellow to help Kincannon find it, and on it, in black paint, were the words "RETURN TO UNIVERSITY OF MICHIGAN, WILLOW RUN, MICHIGAN. ATT: M. H. NICKEL SHIP RR. EXPRESS CHARGES GUARANTEED."

Sturgeon was far from being the only one for whom things had gone wrong. The plain fact is, as White and his colleagues on the crane assured me, that the rockets simply can't be a hundred per cent controlled. "The field's so new," White told me, "that we just don't have enough background yet to be able to say that Incident X happened because of Factor Y." On one occasion, the missile, in the takeoff, had scooted low, just missing a party of dignitaries, including former Secretary of War Patterson, who were visiting the Proving Ground. Another time, a V-2, headed the wrong way, had been exploded in flight. On two occasions, rockets that were going astray had not been exploded. One of them had landed near the town of Alamogordo, and the other had fallen just outside the Mexican City of Juárez, eighty miles to the southeast. This latter mishap, involving a friendly sister republic, had filled the White Sands command with anxiety, but when a group of officers arrived on the scene, they found that no one had been hurt. "A couple of hundred Mexicans," White told me, "made off with the rocket fragments they found in the crater and sold them as souvenirs to American tourists."

At the moment, White continued, he was worried about the next day's weather. The Army's meteorologist had indicated that it might be cloudy, a condition that would make it too difficult for the field crews to follow the V-2's flight. "If tomorrow morning's weather report is bad," White said, "we don't shoot." He looked up at the sky, which was innocently blue and cloudless. "At any rate," he told me, "if we do, and you hear the shout, 'It's a keeper!' you'll know the takeoff's gone well." He asked me where I was going to be for the shoot, and I said that I didn't know. "Why don't you hang out with Walt Hausz, here, our electronics man?" he asked. He indicated a young, alert-looking fellow who, until a few minutes ago, had had his face inside the warhead. "Walt's going to be at Radar Station C, two miles or so from here. Most spectators will be up in camp, but I think seven miles is a little too far. You miss the noise and flame. Besides, we have a little saying here: 'The closer you are, the safer you are.' Some of us even believe it."

I left the instrument men and descended the ladder to the ground, where I met Kincannon again. This time he looked gloomy rather than desperate. "Something's going to go wrong tomorrow," he told me. "I've got a certain feeling in my bones. Every now and then, I get that feeling, but they laugh at me. I had that feeling when the goddam thing landed in Mexico. And they laughed at me the day of the Alamogordo misfire, until that telephone call came in. It was from a lady who said she was calling in to say that the rocket had plopped down right near her. 'Where are you?' they asked her, and she answered, 'The corner drugstore.' "

The next morning, carrying a pillow and binoculars, I met Hausz, and we drove out along a narrow dirt road to our vantage point. He had news for me. Takeoff time, or X Hour, had been set for 11 A.M.; the weather report was good but not wonderful. "Clouds after one o'clock," he said. "We can't afford any bad delays." Radar Station C turned out to be an encampment of eight or ten trailers, which contained not only radar but several other kinds of equipment. The purpose of all the equipment was to keep tabs on the rocket during its eight-minute flight. The radar, for example, enabled one to see, indirectly, the rocket's moving image. "Exactly the same type of radar that picked up most of the V-1s that came over England," Hausz told me. An optical "tracker" at the station would make it possible to follow the missile directly. I looked briefly into its powerful lens and could see heat waves shimmering up from the desert. Hausz's own trailer was fitted out with the receiving end of a telemeter, a remarkable machine that Hausz described as "the rocket's telephone back to earth." The telemeter transmitted twenty-three pieces of information, such as data on temperatures, cosmic rays, and wind pressures. In addition, the G.E. wagon had three special cameras, which would make a pictorial record of the flight. At one end of the encampment was another piece of tracking equipment, known as a sky screen, actually little more than an empty wooden picture frame, that would make it easier to follow the course of the rocket with the naked eye. An Army officer, sitting behind the sky screen, would be one of the two men in the area who, if he decided the missile was off course, could pull a switch to explode it. "Our supply of rockets is limited," Hausz said, "so he has to be awfully sure that it's really off course. But he also has to think fast. It doesn't take long for something that's traveling better than three thousand miles an hour to land in Juárez."

Several dozen men, most of them stripped to the waist and wearing just shorts, were at Radar C. Like the men at other field stations elsewhere in the desert or up in the Organs, they were checking their equipment or simply standing by until the time came for them to go to work. People kept drifting in, coming by the same road that Hausz and I had used. I stood around outside Hausz's trailer. The later the arrivals, the more rank they seemed to have. The last batch consisted of several full colonels. They all seemed cheerful and breezy, with the exception of one, who was implacably gloomy.

"I've been to every one of these shoots," I heard him tell one of his equals, "and each time I get butterflies. I have this notion that the rockets are going to score a direct hit on *me*. As if a forty-five cartridge couldn't also kill me." By ten-fifteen, a communications system whose interchanges were broadcast over a public-address system went into operation. "Son of a bitch" were the first words that came over it. "Just testing," a fellow alongside me explained.

Ten minutes later, it was announced that X Hour had been delayed a half hour. After that the p.-a. system, which encompassed all the field stations as well as the blockhouse, was filled with messages between individuals who wanted to have lunch together after the shoot. A half hour later, an order forbade any more personal messages, and added, "X minus thirty!" A minute later, a pair of Stinson L-5s appeared in the air. They were to hover until X Hour, after which they would help locate the point of impact. Then came the announcement that the phones at another field station had gone dead. "Oh, Lord," the gloomy colonel said. "They better fix that fast. We're racing weather." Five minutes later, I could see, through my binoculars, thick, reddish smoke billowing at the launching site. This was the signal that the V-2 was definitely set to be fired in twenty minutes. Hausz left me and went to his telemeter station.

The blockhouse was now calling out the passage of each minute. Except for that, the p.-a. system was silent. "X minus one!" Forty seconds later, the blockhouse began to count off the seconds. ". . . ten, nine, eight, seven, six, five, four, three, two, one . . . Fire!" No. 27 barely rose. It seemed to stand still. It seemed uncanny that an object burning with nineteen thousand pounds of explosive fuel should be capable of this leisurely hesitation. No. 27 continued to rise slowly. Its awful restraint was ended with a short, definite thrust that seemed unspectacular to me but was enough to cause people around me to shout, "It's a keeper!" An enormous, intensely red lick of flame suddenly shot out from the missile's tail. Then the rocket's sound, traveling across the sand, reached us. It was not a sharp sound but a roar—the loudest I have ever heard. The roar had to it a special quality of potentiality, as though it could, if it felt like it, be even louder. The sound waves brought with them a faint wind. The flame continued to burn, and the roar remained in the air, but by now the V-2 was in earnest ascent, and real distance was being put between itself and the earth. By X-plus-40 seconds, the missile had soared so high that about half the people who were not in trailers were flat on their backs, squinting through their binoculars. I watched No. 27 until my neck could bend back no further. By then, No. 27, with its flame and roar, seemed to have become a puff of celestial vapor. I blinked for an instant, and when I opened my eyes, I saw the same puff and realized that I was no longer watching a rocket but the sky itself.

A few seconds after the disappearance of No. 27, Hausz came out of his trailer and stood beside me. "Almost wish I were with her, so I could know for myself how she's whizzing," he said, as I continued to peer at the sky. "But a gyroscope's reaction time is only one-fifth of a second—a lot better than mine. And our eye isn't as sensitive as a television camera's. Our ear doesn't compare to radio's, and soon our noses won't be so wonderful. Up in Schenectady, something called an ozotron has been developed. It detects smells that are too weak for us to sniff. But judgment—that's all ours. Only it's unreliable." Like Hausz, others had also emerged from their trailers. The eight minutes of flight had not yet elapsed, but the rocket's radio beacon, which made possible communication between No. 27 and the ground, had been lost. Hausz thought that the cabling inside the missile had accidentally burned. That had happened twenty-five miles up. At that height and at the speed at which it was traveling at the time, Hausz calculated that the missile would attain an altitude of a hundred miles. As far as G.E. was concerned, he told me, No. 27 had stayed aloft long enough for the thermometers to transmit the desired information to the telemeter. G.E., unlike Sturgeon, the Naval Research Laboratory, and Professor Whipple, did not need to recover the instruments themselves. People were standing around in groups, discussing the lost beacon and spreading rumors about left-field fences and right-field fences. As Hausz and I headed for our car, the anxious colonel was hoping aloud that by now No. 27 had definitely and harmlessly hit somewhere.

We drove to the blockhouse quickly, but when we got there, I found Sturgeon, not Kincannon, at the wheel of the Monstrosity. The lost beacon had created doubt as to where the impact point was, and the diligent Recovery Officer had taken off in a Stinson L-5 to scout the terrain. In the meantime, Sturgeon and I were to proceed in a general southwesterly direction until we received specific information over the Monstrosity's two-way radio set. A jeep with two sergeant-photographers and a Naval Research Laboratory man who was after his spectrograph trailed us. We sped past the M.P. sentries at the camp's gate and out onto a broad public highway. The noon sun was extremely hot. The sky had clouded up, and Sturgeon, an appreciative meteorologist, paid a tribute to the Proving Ground's weatherman. "Cirrus clouds," he said. "Wish they'd filter the sun's heat better than they do, but, after all, we're four thousand feet above sea level." After forty-five minutes on the highway, we got word to make for the Joranada Agricultural Station, a Department of Agriculture installation that was investigating methods for handling desert crops and cattle. Fortunately, Sturgeon knew where it was, having visited the place several months ago. He was on edge. His colleagues at the University of Michigan laboratory were waiting for a telegram from him. "Four times I've wired them about our air bottle," he said, "and each time rotten news."

We cut off the highway to a narrow, unpaved road that led to the Joranada headquarters. The station, judging by the lush crops and fat cattle we passed, was doing good work. At the end of four miles, on the other side of the road from the headquarters, we saw an air strip, on which one of the Army's L-5s was already sitting. A second plane was coming in for its landing. We pulled up behind a farm truck, near which Fred Ayres, the Joranada superintendent, and his collie were standing. Ayres, a spare, gray-haired man, had been up in the L-5 that was on the field. He had seen the rocket descending and phoned in this information to the Proving Ground. An Army plane had fetched him as a guide. "Heard her come whooshing down," he said. "Lucky she just missed dropping into Mayberry Canyon. You couldn't get in there with a horse." The second plane taxied up to us, and Kincannon leaped out and climbed into the jeep. Sturgeon obligingly squeezed into the rear section, which was crammed with equipment. Ayres thereupon hopped into his truck and tore off at a wild speed, the Monstrosity and the photographers in his wake. We bumped over a series of cattle guards, and finally wound up in front of a corral, whose fence was closed. A few steers were inside. Their owners, a man and woman who were drinking milk on their back porch nearby, gave us a bored look, as though rocket chasers pestered them every day.

I unhinged the fence for us, and when we were on the other side of the corral, we were no longer on a road, not even the well-disguised one we had traveled so far. It was simply a trail of sand, unevenly and inexplicably flattened. Cactus trees along its edges flicked into our vehicles at us, but on both sides of us were high, round dunes, which made the trail's flatness too attractive to give up. A short distance later, we came across two possible clues to the trail. First, ahead of Mr. Ayres' truck, a half dozen graceful Palominos confronted us. Our caravan startled them, and for a few seconds they galloped in our lead, as if they, too, were in pursuit of science. Then they discovered their error and bounded off to the dunes. Possibly a herd of whitefaced Herefords that we encountered a hundred yards beyond were more responsible than the horses for our trail. They stood dumbly in our path until they were routed by Kincannon, who yip-ay-yeed at them. They had hardly scattered when Kincannon himself delayed us briefly by slamming his brakes and leaping out of his jeep to the ground. There he pulled out his forty-five and rapidly shot three slugs at the sand. His target, I finally saw, was a rattler. "Goddam diamondbacks!" he said, taking the wheel again. "That's the forty-ninth I've drilled on these impact hunts."

After that, there were no more creatures. There was no more trail, either. There was only two miles of rising and falling dunes. Once we plummeted into an arroyo. I was thankful for my pillow. Then Mr. Ayres halted his truck on the crest of a dune and benignly waved us on. Fifty yards ahead, near two yuccas, we could discern a whitish object. An L-5 was circling over the spot. When we reached it, we saw that No. 27 had successfully come apart. The warhead and body had fallen elsewhere in the desert waste, and it was the tail, containing the air bottle and corn seeds, that we had come upon. It was smashed, of course. Wires protruded from it every which way, looking like messy hair. There was a stench of alcohol. The seeds were found almost immediately, in a small metal container that had been thrown clear of the tail. We searched the missile's battered hulk for more treasure. Then Sturgeon, on his knees, yelled, "There it is!" and pulled his air bottle from the wreckage. Its yellow paint had been chipped, and it was dented in the middle, but it was intact. "Shoot him!" Kincannon ordered the photographers. Their bulbs flashed. Sturgeon, on his knees, was patting his bottle.

Directly after his capture by the U. S. Army, Dr. Wernher von Braun, Hitler's missile expert, was kept away from interviewers; military authorities felt that it was too soon for the American and British publics to comprehend that enemies could be used as well as killed. When Dr. von Braun was largely instrumental in sending aloft America's first satellites, in 1958, the same authorities again made it difficult to approach him, this time on the ground that the United States could ill afford to have him distracted from the drawing board. Between these two periods, though, it was possible to sit and talk with Dr. von Braun, an indispensable man who had survived his Nazi past and was driving hard toward a future that was literally without bounds.

CHAPTER 13 | OCTOBER, 1950

A ROMANTIC URGE

AMONG THE SPOILS of the Second World War that still belong to the Americans—and to the Russians and the British and perhaps another victor or two—are some of the German scientists whose creative ingenuity accounted for so many Nazi military successes. Not long after the Allied armies crossed the German borders, their commanders, possibly more realistic than the millions back home who were cheering the arrival of what they thought would be a long peace, dispatched carefully chosen units to forage for this human booty. The roundup was not a joint operation. Each of the powers was out to acquire for itself, against the day when it might again be at war, the services of as many of these gifted enemy specialists as possible—airplane designers, guided-missile men, physicists, and the like. The American entry in the free-for-all was known as Operation Paperclip, and as a result of the efforts of its uniformed talent scouts, hundreds of strategically valuable German expatriates have been engaged in the United States on projects for its Army, Navy, and Air Force, as well as for such large industrial companies as Bell Aircraft and General Electric. The Russians, of course, gave Operation Paperclip stiff competition, and succeeded in making off with a number of scientific catches, but American military leaders are of the opinion that the Paperclip agents got the better bag.

Whatever the score, a man who was one of the most sought-after prizes of this melancholy contest is now cerebrating for the U.S. Army within the borders of the United States, and it was through the military's good offices that I was enabled to have a talk with him, not long ago, during which he discussed his career in Germany, his life in this country, and his thoughts about the future. The man is Professor Wernher von Braun, a scientist who served Hitler as head of the experimental guided-missile station at Peenemünde. It was at this seacoast town on the Baltic that von Braun, with five thousand men working under him, developed Germany's *Vergeltungswaffe Zwei* (Revenge Weapon Two), the famous V-2 that pounded London and Antwerp. The mounting of rocket engines on conventional Messerschmitt fighters was another innovation in which he had a hand. So was the *Wasserfall,* a guided anti-aircraft rocket that, after many successful test flights, was about to be turned loose against Allied planes just as the war ended. "I maintain that the *Wasserfall* is an effective way of defending cities like New York against air raids," von Braun told me. Only two months before Operation Paperclip brought about his transfer to his current sponsor, von Braun was poring over detailed plans for yet another revenge weapon—a transoceanic missile that could pound New York.

My interview with von Braun took place in his home near the reservation at Redstone Arsenal, just outside Huntsville, Alabama, where he is director of research-and-development projects at an Army Ordnance Guided Missile Center. The center used to be at Fort Bliss, near El Paso, but was shifted east when the Redstone reservation, a much larger area, was made available. Details of rocket developments at Redstone are, of course, secret, but there is nothing secret about the broad objective of all such centers, in the United States and elsewhere. That objective is to build a guided missile capable of carrying an atomic warhead to any point on the face of the earth. As might be expected, von Braun is an important factor in whatever progress is being made at Redstone. The setup there is very much the same as the one he knew at Peenemünde: He is a civilian with a civilian staff, the core of which consists of a hundred and seventeen German scientists, engineers, and technicians who worked under him in the old days, and his immediate superior is an Army man. This man is Major James P. Hamill, the administrative officer in charge of the German contingent, a thirty-one-year-old physicist and Fordham graduate who speaks German. He was a member of Operation Paperclip and has known von Braun and the others since the day they entered American employ. Before meeting von Braun, I had a talk with Hamill in his office, where he told me something about the unusual command that came his way after the war. His security officer, Major Joseph Sestito, a large, cheerful man, was present.

Hamill's opening remark was automatic; he asked me not to discuss the Center's work with von Braun. "He wouldn't tell you anything anyway," Hamill said. "None of them would. They've been security-conscious a long, long time. After all, Peenemünde was Germany's Oak Ridge." Sestito observed that he thought the scientists' sense of protocol was every bit as strong as their security-consciousness. "In spite of all they've been through together, the non-Ph.D.s wouldn't dream of entering an automobile ahead of the Herr Doktors," he said. "The Herr Professors receive the same respect from the Herr Doktors. And all defer to von Braun, although he's only thirty-nine. He has an office of his own, by the way. Right above this one."

"He's among the youngest, in fact," Hamill said. "He and his brother, Magnus, who's a chemist here." He smiled as he continued, in a reminiscent mood, "You know, the instinctive dread these Germans have of ruffling a superior got me into a jam a couple of years ago, when an influential member of the Research and Development Board flew out from Washington to visit us at Fort Bliss. We were coming out of one of the buildings there when he said to me, 'I hope you're letting them feel they can discuss scientific matters in a free-and-easy way. We certainly don't want some young major putting them through infantry drill or anything like that.' 'Naturally not,' I said. Just then, a half-dozen Paperclip boys came along. When they saw me, they immediately flattened themselves against the building wall, whipped off their hats, and shouted in unison, 'Good morning, Major Hamill!' My visitor was charitable enough to change the subject."

The Germans, I learned from Hamill, started arriving in this country late in the summer of 1945. They came as "wards of the Army," and thus required no entry permits. Each of them voluntarily signed a one-year contract with the Army. Subsequently, new five-year contracts, subject to termination in three years at the Army's discretion, were drawn up, and these were signed by one and all. (They were later renewed.) "I can't disclose the men's salaries," Hamill said, "but they're modest compared to what they would earn in private industry." In 1947, the Peenemünde scientists at Fort Bliss were joined by three hundred more wards of the Army. These were the parents, wives, and children of the scientists, who up to that time had been cared for at a camp for Paperclip dependents in Landshut, Bavaria. Two of the new arrivals were von Braun's parents, the Baron and Baroness Magnus von Braun, whose ancestral estate in Silesia had been confiscated by the Russians. A third was his eighteen-year-old bride, a second cousin he had known all his life and to whom he proposed by mail; von Braun had been permitted to leave El Paso and go to Landshut to marry her and accompany her back to Fort Bliss.

The Germans, who at Fort Bliss were quartered in a former hospital annex, kept pretty much to themselves at first, but gradually, as some of them acquired automobiles, they began spending more and more time in El Paso, where they shopped, went to movies and night clubs, and became acquainted with the residents. "They learned English with a Texas twang," Hamill said. "They had sombreros and cowboy boots to go with it. Their children went to El Paso schools, where they generally received high grades from their teachers, and bloody noses from the American and Mexican kids, who thought the war was still on. Their parents never came to us about that, though. They just told their kids to take care of themselves." Unlike the children, the parents ran into hardly any antagonism in El Paso. What little there was came from a few G.I.s on the post, who made a point of telling the Germans they were lucky to be eating three squares. "Nowadays they'd complain about such treatment, but at the time they didn't let out a peep," Sestito said. "They seemed to have a group spirit, based on the idea that on each one's model behavior rested the glory of the Reich. Also, they may have figured they'd be sent back to Germany if they showed any resentment. An aerodynamics man who was telling me one day about an unfriendly G.I. wound up by saying, 'Maybe he lost someone in the war. I can understand.' "

As it happened, two of the Paperclip men *were* sent back to Germany, but not for showing resentment. One was incompetent. The other went off to Juárez on a lark. It was then a violation of an Army order to cross the short bridge over the Rio Grande that connects El Paso with the Mexican town. "The Germans were our wards," Hamill explained, "and we didn't want to risk any possible international incidents. Fortunately, this particular fellow wasn't much use to us and wouldn't be to the Russians, so I didn't hesitate to make an example of him." Sestito said that two years later, in 1948, the Army found itself in the position of requiring the scientists to cross the bridge. This was done at the insistence of the State Department, which complained that technically the Germans weren't in the United States at all. Von Braun and his colleagues, following instructions, therefore showed up at the American Consulate in Juárez, where they filled out visa forms. "Port of embarkation was given as Ciudad Juárez," Sestito said. "Port of arrival, El Paso. Method of travel, El Paso City Lines. That's a trolley line. The fare's four cents."

When the scientists and their families had their visas, they became resident aliens and, except for certain standard reservations, were on an equal footing with American citizens. The Army thereupon lifted some of the restrictions that had been placed on the Germans. Censoring of their mail ceased, although for months afterward the Germans insisted on showing their letters to Hamill or Sestito. Increasingly, classified information was made accessible to them, and they were no longer under surveillance when they traveled. (Previously, when it had been necessary for them to make trips to places like the General Electric plant, in Schenectady, agents of the Counter Intelligence Corps had checked their trains or planes at stops along the way to make sure they were still aboard.) Furthermore, the Germans were informed that when their contracts expired, they might, if they chose, quit working for the Army and enter private industry. On the face of it, Sestito told me, the scientists can even return to Germany upon the expiration of their contracts. "However," he added, "they possess knowledge of classified information, and so, I believe, there are certain legal provisions whereby their return could be prevented, if any of them *should* want to go back." Three other

Germans besides von Braun have been back to their homeland on brief visits, one of them also to be married in Landshut and the others to receive long-overdue Ph.D. degrees at the University of Darmstadt. "Resident aliens or not," Sestito said to me, "they were restricted to Western Germany, and C.I.C. men kept tabs on them all the time. And they most certainly weren't allowed to go to Berlin. Why run the risk of Russian kidnappings?"

As resident aliens, the Germans were entitled to apply for American citizenship. All of them did, and now have their first papers, Hamill told me. "By the way," he added, "the group has been investigated thoroughly by both the Army and the F.B.I. You never know when someone's going to ask about that." In Hitler's day, Sestito said, about eighty per cent of the Redstone Germans were members of either the National Socialist Party or some other Nazi organization. "Von Braun himself joined the Nazi Party in 1940," he went on. "I'm fairly sure that these men became members more or less as a matter of expediency, rather than ideology. Not that I'm swearing they're one-hundred-per-cent sold on American institutions. In fact, any political attitude they may have toward their work seems to shape up as a neat syllogism out of some latter-day Goebbels: Germanic culture has always been the leader of Western culture; Western culture is now being championed by the United States against Russia's Eastern culture; therefore, the United States is the champion of Germanic culture. I believe they joined Nazi organizations primarily to hold on to their jobs. Their work is the driving force in their lives, not just a way of making a living. I'm glad they're working for us and not for some other country, and I hope they all keep renewing their contracts. They're good, very good." Hamill indicated several documents with red covers marked "SECRET." "We're making progress," he said. Then he looked up at the ceiling. "That guy upstairs wants to go to the moon," he said. "That's his passion—space travel. Whether it will be war or peace on earth comes after that for him."

Hamill told me that his assignment had been gratifying to him for personal as well as military reasons. He has derived deep satisfaction from watching the Germans gradually adjust themselves to their new environment. "They're eating hominy grits," Sestito put in. "Also enchilada sauce. That's the Mexican influence from El Paso. On the other hand, the Huntsville grocery stores are selling sauerkraut for the first time." I asked Hamill whether he thought von Braun and the rest would be able to readjust to their old environment if they ever found themselves back in Germany. "I'm not sure," he said slowly. "The kids they brought with them were three to eighteen when they came over. Already, two of the eighteen-year-olds have married Americans—Texans, incidentally. Thirty children have been born here. Children are anchors, you know. No, I'm not at all sure. These people have become used to things. It might be too much of an effort for them to migrate again. I don't mean as scientists—they could be that anywhere. I mean as human beings."

At Hamill's request, Sestito led me up a flight of stairs to von Braun's office, a large room containing a conference table as well as a desk. As we entered, von Braun rose from the desk and strode buoyantly toward us. He is a startlingly handsome man, over six feet tall, blue-eyed, blond, athletic-looking. His expression struck me as exuberant rather than reflective, and his manner as that of a man accustomed to being regarded as indispensable. He shook my hand energetically. "I will pick you up at your hotel after dinner and drive you to my house, where we will talk," he said. He laughed heartily and continued, "Germany is three countries. The Rhineland is the wine country. Bavaria is the beer country. Prussia and Silesia are the land of schnapps. I am from Silesia, so tonight you and I will have schnapps together."

Von Braun and I arrived at his home, a small two-story frame house, shortly after eight o'clock. His wife, an extremely pretty young woman, met us at the door and anxiously asked my indulgence for the appearance of the place. "We're moving in a few days," she explained. "We're in the middle of packing."

"We've just had a new house built," her husband said. "Much more room in it than here. Especially for my daughter. She's two. We're going to have three bedrooms, a terrace, and a porch. And a white shingle exterior. The house is on top of a hill, so we'll have a view, too. Huntsville, with its green and mountains, reminds me of Silesia. I found El Paso sandy and dry."

Actually, the von Braun living room, in which I spent the evening, showed only minor signs of decamping. Three packing cases crammed with furnishings stood off to one side, and the light was dim because, Mrs. von Braun said, a couple of lamps had already been removed to the new house. Apart from that, all appeared to be in order. Von Braun and I seated ourselves on two comfortable facing sofas beneath a dark Rembrandt reproduction that gazed down on us from the wall. Between us, on a low table, rested an Americanized version of Silesian hospitality—bourbon and soda. Mrs. von Braun brought in a tray of small sandwiches and cakes from the kitchen and then excused herself, saying that she must go upstairs and continue her packing.

Von Braun started off by telling me that his childhood had been spent in first one German city and then another, depending on where his father, who worked for the Ministry of Agriculture, happened to be stationed. His absorption with rockets began in 1930, when he was eighteen and was just embarking on the studies that eventually led to a Ph.D. in physics at the University of Berlin. Specifically, it was an article in a magazine devoted to astronomy that inspired his fervor. "I don't remember the name of the magazine or the author, but the article described an imaginary trip to the moon," he said. "It filled me with a romantic urge. Interplanetary travel! Here was a task worth dedicating one's life to! Not just to stare through a telescope at the moon and the planets but to soar through the heavens and actually explore the mysterious universe! I knew how Columbus had felt." Von Braun's romantic urge led him to consort with some talented but impecunious rocket enthusiasts who had banded together to form an organization called the *Verein für Raumschiffahrt* (Spaceship Travel Club) and were using an abandoned three-hundred-acre arsenal, which they called their *Raketenflugplatz* (Rocket Flight Place), on the outskirts of Berlin, as a proving ground for some rudimentary missiles they had built. The members of the club, many of whom later figured prominently in the doings at Peenemünde, had wangled a free lease on the dump from the municipal authorities and went about scrounging materials from manufacturers by talking fast about the rosy future of rocket travel. They recruited free manpower by letting unemployed mechanics live in the concrete igloos and warehouses that dotted the area. In spite of their penury, the members steadily improved their rockets, and word of their accomplishments began to get around.

One day in the spring of 1932, a black sedan drew up to the edge of the *Raketenflugplatz* and three passengers got out to watch a rocket launching. "They were in mufti, but mufti or not, it was the Army," von Braun said to me. "That was the beginning. The Versailles Treaty hadn't placed any restrictions on rockets, and the Army was desperate to get back on its feet. We didn't care much about that, one way or the other, but we needed money, and the Army seemed willing to help us. In 1932, the idea of war seemed to us an absurdity. The Nazis weren't yet in power. We felt no moral scruples about the possible future abuse of our brain child. We were interested solely in exploring outer space. It was simply a question with us of how the golden cow would be milked most successfully." After the appearance of the black sedan, the golden cow supplied the members of the *Verein für Raumschiffahrt* generously with equipment, proving grounds, and skilled workmen. Von Braun, I gathered, was singled out by the Army as the group's boy wonder. He spent the Christmas of 1935 at his father's estate in Silesia, and while there he mentioned that he was scouting for a coastal site that could be used as an experimental station. "Why don't you look at Peenemünde?" his mother asked. "Your grandfather used to go duck-shooting there." Von Braun did so. "It was love at first sight," he told me. "Marvelous sailing."

Hitler, upon coming into power, poured twenty million marks into Peenemünde and speeded its construction by granting it priorities on material and labor. By 1937, the station was completed, and von Braun, now attached as a civilian to the German Army's Ordnance Department, took over as technical director. His titular superior was Major General Walter Dornberger, a physicist himself, with a Ph.D. from the University of Berlin, who had long been interested in rockets and who had been one of the three passengers in the black sedan. (General Dornberger, another Paperclip find, is today with the Bell Aircraft Company.) From the outset, the experiments were aimed at developing the V-2. "Many fanciful stories have described the V-2 as part of a devilish plan devised by Hitler for use against the city of London," von Braun said. "The real story is much less sinister and dramatic. One day, a year before Peenemünde opened, Dornberger said to me, 'The Ordnance Department expects us to make a field weapon capable of carrying a large warhead over a range much beyond that of artillery. We can't hope to stay in business if we keep on firing only experimental rockets.' "

Bounding up from his sofa, von Braun went to a table and came back with an album of snapshots taken over the years at Peenemünde. Turning its pages, I saw pictures of him in a blockhouse, at test stands, and in a deep-sea diver's costume, about to plunge into the Baltic to retrieve the parts of a missile that had landed in the sea. One picture was of a banquet given at Peenemünde in von Braun's honor. "That was taken in 1944," he said. "I'd just received the Knight's Cross for the V-2. I was also given the honorary degree of Research Professor by Hitler. That's why I'm called Professor today. A very high award—Willy Messerschmitt [inventor of the fighter plane named after him] was given one, too. Not many people knew about it, because our work was always kept so secret. It's odd, but I'm better known in your country than I was in my own."

Putting the album aside and returning to the story of Peenemünde, von Braun said that after the Nazis marched against Poland, the Luftwaffe became Hitler's great pet and his interest in guided missiles lagged. Peenemünde's priorities dropped lower and lower. Technicians there were refused military deferments and were converted into infantrymen. Early in the summer of 1942, Dornberger and von Braun visited Hitler at his headquarters in East Prussia. They tried to persuade him that, in view of the way the Luftwaffe was flagging, guided missiles were Germany's one sound offensive bet. "No luck," von Braun told me. "The next day, we received word that *der Führer* had dreamed during the night that our rockets would not work." On October 3, 1942, von Braun said, a launching, or, as he called it, a shoot, at Peenemünde was so successful that Dornberger was moved to exclaim, "This afternoon the spaceship was born!" Further encouraging shoots took place, and in July 1943 the General and von Braun made a second pilgrimage to East Prussia. "*Der Führer* looked much older, and he was wearing his first pair of glasses," von Braun recalled. "But when we described our accomplishments to him, his face lighted with enthusiasm. He revoked his dream."

Hitler's enthusiasm was almost as trying as his indifference had been. Peenemünde became overrun with officials wanting to know how fast mass production of the V-2s could get under way. Von Braun protested that his rockets were still in the experimental stage, but Hitler's lieutenants couldn't wait. By February 1944 the Baltic station was so firmly entrenched as Hitler's pet that Heinrich Himmler, the chief of the Gestapo, approached von Braun with a proposal that it be transferred to S.S. sponsorship. "He assured me that Hitler's door was always open to him," von Braun said, "and that with him I would not be bothered by the red tape that the Army always put in the way of gifted inventors." Von Braun informed Himmler that he admired General Dornberger and that mass production was being held up by technical problems, not red tape. Apparently, Himmler was miffed, for three weeks later von Braun was awakened at two in the morning by three Gestapo agents, taken to Stettin, and put in a prison. He was held there for two weeks. During this time, a court of inquiry asked him to disprove a charge that he had been planning to fly to England with secret documents in a small plane the Army had placed at his disposal. Von Braun could only deny the charge. "One day while the inquiry was in full swing, Dornberger burst into the room and presented some papers that brought about my immediate release," he told me. "Dornberger had gone directly to Hitler's headquarters about my predicament."

Despite various ups and downs, von Braun continued, the V-2's accuracy was improved, hundreds of soldiers were trained in the firing of rockets, and a vast subterranean production plant was set up at Nordhausen, two hundred miles southwest of Peenemünde, in the heart of Germany. On September 7, 1944, the first V-2 was fired at London. "The Allies had bombed us several times at Peenemünde," von Braun said, "but we felt a genuine regret that our missile, born of idealism, like the airplane, had joined in the business of killing. We had designed it to blaze the trail to other planets, not to destroy our own." Then, almost harshly, he said, "But it was too late for the V-2 to stem the tide. We needed another year. *Der Führer* didn't seem to realize how immature our weapon still was." Von Braun shrugged, and added, "If Germany had won the war, *der Führer* would probably have lost interest in rockets. His enthusiasm would have shifted to a huge reconstruction project in the Ukraine or some such. I just know it."

After a moment's silence, von Braun unexpectedly let out a jolly laugh. "The amusing thing about my country's collapse was that the V-2 crowd had its choice of what to do," he said. "The High Command and the Ministry of Armament wanted us to move west. The Army corps commander defending Pomerania wanted us to stay and help him. In the end, we decided for ourselves. That was at the beginning of 1945. The Russians were only a hundred miles away, and we could already see that an Iron Curtain was coming down. General Dornberger and I wanted our outfit to fall into American hands." I asked why, and von Braun smiled. "My country had lost two wars in my young lifetime," he replied. "The next time, I wanted to be on the winning side." Not everyone at Peenemünde shared von Braun's views, with the result that when, during January and February, he and some four hundred of his most skilled colleagues headed for the so-called Bavarian Redoubt to hide out from the S.S. until the end of the war, a good many others stayed behind to await the arrival of the Russians. Thanks to Peenemünde's restored high priority rating, the railroads provided transportation for von Braun and his party, and the Navy agreed to ship twelve thousand tons of his technical equipment to Lübeck, where it was to be loaded on barges and sent up the Elbe to Magdeburg, and then moved by train from there to the Redoubt. Seventy per cent of this equipment, stranded on the docks at Lübeck and Magdeburg, was eventually grabbed by the Russians.

The guided-missile people, scattered throughout twenty-five closely bunched but isolated Bavarian villages, settled down to await capture. The waiting lasted from early April until the middle of May. "There I was, living royally in a ski hotel on a mountain plateau," von Braun said. "There were the French below us to the west, and the Americans to the south. But no one, of course, suspected we were there. So nothing happened. The most momentous events were being broadcast over the radio. Hitler was dead, the war was over, an armistice was signed—and the hotel service was excellent." Finally, on May 10th, von Braun grew tired of waiting and sent his brother Magnus down the mountain on a bicycle in search of the American Army. With the help of a G.I. he came across at the foot of the mountain, Magnus made his way to a Counter Intelligence Corps headquarters in the small Austrian town of Reutte, where he informed the officer in charge that the top V-2 men were only a couple of miles away. The officer, who had not yet been briefed on Paperclip objectives, told Magnus to come back the following day and bring his colleagues. The next morning, the party drove down the mountain in a fleet of cars. "Did you think you might be arrested and punished?" I asked von Braun. "Why, no," he replied in a tone of surprise. "We wouldn't have treated your atomic scientists as war criminals, and I didn't expect to be treated as one. No, I wasn't afraid. It all made sense. The V-2 was something we had and you didn't have. Naturally, you wanted to know all about it." He laughed, and added, "When we reached the C.I.C., I wasn't kicked in the teeth or anything. They immediately fried us some eggs."

From Reutte, von Braun and his associates were taken to Garmisch-Partenkirchen, where a Paperclip interrogation camp for German scientists had been set up. Here, he told me, he was questioned by Dr. Richard Porter, of General Electric, and Dr. Fritz Zwicky and Dr. Clark Millikan, of the California Institute of Technology. "Their questioning, of course, was extremely intelligent," von Braun said. "Those men are top scientists. I still do business with them." British scientists were eager to talk with him, and in August he was flown to London. He spent two weeks there. He and some other German rocket experts were billeted at an Army camp near Wimbledon, where they were picked up daily by an Air Force Intelligence officer and driven to the Ministry of Supply. "I must admit that I thought the British might be unfriendly to me," von Braun said, "but I found I was wrong the first day I spent at the Ministry. I was interviewed there by Sir Alwyn Douglas Crow, the man in charge of developing British rockets. I was hardly inside his office before we were engaged in friendly shoptalk. He was curious about the headaches we'd had at Peenemünde, and he gave me a good picture of the damage the V-2 had done in England. He told me that in June 1944 the British had learned the details of what we were up to at Peenemünde by piecing together the debris of one of our test rockets that had accidentally landed in Sweden. I must say they made an excellent analysis."

In the course of his commuting between Wimbledon and the Ministry, von Braun, who had got to know London fairly well while on a pleasure trip there in 1934, during his student days, had a chance to observe some of the damage that had been wrought on the British capital. At first, he said, he was amazed by how much less rubble there was in London than in Berlin, but then he realized that it was because Berlin, having taken its worst punishment at the very end of the war, hadn't yet had time to clean up its debris. "One day, the Air Force officer driving me in to London stopped our car in front of the remains of a downtown building that had been struck by a V-2," he said. "It looked as if it had been a six-story office building, but I was unable to tell the precise way in which the V-2 had done its damage, because the rubble had been cleared away. The officer started up the car again after a few minutes, and, for some reason, I found myself wondering as we drove off where our German agents in London had disappeared to. I never did find out, but one thing I know is that we had some good ones there. Our battery commanders on the French coast used to have reports on V-2 effectiveness within an hour after a rocket had been launched. I've never heard in so many words how the reports reached them, but I assume it was by radio."

Early in September, von Braun and four other German scientists were flown from London to Fort Strong, near Boston. They were the first of the Peenemünde group to reach this country. Von Braun's companions were sent on to the Aberdeen Proving Ground, in Maryland, to help American scientists there fathom the contents of documents concerning German rockets that had come into their possession. Von Braun was met at Fort Strong by Major Hamill and driven to Washington, where he had several long conversations with Army Ordnance officers in the Pentagon. He and Hamill then left by train for the West, where von Braun, as his first American assignment, joined some other Germans in teaching military personnel how to launch captured V-2s at the Army's White Sands Proving Ground, the New Mexican desert outpost eighty miles from El Paso. "That job took eight months," von Braun said. "We seemed to be expected to do it in two weeks, but shooting a V-2 is a complicated and dangerous business. Especially the rusty, dried-out V-2s we had at White Sands. And the facilities there were unsuitable for efficient shoots. Frankly, we were disappointed with what we found in this country during our first year or so. At Peenemünde, we'd been coddled. Here they were counting pennies. The armed forces were being demobilized and everybody wanted military expenditures curtailed. Of course, our facilities are more adequate now. The situation has improved."

I asked von Braun if the working conditions he had found here had caused him to regret not having signed on with the Russians. "No," he replied, "but working in a dictatorship can have its advantages, if the regime is behind you. I'm convinced that the man in charge of Stalin's atom bomb just has to press a button and he'll be supplied with a whole concentration camp full of labor. We used to have thousands of Russian prisoners of war working for us at Peenemünde. But I'm also convinced that living conditions in Russia can't compare with America's. The Russians are probably paying the scientists they got from Peenemünde well, but a refrigerator or an automobile just isn't there to be bought. I recently read in a German newspaper that some of my former colleagues at Peenemünde are living near Moscow in crowded prefabricated log cabins sent by Finland as reparations. I often get to thinking about the scientists I knew in Germany who I presume are in Russia now. There was Gröttrop, for one —an excellent electronics and guidance-control man. And Putzer, a first-rate production man, who managed the Linke-Hofmann heavy-machinery plant in Breslau. And Schierhorn, who knows everything about aluminum welding. I wish I had them and some of the others here with me, but I do think the United States got the best of our group. The Americans looked for brains, the Russians for hands. The Russians have a great many production engineers who can make wonderful copies of V-2s. The American approach has been to see the whole business as a field for development, to try for something better than anything made at Peenemünde."

Von Braun shook his head. "I can't understand about Gröttrop," he said. "He was the only one of the inner circle at Peenemünde who deliberately went over to the Russians. He may have thought they would make him the key man in their guided-missile projects. Perhaps they have, but Gröttrop was the kind who talked back if he didn't like something—he didn't care who it was. He believed in his personal freedom. I think he made a mistake in choosing Russia."

Once the White Sands teaching chore was out of the way, von Braun settled down to research at Fort Bliss. At first, most of his off hours were also spent there. He told me that when he did go in to El Paso, he encountered practically no hostility. "Some D.P.s in El Paso who learned who I was treated me distantly," he said, "but there were also some D.P.s, with an interest in history, who came and looked me up. Apparently, what had gone on in the Third Reich was still a mystery to them, and they thought I could explain it to them." In the spring of 1947, von Braun went to Germany for his wedding. "I had a feeling of narrowness there," he said. "In Europe, one is always crossing borders, but here one can travel thousands of miles without a passport." The arrival of his bride and of his parents made the United States seem less strange to him as a new home, and being married gave him a more active social life. It also made him aware that his quarters at Fort Bliss weren't ample enough. "Even this house we're leaving now would have seemed like a mansion in Texas," he told me. Late in 1948, the von Brauns' daughter was born, and their house became even less adequate. "My daughter is beautiful," von Braun said. "Perhaps you will see her. My wife picks her up at ten each night for a few minutes."

As his domestic and social interests broadened, von Braun said, so did his professional life. The laboratories at Fort Bliss and the scope of the research projects there were enlarged. He was pleased, too, with a variety of new equipment that was installed at White Sands. "Shoots are the climaxes in my field," he said. "A first-rate proving ground is essential. You put six months of work into a missile and inside of a minute it's either a failure or a success." In 1948, the Army gave von Braun permission to attend scientific conventions. At one of these, in Chicago, assembled by the Air Force Surgeon General to consider medical problems associated with interplanetary travel, von Braun read a paper on man-made satellites. "Everyone has been most friendly to me at meetings," he said. "Science is as much a universal language as music." In August 1949 the British Interplanetary Society invited von Braun to become an honorary fellow, "in recognition of your great pioneering activities in the field of rocket engineering." In accepting, von Braun replied, in part, "Despite the grief the work of me and my associates brought to the British people, [your invitation] is the most encouraging proof that the noble enthusiasm in the future of rocketry is stronger than national sentiments."

The headlights of an automobile coming out of a driveway across the street shone brightly into von Braun's living room, lighting up the gloomy Rembrandt and the packing boxes. When the car had gone and the room was somber again, von Braun told me that the shift to Alabama, in 1950, had seemed no wrench at all. By then, he said, he and his wife had become used to thinking of the United States as their home. "We were no longer surprised when people called each other by their first names a few minutes after being introduced," he went on. "And when we saw a supermarket here in Huntsville, we knew we were all set. Everything in one store! In Germany, even vegetable shops are specialized." Soon, von Braun told me, he and his family would be enjoying the view from their new house. As for his parents, they have a comfortable home near by. "They are our sitters," he said.

Certainly, von Braun assured me, the move to Alabama hadn't interfered in the slightest with his research. "I can work anywhere in the world," he said. "I've finished *Mars Project* since coming here. That's my novel. I worked on it for three years. It deals with a trip to Mars by seventy passengers aboard ten spaceships. The first half describes preparations for the flight and the second tells about settling on Mars. That second part shows what scientific developments will be able to do if our civilization succeeds in surviving a few more years. My characters live underground in pressurized, air-conditioned homes, and all their food is synthesized. In the end, Mars and Earth work out their scientific problems through mutual aid."

"But what about the moon?" I asked.

"Mars is more of a challenge," von Braun replied. "It would take two hundred and sixty days to get there. To the moon it's only a hundred hours." He hesitated momentarily. Then he spoke with an intensity he had not shown all evening. "Personally, though, I'd rather go to the moon than to Mars, even if the trip is shorter," he said. "After all, a journey to the moon is unquestionably a possibility. The moon's face, thanks to telescopes, is more familiar to us than even some parts of the earth—the mountain ranges in Tibet, for example. All that's needed is adequate funds and continuity of effort. Spaceships will eventually be used by everybody. All this military application of rockets—it's only a part of the picture. A means to an end."

I asked von Braun if he had ever regretted the arrival of the black sedan two decades ago at the *Raketenflugplatz*. He shook his head. "Someone else would have done the job if I hadn't," he said. "Rockets were a new idea, and a new idea is stronger than one man's feelings. Once civilization is committed to technical advance, we have to keep going. We can't go back to a pastoral existence. That would destroy the social bases of our modern life. Think of the men in industry who would be thrown out of work. Think of the way populations are increasing—those people couldn't be fed. The main question is how we use our technical advances. They can either kill us or elevate us. In ancient Greece, slaves did the dishwashing while Sophocles wrote his tragedies. Literally, we don't have slavery today, but the bulk of humanity is in bondage to physical chores. Technology offers millions a chance to investigate the higher aspects of life. But you don't get something for nothing. There are strings attached to that chance." Von Braun paused, and then continued, "The same things would have happened at Peenemünde without me. Do you think scientists should be blamed for wars? Einstein? He looked for fundamental truths and his formula was used for an atomic bomb. Alexander Graham Bell? Military orders that kill thousands are transmitted over his telephone. Why not blame the bus driver who takes war workers to their factories? How about movie actors who sing for the troops?"

"Have you any answer for it all?" I asked.

"Religion," von Braun replied at once. "As long as national sovereignties exist, our only hope is to raise everybody's standards of ethics. I go to church regularly now."

"Did you at Peenemünde?"

"I went occasionally," he said. "But it's really too late to go to church after a war starts. One becomes very busy." He waved his hand vaguely. "Any real scientist ends up a religious man. The more he learns about natural science, the more he sees that the words that sound deep are really poorly contrived disguises for ignorance. Energy? Matter? We use them but we don't really know what they are. Or take the mystery of heredity. It will never be solved." He laughed. "None of us have anything to do with the most fateful event of our lives—picking our parents."

Right now, von Braun said, world conditions being what they are, he can't see himself doing anything other than continuing at Redstone. He regards his present course as essentially the one he followed at Peenemünde. "Still developing military rockets. And still hoping for spaceships," he said. "Only now I'm doing it in a different country. But soon it won't even seem like a different country. I used to spend my week ends sailing on the Baltic. Now I fish in T.V.A. lakes. Sometimes, at Redstone, soldiers in training for technical jobs have to mop our laboratory floors. They gripe about it the same way the soldiers did at Peenemünde. Gröttrop is probably listening to the same gripes in Russia."

We heard Mrs. von Braun coming down the stairs. "Wernher!" she called out softly as she stepped from the landing. Their daughter, half asleep, was in her arms. Von Braun and I stood up, and he walked toward his wife. She glanced at me to see if I was admiring the baby. I was indeed. She is a beautiful child—blond, curly-headed, lanky for her age. The living-room lights gradually roused her. She blinked several times, and then her blue, still-sleepy eyes opened wide. She caught sight of her father and drowsily reached out a hand toward him. He touched her fingers, bent down, and kissed her.

Von Braun and I didn't sit down again after his wife and daughter left. The interview was over. "I'm going to do some work at home tonight, and I have to be in at Redstone very early in the morning," he told me jauntily. "I leave for a shoot at White Sands in a few days."

Scientists, quietly persevering with their tasks throughout the war, knew that the lives of millions everywhere would be irrevocably altered if their researches proved successful, but it was not until this came about that particular faces of Atomic Age humanity began to emerge, men and women with names and addresses, parents and insurance policies. When those faces did appear, the faces of the explorers of radiation were among them. It was clear that they had not experimented with inorganic matter alone. They had experimented with their own lives as well.

CHAPTER 14 | FEBRUARY, 1954

A DEACON AT OAK RIDGE

MOST SCIENTISTS, like most other people, are too preoccupied with their daily work to ponder its moral implications, but those who do sometimes reach fairly sweeping conclusions. Certain physicists, for example, won't have anything to do with military projects; others, equally conscientious in their self-searching, feel that at the present time they would not be justified in trying to do anything but make atomic weapons more lethal. Extreme as both positions may sound, the one that has recently been taken by Dr. William G. Pollard, the executive director of the Oak Ridge Institute of Nuclear Studies, in Oak Ridge, Tennessee, is, for a man of science, even more radical. After twenty years as a physicist, during which his philosophic point of view has been just as objective and just as skeptical as that of any of his colleagues, Pollard has been ordained a deacon of the Episcopal Church. A week before Christmas, 1952, at the age of forty-one, with his four sons serving as acolytes, he was invested with holy orders in ceremonies held at St. Stephen's Church, in Oak Ridge—a building he had helped put up with his own hands. His ordination came at the end of two and a half years' intensive study of theology, culminating in an examination that he found more rigorous thran any he had taken as a graduate student at Rice Institute, in Houston, Texas, while preparing a doctoral thesis entitled "On the Theory of Beta-Ray Type of Radioactive Disintegration." "I think my theological examiners wanted to be certain I wasn't just pulling an intellectual stunt," Pollard told me.

Working simultaneously as a physicist and as a religionist, Pollard has found, leaves him practically no free time. Most of his weekdays are spent supervising the affairs of the Institute, a scientific alliance of thirty-two Southern universities that operates on an annual budget of about two million dollars, which is put up by the federal government, but on Sundays, wearing his vestments, he is busy at St. Stephen's, where he assists at Holy Communion. In addition to carrying on his work with the Institute, he has for several years been engaged in secret military research; nowadays, upon returning home from a conference at a certain Oak Ridge war plant where he has presented his latest findings in connection with this project, he may don his clerical dress and pay a pastoral call on some ailing and frightened elderly parishioner. Some time ago, having read a paper on "The Separation of Isotopes by Gaseous Diffusion" at a scientific meeting at Ohio State University, he stayed over a day to address three hundred members of the university's business school on "Revelation and Response."

Pollard says that he has no interest in trying to reconcile faith and skepticism. He considers them mutually antagonistic, and has chosen faith, in which, as he puts it, "explanations are useful but not necessary." "I no longer believe that the approach of size-up-and-solve will produce a formula explaining all natural phenomena," he says. "If this sounds like heresy to any of my scientific colleagues, I can only say that the more I have learned of science, the more I have become convinced that the origin of the universe will forever remain a mystery to us. And I say this with sympathy for those who disagree with me, for, like them, I have been an agnostic who was sustained for many years, and happily so, by the hope of that master formula. Ten years ago, I would have been incapable of taking the step I have taken. Wars, social upheavals, nationalism—I once reacted intellectually to such things, but now I see them as perhaps containing elements of God's judgment. I'm less worried now about these problems than I used to be—though not because I have any greater confidence in man's being able to cope with them."

A year or so after he had been ordained, I visited Pollard in Oak Ridge, and far into the late hours of a mild Southern night listened to his account of how he had arrived at his religious decision. We sat talking on a narrow wooden porch outside his house, which overhangs a gully filled with pines and dogwoods, while from time to time his wife, Marcella, a spirited woman with an oval face and hazel eyes, made us comfortable with highballs of Tennessee sour-mash whiskey. "After Bill's ordination," Mrs. Pollard said, with a smile, as she brought in a round of drinks, "a Hard-Shell Baptist wrote him that he shouldn't have picked a denomination that lets its ministers drink." She sat with us most of the evening, rarely speaking and periodically looking in on her four sons, who were reading and listening to the radio in the living room. Occasionally, one or another of the boys, who range in age from twelve to nineteen, joined us for a brief period. At first, I ascribed these appearances to curiosity about an unfamiliar guest, but, watching them as they listened intently to their father, I gradually came to suspect that they were still curious about his having adopted a second career; Pollard, I discovered, has never been able to give a specific explanation for it. "I'm fuzzy when it comes to reasons," he told me, "and I've heard them all, including the one that I may have deliberately overstated a position that many scientists have informally come around to. But I'm serene about the decision itself, and that's what really counts."

Pollard is a rather good-looking man, with a high forehead, brown hair, a thin nose, and inquisitive gray eyes, and he is, of course, well educated. (He has five degrees, two of them honorary.) There is nothing sanctimonious about him; he talked to me with candor, and there were times, indeed, when he discussed his new status with open amusement. Pollard told me that he was born in Batavia, New York, and that when he was twelve his family moved to Knoxville, Tennessee, where his father, who had been a mining engineer, became the regional representative of an electrical-equipment firm. Pollard was brought up in the Episcopal faith, but he lost interest in it as a high-school student and turned to the Unitarian Church. After three years he also gave that up. By the time he married, which was in 1932, shortly after graduating from the University of Tennessee, he had come to look upon religion as, in his phrase, "a fairy tale." "To me, it seemed to be a matter of Bible fundamentalists insisting that Adam was the first man and that the world was created in 4004 B.C.," he told me. "I was by then immersed in my graduate work at Rice and I didn't see how anyone could fail to realize that the only rational way for us to make the best of the universe was to comprehend its material nature."

His bride, Pollard went on, held an opposite view. Her parents, who were Presbyterians in Nashville, had brought her up as a regular churchgoer (she became an Episcopalian while a student at the University of Tennessee), and she was determined not only to remain a regular churchgoer but to bring up any children she might have in the same fashion. "In the early days of our marriage, we had many crises over that," Pollard said. "Three months after our wedding, I remember, Marcella very much wanted me to go to church with her one Sunday, but I told her that the studying I was planning to do at home was more important. The church was a mile away, and she told me later that as she walked toward it alone, she kept looking back, hoping that I would be trying to catch up with her. I was doing no such thing, but neither could I get any work done as I sat at home thinking of her. And since I couldn't, I figured that one of us might as well have our way, so after that I went to church with her. But I wouldn't say the Creed. I considered it too ridiculous."

In 1936, with a Ph.D. in physics from Rice, Pollard returned to the University of Tennessee as an assistant physics professor. Five years later, he was an associate professor and two years after that a full professor. He was also the father of four little Episcopalians—baptized in that church at his wife's insistence—but he was far less interested in their religious upbringing, he told me, than in his research. In 1944, he was asked to join Columbia University's Special Alloys and Metals Laboratory, which was a cover name for one of the wartime Manhattan District's most important scientific units. He did research there on the gaseous-diffusion method of extracting U-235—the explosive in atomic bombs—from common uranium. Moving to New York meant two months' separation from his family, who had to remain in Knoxville until he could make arrangements to bring them North, and during that period he lived in the King's Crown Hotel, on Morningside Heights, not far from the Pupin Physics Laboratories, at Columbia University, where his unit was then situated. Even without his wife to act as a spur, Pollard said, Sunday as often as not found him in church; he wasn't sure whether he went there just as a matter of habit or in order to provide cheering items for his letters to his wife, who was concerned about the logistics of moving their children and furniture to New York. When his family at last arrived, he told me, he was relieved, because that meant he could once again assure himself that he was attending church simply in the interests of domestic accord. "I saw myself as just a father taking his wife and four small boys somewhere on Sunday morning," he said.

"We moved into a fairly nice house in Mount Vernon," Mrs. Pollard recalled. "Bill became a commuter. By that time, the Laboratory had been moved to the old Nash automobile building, on Broadway at 133rd Street. It was quite a far cry from the campus at Tennessee."

Although in the course of his work, Pollard had occasion to visit the then secret city of Oak Ridge, where there was an enormous gaseous-diffusion plant, he and his associates at Columbia were told no more than was necessary about what was going on and knew nothing of the successful atomic-weapons test that took place in New Mexico on July 16, 1945. They did, however, know that something was brewing and they were therefore not quite as surprised as most people when, three weeks later, President Truman announced that an atomic bomb had been dropped on Hiroshima. "I was exhilarated," Pollard said. "I was in the Nash building at the time, and my colleagues and I kept the radio going all that afternoon and took turns rushing out for the latest editions of the newspapers. We finally knew for certain that our work had been effective." Three days later, he continued, when the Nagasaki bomb was dropped, his mood changed. Mrs. Pollard shifted restlessly in her chair at this point, and her husband, after glancing over at her, went on to explain, "Marcella doesn't want me to say what I'm about to say."

"You know how people are," Mrs. Pollard said. "They'd think Bill turned to the church because of a sense of guilt."

"They'd be mistaken, I believe," Pollard said. "But whether they'd be right or wrong, I don't see why that should keep me from talking about a meaningful experience." He hesitated briefly, and then resumed where he had left off. "After the Nagasaki bomb, my exuberance was replaced by something approaching terror," he said. "I thought the bombs would be sprinkled all over Japan. When I got back to Mount Vernon that evening—it was a Thursday—I picked up a newspaper and saw on the religious page that I had just enough time to get to a service in New Rochelle. I walked out of the house alone and took a trolley to Trinity Episcopal Church there. This time, there were no little boys along. As the service progressed, I became conscious of a feeling that it wasn't just an empty rigmarole, and when I got back home, I was no longer disturbed. I slept calmly that night."

Shortly after V-J Day, Pollard said, he returned to the University of Tennessee. He had not been there long when he heard a physicist, Dr. Katherine Way, at a party in Knoxville, outline an idea that stirred his enthusiasm, as well as that of several others present. Now that the war was over, she suggested, it would be a fine thing if university researchers in the Oak Ridge region could use some of the elaborate facilities there, which were far beyond the means of any school. Her suggestion led to a conference of Southern scientists in December, 1945, at which Pollard was chosen chairman of a committee whose purpose was to sound out federal and academic officials on the idea. After months of scurrying about between Washington and various campuses, the committee succeeded in winning both government backing for the project and the sponsorship of fourteen leading Southern schools, and the Oak Ridge Institute of Nuclear Studies was well on its way. In October 1947 the sponsors appointed Pollard executive director for a five-year term, and he thereupon resigned from the Tennessee faculty. Two months later, the Pollards set up housekeeping in Oak Ridge.

If he and his family had moved to a more settled community, Pollard told me, he might never have taken holy orders. "At best, I might have wound up a good, solid Episcopalian," he continued, smiling. "But Oak Ridge was only five years old and its churches had little or no resources. It was hard not to lend a hand, but if you did, you let yourself in for more than you'd bargained for." However, Pollard's first concern at Oak Ridge was to organize the Institute, and to judge by its growth, he would appear to have accomplished this effectively; the number of its academic sponsors has more than doubled in its first six years, and its staff, which at first consisted only of Pollard, an administrative assistant, and a secretary, totals a hundred and seventy-five. The Institute trains scientists from American and foreign universities, medical schools, and industrial firms in the use of radioisotopes, or "tracer atoms"; it provides the facilities for scores of university teachers to do research; it awards Atomic Energy Commission fellowships to young physicists to study the latest methods of guarding against radiation hazards; and it operates a thirty-bed hospital and a laboratory for the study of the effects of radioactive materials on cancer.

It was plain to Pollard that the local Episcopalian affairs were just about as badly in need of spadework as the infant Institute. He and his fellow-parishioners had no church building; like the members of several other sects represented in Oak Ridge, they worshipped in a high-school gymnasium. One Sunday, as he and his family were leaving the gymnasium after the morning services, he casually inquired of the rector, the Reverend Stephen Davenport, if he thought the parish would ever have a church of its own. Davenport replied that only a few days previously he had received word that the Atomic Energy Commission was about to allocate land to the various denominations that wanted their own churches. Then the Rector startled Pollard by inviting him to head a drive for a building fund. "I could have pleaded pressure of work, I suppose, but since I was the one who'd brought up the matter, I didn't see how I could back down," Pollard told me. "Anyway, I took the job on, and we raised eight thousand dollars."

In August 1948 the church's Sunday-school superintendent and lay reader, an engineer named John Bull, left Oak Ridge to study for the ministry. A month later, the Rector, perhaps recalling Pollard's diligence as a fund-raiser, asked him to fill Bull's Sunday-school post. "I wanted to turn him down," Pollard said, "but I had four children going to Sunday school—more than most of the parishioners—so I was stuck. Now that I look back, practically all the steps that led to my ordination seemed just temporary and inconsequential at the time." As Sunday-school superintendent, Pollard led a fifteen-minute service for the whole student body, which numbered about a hundred, and afterward, like ten other volunteers, taught a small class. He found that the questions his pupils asked in class made teaching unexpectedly interesting. "The children wanted to know things like how various feast days came into being and why we have Lent and where this or that canticle came from," he said. "Since I didn't know, I had to read up on the subjects at the library. I was amazed at how absorbing the material was."

That fall, the persuasive Davenport gave up his post in Oak Ridge to become rector of a church in Massachusetts, and he was presently replaced by the Reverend Robert F. McGregor. McGregor also proved to be persuasive. Inquiring around for likely nominees to fill Bull's position as lay reader, he was told by several of his parishioners that their children were enthusiastic about Pollard's Sunday-school services. Impressed, McGregor asked Pollard how he would feel about becoming a lay reader. "He made it sound so easy that I wondered why he needed anyone," Pollard told me. Lay reading, the Rector explained, merely meant reading the appropriate prayers from the Book of Common Prayer at morning or evening services; if Pollard agreed, McGregor would arrange with the Bishop of Tennessee to have him licensed as a lay reader. "I agreed," Pollard said, adding, with a shrug, "It was another of those steps."

As a lay reader, Pollard told me, he enjoyed leading prayers but found the contents of the prayers themselves even more rewarding. As he grew increasingly familiar with their wording, he began to wonder about their origins. Accordingly, just as he had done in response to the questions of his Sunday-school pupils, he embarked on a reading program, but this one was on a formidable scale. He bought books—dozens of them—and spent all his free hours studying them. From time to time, glancing at his bookshelves, he would find himself smiling at the incongruous juxtaposition of his worn scientific volumes with such titles as *Early Traditions of Israel, Source Book of Church History for the First Six Centures,* and *Doctrine of the Trinity*. His reading program gave him an entirely fresh view of the Bible. "I'd previously taken it at its face value," he said, "but now I discovered that it was a highly complex blending of independent literary sources that were fascinating to disentangle. Here was a field of bona-fide scholarship that commanded my intellectual respect, without which, I imagine, I couldn't have embraced religion. It was exciting to find that the Bible didn't have to be accepted solely on the basis of its philosophical and metaphysical values. It could be accepted as a piece of history describing the unique fortunes and experiences of a people, which culminated in the revelation of God among them. Through the Bible,

I now saw, the Judaeo-Christian civilization could be studied in the same disciplined way as, say, the Greco-Roman civilization. In fact, one Hebrew writer—theologians differ over his identity, but I believe it was Ahimaaz, the son of a priest of David—impressed me as being much more truly the father of history than Herodotus. If I'm ever at a university again, I may learn Hebrew, so that I can read the work in the original."

Pollard was happily persevering at his private research when, in June 1950, Davenport and Bull returned to Oak Ridge for a sentimental but formal occasion; Bull had completed his training for the ministry and had asked Davenport to preach the sermon at his ordination. In his sermon, Davenport pointed out that, like Bull, many lay readers had gone on to prepare themselves for the diaconate—an order of the ministry, just below the priesthood, that carries with it the privilege of assisting at Holy Communion and, if the deacon is licensed to do so by the bishop, of preparing and delivering sermons. "Listening to him, I gathered that the duties of a deacon were only slightly greater than those of a lay reader," Pollard said. "The training, I knew, took three years at a seminary under ordinary circumstances, but I'd already read so extensively in church history and liturgics that I felt I must have already completed some of it. The idea of having my religious studies organized, as my scientific studies had been, appealed to me. Anyway, I thought, there'd be nothing final about deciding to study for the ministry. I'd have to be admitted first as a postulant and after that as a candidate for holy orders, and I could always quit at any time along the way. I'd say that my approach then was more curious than dedicated."

For a few weeks after the visit of Davenport and Bull, Pollard said, he talked over the idea of studying for the ministry with a close friend—a biochemist in cancer research at the Institute—who also had leanings in that direction. "It was an odd time to be discussing such matters—just when the Institute was coming along so wonderfully," Pollard observed to me. Then, one evening, McGregor came by the Pollards' house on church business of an unrelated nature, and when it had been disposed of, Pollard brought up the subject of preparing for ordination. McGregor remarked simply that he had suspected his lay reader might be contemplating such a step. "He was letting me know that the decision had to be my own," Pollard told me. Shortly thereafter, Pollard and the biochemist began meeting at regular intervals with McGregor, who mapped out a program of study for them, and late in 1950 they were admitted as postulants. The biochemist dropped out in April 1952 because he could not afford the time, but Pollard, although he, too, was busy, stayed on. "I became deeply interested in the curriculum," he said. "Marcella and I cut our social life to the bone. If I had to go out of town for the Institute, I studied on the train or plane, and in my hotel room."

"Bill's only recreation was doing carpentry and rolling asphalt walks for the church we were building," Mrs. Pollard said. "And even that stopped in the middle of 1951, when St. Stephen's was finished."

A year after Pollard started his formal studies, he was admitted to candidacy for holy orders. That was in October 1951. Three months afterward, he took the first part of the examination required for ordination as a deacon at the Episcopal rectory in Maryville, a few miles south of Oak Ridge, before a Board of Examining Chaplains that consisted of two of the most learned theologians in the diocese. For an entire day, they questioned him exhaustively on the subjects of the Old and New Testaments, liturgics, and such branches of practical theology as homiletics, pastoral care, and pastoral administration. Two days later, he received a letter informing him that he had acquitted himself well and could go on preparing himself for the second —and final—part of his examination.

Pollard said that the deeper he got into religion, the more frequently he found himself uneasily comparing its point of view with that of science. He discovered that it wasn't easy to relinquish the secular beliefs that he had relied on for so long. "Each time I was about to tackle a new aspect of religion, I'd be sure there was going to be something in it that I wouldn't be able to swallow," he told me. "Dogmatic theology, I remember, had me especially worried." Eventually, after a trying period of several months, he succeeded in reaching certain conclusions that, while many scientists would undoubtedly consider them false, enabled him to cross the line between mere curiosity and dedication. "I decided that a person could, without violating his intellectual integrity, both think within the framework of a Judaeo-Christian view and believe all scientific knowledge of the structure of the world," he said slowly. "I decided that science was a way of investigating the wonders of God's creativeness, such as the marvelous unity of a living cell and the intricate combinations of particles that make up matter. That being so, it seemed to me irreligious to oppose the work of science."

But while this reasoning made it possible for a religious man to be a scientist, Pollard pointed out, it scarcely bridged the philosophical chasm between the two fields—between the religious view that man is a creature of God, dependent on Divine Providence, and the view, implicit in much of science, that everything in the world as we know it is dependent upon prior sets of conditions, which we need only to understand and place in their proper sequence in order to control the future. Thus, Pollard said, a leading educator has declared that a complete science of psychology would make it possible for us to become "masters of our souls as we are now masters of heat and light." Pollard smiled as he let me ponder the implications of that thought, and then he dismissed it by saying, "That's about as likely as a carbon atom explaining the solar system." During this period of introspection, he went on, it occurred to him that physics itself, like other sciences, has its share of paradoxes, a fact that would seem to disprove the theory that all phenomena can be arranged in a neat pattern based on cause and effect. As an example, he cited the famous argument that scientists got into a quarter of a century ago over whether light is composed of electro-magnetic waves or particles; each side, accepting the premise that there could be only one true concept of the atom, assembled convincing data with which to discredit the other. In the end, Dr. Niels Bohr, the Danish physicist, showed, by means of his principle of complementarity, that while the two concepts were contradictory, both were essential to an understanding of physical phenomena. "As many scientists are beginning to recognize, the more knowledge we accumulate, the clearer it becomes that science is unlikely ever to lead us to an orderly arrangement of nature's ways," Pollard said. "And certainly our scientific achievements haven't affected our freedom of will to use them for either building a utopia or destroying civilization. I have come to interpret events as revealing the acts of God—an interpretation that I know the single-minded scientist will have nothing to do with, because I can't prove it. But isn't one look at the armed world today enough to suggest that he, with his conviction that increased knowledge means progress, is also guilty of some sort of faith?"

Except for a few intimate friends, Pollard said, he had planned to tell no one what he was up to until he had passed his examination. Two weeks before the second part of his examination, however, he changed his mind. A quarterly meeting of the Institute's board of directors was coming up, and he felt that the members—a group of nine distinguished educators and scientists—were entitled to advance warning about the possibly controversial step he was hoping to take. At the meeting, which was held in a walnut-panelled room in one of the Institute buildings at Oak Ridge, the board disposed of several items on the agenda and then the chairman asked Pollard to leave the room. "That was when I had to speak up," Pollard told me. "I knew they were about to take up my reappointment. So I said to them, 'There's something you ought to know,' and then I told them what I'd been doing and what I was planning to do. I said that while I didn't think it would affect my direction of the Institute, I was aware that the denominational universities among the sponsors might object. If I was ordained, I said, I would make it a point to wear clericals at the Institute only when my pastoral duties made it necessary, which would be infrequently, because that might annoy some of the other scientists. I said that I didn't want to leave the Institute but that I'd understand if they asked me to. And I suggested that if they wanted me at all, they might reappoint me for just a year, rather than for the maximum five years, and see how things worked out. When I had finished, no one said a word, and I could sense an embarrassment among the members that I was afraid would prevent a free-and-easy discussion. I hoped someone would say something, and finally, to my relief, one of the directors asked me if I thought my position would be any different from that of other laymen who devote some of their time to church work. I replied that I didn't think so. Then I was again asked to leave the room, and in five minutes they called me back. They'd voted me a five-year term and a raise."

In November, 1952, two and a half years after his Sunday-school pupils had asked him their first questions, Pollard appeared again before the two examining theologians at Maryville. They interrogated him—this time for two days—about church history, moral theology, dogmatic theology, and the history of religion. A few days later, he was informed that he had successfully completed his studies. His ordination was set for Ember Wednesday, December 17th, in St. Stephen's. At the end of November, happening to be in New York on Institute business, he dropped in at the J. M. Hall vestments shop on West Fortieth Street and had himself fitted for a clerical vest and collar. "I looked in the mirror and felt pretty good," Pollard said.

St. Stephen's Church was crowded for Pollard's ordination. Three bishops were on hand, including the Bishop of South Carolina, who had been rector of the church in Houston that Mrs. Pollard had so much wanted her husband to attend twenty years earlier and who now delivered the sermon. The presence of the four Pollard boys as acolytes gave the traditional ceremonies an unusual family touch, which was somewhat blurred by the fact that the idea of a nuclear physicist's taking holy orders attracted several reporters, as well as photographers who punctuated the proceedings with the click of cameras. Numerous Oak Ridge scientists were in the church, and Pollard suspected that it was the first time some of them had been in any church. Dozens of employees at the Institute left their desks to watch their chief being ordained, although it meant that they would be docked half a day's pay. After the ceremonies, Pollard was the guest of honor at a luncheon given by the women of the parish, and more pictures were taken.

The resulting newspaper stories and pictures brought Pollard scores of letters and telegrams from all parts of the country. Some of them were not wholly friendly. Several complained about his choice of a denomination. Others warned him against attempting to insinuate scientific cant into religion. A Midwestern well-wisher called his act proof that science was at last waking up to the true meaning of cosmic rays. One correspondent thought it a shame that a man of Pollard's education should surrender himself to the rigid rituals of the church. "Scientists who don't surrender themselves to research techniques that are just as rigid run the risk of sloppy data," Pollard remarked to me mildly. The day after the ceremonies, he discovered that, as an inverted Faust, he was in a position to make money out of his ordination when a garrulous executive of a television network in New York called him up and urged him to fly north to take part in a program. "I agreed, then wondered why, and turned him down," Pollard said. "That wasn't exactly the sort of redemption I'd been seeking." Soon lecture-circuit managers were imploring him to take to the road under their banners, and magazine editors were making him impressive offers for a first-person story describing in detail how he had met God while walking in a garden. "They all had the same hell-fire-and-damnation yarn in mind," he said. "I was to be a disillusioned scientist who felt guilt-ridden about the bomb but was finally saved by a sudden revelation of God."

In Oak Ridge itself, Pollard continued, nearly all the people who talked to him about what he had done commended him for it, but he could not always be sure whether they meant it or were just being polite. Some of the felicitations, he said, were less welcome than others—especially those of certain churchgoers who, in his opinion, looked upon religion as fashionable and therefore an asset to their social life. "I must say I hadn't thought of the ministry in that way," he said. He was also not impressed by a brother-clergyman who, at a diocesan meeting, treated him rather airily for having been "so tardy in seeing the light." "Such fatuousness isn't likely to help religion," Pollard said. Some of his scientific colleagues said nothing about the matter; he presumes that while several of them indubitably regard him as a renegade, the others simply feel it's his business, and not theirs. Pollard told me that one scientist did try to badger him one evening while they were listening to a concert of records at the home of a friend, by rather pointlessly ridiculing the Trappists. "I suppose you might call it just a coincidence, but Bach's 'St. Matthew Passion' was being played at the time," he added.

Encounters of this sort faded into insignificance when Pollard heard a rumor that one of the ranking medical officials at the Institute was considering resigning in protest against his ordination. According to Pollard, this man, a gifted researcher, is so outspoken about his antipathy toward religion that someone once referred to him as the founder of the First Evangelical Atheists' Church of Oak Ridge. "He was not only important to the Institute but someone I admired as a friend—and also, frankly, for his bluntness," Pollard said. "I dropped everything and went to see him. We talked for two hours." It turned out that the man was upset because he was afraid that his professional colleagues throughout the country would infer that the Institute was dominated by religious influences, and therefore might begin to suspect the value of its medical work. "He was apparently afraid of being found guilty by association," Pollard observed wryly. "After he got it all off his chest, I reminded him that I was the same fellow who had collaborated with him on a paper that was just about to appear in a technical journal. I assured him several times that I had no intention of misusing my directorship, but that I had to insist on my right to live my own personal life as I saw fit. If he doubted my word, I said, it was his duty to bring the matter up before the board of directors. He told me he didn't want to do that, because he respected me as a scientist and it might mean that I'd be fired. I realized then that since neither of us wanted the other out of the Institute, we were going to be able to patch things up." And eventually the medical man agreed to stay on, but not before he had diagnosed Pollard's mental attitude as that of a man suffering from a type of aberration that not infrequently afflicts those who have reached the age of forty. "He told me I could read it all in William James," Pollard said, with a chuckle. "And I replied that since my new point of view showed me that *he* was clearly living in an illusory world, the best thing for us to do was regard each other as mentally ill and continue to collaborate on research."

As a deacon, Pollard has undertaken a variety of new tasks. He gives occasional sermons at small missions in Tennessee hill towns that cannot afford their own preacher. He assists McGregor at Sunday services, and also at Wednesday-evening Holy Communion, to which, at the end of his workday, he goes directly from the Institute. If McGregor is out of town—on church affairs or on vacation—Pollard acts as the pastor of St. Stephen's, leading the congregation in worship and conducting burial services if the need arises; occasionally at such times his two careers cross paths. Once he was hurriedly summoned from a meeting of the board of directors at the Institute to baptize a dying newborn child. There are also pastoral calls to be made at the Institute's cancer hospital, a place Pollard used to be interested in primarily from the administrative point of view. "It felt strange, the first time, to be wandering around that familiar ward in my clericals," he told me. Even when McGregor is on hand, Pollard is called upon every now and then to pay a pastoral visit. Not long ago, for instance, a neighbor of his, an elderly woman who was going to have an operation, sent word by her niece that she wanted to see him. For two weeks, Pollard stopped in daily to pray with her. He also prayed with her twice in the Oak Ridge general hospital, just before and just after the operation was performed.

Unlike the majority of scientists, Pollard said, his parishioners are not in a perpetual state of intellectual ferment, although among them are a number of people of high intelligence, including a few scientists. The core of their attitude, it seems to him, is an acceptance of what he calls "the drama of existence"—a feeling of being swept along by a force over which they have no control. "They think in terms of responsibilities, hopes, decisions, and an eventual necessity to account for everything they do," he said. "To men who spend most of their time on formulas and equations, such matters do not seem of paramount importance. Naturally, scientists are not untouched by them, but they tend to dismiss them whenever possible as unruly and trifling, if sometimes puzzling, impositions upon their orderly scheme of things. After all, how can you subject a hope to external verification? As one theological writer has said, the scientist's approach to life differs from that of the religious man as much as a sociologist's approach to women differs when he is preparing a treatise on women and when he is marrying one. After I ceased to be wholly dependent on the scientific approach, I lost the feeling that all phenomena must be explained. Now when I see a thunderstorm brewing, for example, I am able to regard it with a sense of wonder, if you will, and let the next fellow worry about air currents, temperature changes, and the rest of the physics going on up there."

While Pollard feels that nowadays he can take external verification or leave it alone, he still has a wholesome respect for the workings of the intellect. "After all, I'd be out of work if I didn't," he said. He believes, indeed, that he himself is far better suited to theological scholarship than to the more temporal aspects of church work, and it is to scholarship—which, as he reminded me, attracted him to the church in the first place—that he is devoting most of his attention. Not long after he was ordained, he spent all his spare time for three months preparing a series of twelve lectures on the Old Testament, which he delivered at weekly intervals at St. Stephen's, before audiences that included many people who were not Episcopalians. (According to McGregor, whom I met briefly before leaving Oak Ridge, few professors of theology could have done better.) At present, Pollard is assembling and editing the writings of the Hebrew historian Ahimaaz, which he expects to bring out as a book, with a long, analytical preface. In June 1953, the *Christian Scholar,* a quarterly published by the Commission on Christian Higher Education of the National Council of the Churches of Christ in the United States of America, ran an article by him on the place of science in religion; he is now a member of the journal's editorial board. He gave up eleven days of his vacation in the summer of 1953 to conduct a seminar on "The Teaching of the Natural Sciences in Relation to Religious Concepts" at Pennsylvania State College; the course was attended by twenty-six college and secondary-school teachers of natural sciences from all over the country. Half the members of the group were biologists and the rest physicists and chemists in about equal numbers.

More than a year having passed since Pollard's ordination, he is now eligible for the priesthood. He does not know whether he will go on to it. "I have a great attachment for the Institute, but it's established now, and no longer the challenge it once was," he told me. "And I often regret the amount of time it prevents me from giving to theology. I guess the relationship between man and the universe has come to interest me more than the one between nucleons and mesons." Pollard thinks more and more scientists will sooner or later come around to the same point of view. He would like to help them do so, but he suspects that he is not quite ready yet to be a proselytizer, because "too many new slants on religion are still hitting me." He believes that science is now at the pinnacle of its influence, and in the years ahead will give way to a religious renaissance comparable in its impact on the world to that of quantum mechanics in the past few decades. The perilous state of man's affairs, he feels, will be only partly responsible for this. "It just happens that there are several theologians of great stature alive today—men with far more gifted minds than their predecessors of the past century," he said. "As their ideas filter down, many scientists may come to realize that the world they think they are investigating simply does not exist."

As for himself, Pollard is uncertain what he will do. Perhaps he will remain at the Institute, perhaps he will teach physics at a denominational school, perhaps he will get out of science entirely. "Of course, I do have a family to support," he said, bowing amiably in the direction of his wife and then nodding toward the door of the living room, which was now empty. The boys had long since turned off the radio and gone to bed. The treetops below us in the gully were black and still. "We'll see, we'll see," Pollard said, rising. His wife shook her head incredulously as she and her husband showed me out. "And all I ever hoped was that maybe Bill would go to church Sundays," she said.

CHAPTER 15 | NOVEMBER, 1953

A FAREWELL TO STRING AND SEALING WAX

DR. SAMUEL A. GOUDSMIT, a reflective and genial, though occasionally sardonic, man in his early fifties who is one of America's leading physicists, readily agrees with the popular view that recent developments in the field of atomic energy may profoundly affect future generations, if any, but he is more specifically concerned with the immediate effect the current scientific boom is having on him and his colleagues. The boom, in fact, has Dr. Goudsmit reeling. Sometimes, when his sardonic mood is on him, he wonders whether the synchrotrons, the betatrons, the cosmotrons, and all the other contrivances physicists have lately rigged up to create energy by accelerating particles of matter aren't playing a wry joke on their inventors. "They're accelerating us, too," he says, in a voice that still betrays a trace of the accent of his native Holland. In protesting against the speedup, Goudsmit can speak with authority, for in the course of only a few years, he, like many other contemporary physicists, has seen his way of life change from a tranquil one of contemplation to a rat race. In 1941, as a professor of physics, he was contentedly dividing his time between laboratory and classroom at the University of Michigan; now, after having twice served overseas with the armed forces, he is the senior scientist and the chairman of the Physics Department at the Brookhaven National Laboratory, at Upton, Long Island, one of the largest nuclear-research centers in the United States, as well as the editor of the *Physical Review,* a professional journal that is to physicists all over the world what *Scott's Catalogue* is to philatelists and the *Al-*

manach de Gotha to European nobility. Every now and then, when he encounters a stranger at a cocktail party or in the club car of a New York-to-Washington train, Goudsmit finds himself listening to a heated denunciation of physicists and all their works. "If it weren't for those damn scientists and their bombs, everything would be all right," says the stranger. Goudsmit turns his soft, brown, unhappy eyes toward the stranger and nods sympathetically, but it is an effort for him to restrain himself from setting the record straight. "*He* tells *me* that the scientists are upsetting everybody," he said recently after one such attack. "They've made him move his family to the country, he says, and he hates commuting. And what do I do? Do I tell him that it's the lives of us physicists that have really been upset? Do I tell him that the hot and cold wars have so changed my profession that I can hardly recognize it any more? I do not. I just say that country air is good for kids, and try to change the subject. What spineless self-restraint! Why don't I have the courage to tell him that we physicists are among the maladjusted veterans of the Second World War?"

Before the war, to hear Goudsmit tell it, physicists were a poor but happy lot. There were relatively few of them, and they kept pretty much to themselves. Those were what he calls "the string-and-sealing-wax days"—an allusion to the makeshift materials with which physicists often put their rudimentary apparatus together in cramped laboratories somewhere out behind the gym on this or that university campus. Nowadays, both government and industry are pumping billions of dollars into this once impoverished profession. "It's been a shock," Goudsmit says. "We've got marvelous laboratories for basic research, which is the real love of any self-respecting physicist, but somehow we don't have the same tender affection for them that we would have had years ago, when acquiring a three-hundred-dollar spectroscope was reason enough for throwing a party. Today we're given a multimillion-dollar piece of equipment, and the minute the dedication ceremonies are over, we're poring over plans for an even more powerful one. In the old days physicists gave themselves up wholly to a single-minded study of the fundamental laws of the universe. Now we feel called upon to do things of a sort we never even imagined we'd be doing—thoroughly unscientific things. We sit down with the Defense Secretary to help him figure out his next year's budget. We brief the President of the United States on the nation's nuclear stockpile. We're at Eniwetok or Las Vegas, or we're talking with troop commanders in Europe or Japan. We teach physics to Navy officers who are going to run nuclear-powered submarines. Air Force generals used to be just newsreel figures to us, but now they're fellows we have to talk over atomic-driven planes and plan offensive and defensive tactics with. Some of us are in industry, designing electronic equipment, and some of us are attached to the American embassy staffs in England, France, and Germany. Colleagues of mine who never even bothered to vote before Hiroshima now sit at the elbows of our United Nations representatives when the subject of atomic energy is on the agenda. And others, who were ill at ease lecturing before a few seminar students, now address large audiences on the fate that threatens the world if atomic energy is not internationally controlled. From timid pedagogue to eloquent Jeremiah—all in the space of a few short years."

Goudsmit himself has done a stint or two as a Jeremiah. On one occasion, in 1949, he delivered a stirring message on the subject of atomic weapons from the rostrum of a Tex and Jinx television show. "It was quite a production," he recalls, with a grimace of stricken incredulity. "Boy Scouts were on the program. So was the pilot who dropped the bomb on Hiroshima. He said that war was hell. I was introduced to Johnny, the Phillip Morris midget. A United Nations chorus of twenty-five voices sang 'Rock of Ages,' and there were two ducks, one of them radioactive, in the cast. My daughter Esther, who was sixteen then, was in the studio, and when I came off the stage, she gave me a big hug and told me I was terrific. She wanted me to take a screen test right away."

Sometimes, when Goudsmit sits back and surveys the scene of contemporary physics, he becomes exasperated by the imperturbable calm with which many of the younger scientists around him—men who have never known the rigors of the string-and-sealing-wax days—address themselves to the momentous, and to him shattering, new order of things. This group of self-assured newcomers is quite large, for half of those who hold Ph.D.s in physics at the present time are under twenty-five. "All these young fellows grew up with the war and some of them were in it," Goudsmit says. "By and large they seem to have been less disturbed by it than the older men. They give you the impression they're just trying to get ahead. Of course, I realize it's not their fault that they weren't around in the old days, but I can't help wishing they'd stop acting as though the profession had always been the way it is now—if only out of respect for old men like me. Lord, the expensive equipment they expect! I gulp at some of the vouchers I'm called on to sign out at Brookhaven. Right now, it seems, everybody there wants a new type of oscilloscope that sells for thirty-five hundred dollars. Someone walked into my office the other day and complained that he had to share the one we'd got for him with another researcher. These new machines do make the work easier, but that doesn't keep me from wondering if, in the long run, it's best for everyone to own a Cadillac. Oh, well, I'm probably in my dotage."

Currently, Goudsmit points out, a young man of average ability who has a desire to earn a Ph.D. in physics can count on free tuition and a fellowship worth fifteen hundred dollars a year; in 1933, an outstanding graduate student of physics was grateful if he was given six hundred dollars a year, and willingly paid a third of that for tuition. A newly ordained physics Ph.D. today can reasonably look forward to a starting salary of about five hundred dollars a month in industry or the government, or, if he prefers basic research, he won't have much trouble finding an opening in a university laboratory at four hundred dollars a month; twenty years ago, there were no government opportunities for such a man, and few in industry, and unless he was very lucky, he had only one prospect—becoming a full-time assistant in a university at around two hundred dollars a month. "I'm naturally pleased to see our youngsters getting a break," Goudsmit says. "But why don't *they* act a little pleased about it? Back in 1927, I came to this country from Holland to teach at the University of Michigan. I was a Ph.D. and I was also married, and all my wife and I could afford was one room, without bath or kitchen, in a rooming house. And things really looked gloomy. Our room had two windows—one looking out on a hospital and the other on a cemetery."

It further distresses Goudsmit to see the apparent equanimity with which some of his younger colleagues regard nuclear weapons, for to him they are a frightening and ghoulishly unexpected application of atomic energy. "Several of the young physicists I've seen going off to watch bomb tests at Eniwetok or Las Vegas were as jaunty about it as if it were a holiday excursion," he says. "Some of them attend as 'observers.' Congressmen who witness the tests are given the same label, and as far as contributing to the success of the tests is concerned, I have a hunch that one set of observers is about as valuable as the other. When the young men get back—and other old-timers tell me they've noticed this, too—they're full of jolly little reminiscences about going swimming in the Pacific near dangerously radioactive reefs, and the foul-ups in the military's air shuttle, and that time out on Eniwetok when a workman spent a whole day carefully painting a dummy structure that was blown to bits the next morning. You rarely hear them so much as mention the terrible potentialities of the weapons they've seen in action. Maybe their small talk is a form of escapism, but if that's so, why don't my contemporaries talk the same way? Rabi, Bacher, Oppenheimer—a detonation leaves them awed and anxious." Dr. I. I. Rabi is chairman of the general advisory committee to the Atomic Energy Commission and a member of the Physics Department at Columbia University; Dr. Robert F. Bacher, a former member of the Atomic Energy Commission, is now at the California Institute of Technology; and Dr. J. Robert Oppenheimer, formerly director of the Manhattan District Laboratory at Los Alamos is now director of the Institute for Advanced Study, at Princeton.

Goudsmit himself has never seen an atomic explosion. "I'm like Ferdinand the Bull," he says. "I prefer to sit under a tree and smell the flowers." Actually, since the tests are not directly related to his work, he feels that he simply hasn't time for prolonged journeys to witness spectacles. "If you want to see a show, why don't you buy a ticket to some big Broadway hit?" he once asked a twenty-three-year-old Nevada-bound physicist who was urging him to come along. "That might help you more with your work than going West. Pauli [Dr. Wolfgang Pauli, who is now teaching in Zurich] won the Nobel Prize by going to the theater, you know. He was watching a revue in Copenhagen when the idea for his Exclusion Principle came to him." It might be argued that Goudsmit has been to Las Vegas vicariously. In the fall of 1951, at Brookhaven, he gave a young lady scientist, who was about to set out for a Nevada test, a quarter to play for him at one of the town's casinos. On her return, she handed him seventy-five cents.

The methods by which graduate students select their schools also cause Goudsmit to feel out of step with the times. The schools that attract them, he finds, are the ones that are lavishly supplied with elaborate modern equipment. He concedes that to a certain extent this approach makes sense, for there is no denying that equipment plays an important part in scientific progress. But he suspects that the search for the latest in equipment often overshadows the search for an inspiring teacher. "Back in the twenties, we looked for the man rather than the machine," he says. "And I, at least, found the man—Bohr, of Copenhagen." Whenever Goudsmit speaks of Dr. Niels Bohr, the Danish scientist who, with Dr. Albert Einstein, is generally regarded as one of the two foremost figures of modern physics, he becomes more than ever the wistful old codger unashamedly pining for the days of his youth. Bohr, a septuagenarian now, has headed the Institute for Theoretical Physics in Copenhagen since 1920. Until 1943, when, to his relief, the British whisked him out of Nazi-occupied Denmark so that he could lend a hand to Allied research, he and his wife lived in an apartment at the Institute. At present, they live in a Copenhagen mansion, complete with greenhouse, that the Carlsberg beer family has turned over to the nation in perpetuity for the lifelong use of whatever individual the Danish government decides is the country's outstanding intellectual of his time.

"In the 'twenties, Bohr's modest Institute, on Blegdams Vej, was the physicist's spiritual capital," Goudsmit says. "All roads led to Copenhagen. Physicists fortunate enough to be invited made the pilgrimage from everywhere—Sweden, Germany, England, the United States, Russia, India, Japan. No more than twenty were ever there at one time, except when Bohr organized a conference to review the state of physics. Then the number might rise to fifty. We would drop everything when an invitation came to go to Copenhagen—just to think and talk. We would go there to have our ideas confirmed, or refined, or picked to pieces. And we would stay until that was accomplished—several days, perhaps, or several months—discussing and discussing in Bohr's study, while Mme. Bohr saw to it that we had plenty of tea and sandwiches. Our talks might last all night. Sometimes we'd do our talking over beers at the Wivel, and once, I remember, I even debated a formula with a colleague during a wild roller-coaster ride at Tivoli."

Despite the limitations in the way of equipment, the 'twenties, in Goudsmit's opinion, were heroic years in the history of atomic physics. "Bohr had written a marvelously intuitive paper on the structure of the atom, and suddenly five fat volumes of unexplained observations on spectral lines began to make sense," he says. "We were as happy as Egyptologists must have been a century earlier, when Champollion succeeded in deciphering hieroglyphics. The 'twenties were a period of such optimism that physicists everywhere believed they were on the verge of explaining all the phenomena of the universe. One of the most eminent of them told a meeting of the Physical Society in London that soon the only problem left would be what he considered a comparatively simple one —the origin of life. The physicists proved to be a little over-optimistic, of course. We are still confronted by riddles, the chief one right now being the nucleus of the atom. Who knows how long we will have to wait before another breakthrough takes place? The conditions we work under today certainly aren't hastening that breakthrough. A quarter of a century ago we could exchange ideas in Bohr's study with no government secrets, weapons programs, or spy cases to bother us. No Tex and Jinx, no autograph hounds. None of us were distracted by offers to become college presidents or big wheels in industry, and governments didn't give a hoot about physicists. There was no trying to elbow one's way to power, for the simple reason that there wasn't any place to exercise power. No huge laboratories, no military projects. A Rockefeller Fellowship was considered quite sufficient. We all felt that we belonged to a sort of lodge, with a worldwide membership of only four hundred or so, and everyone knew everyone else well—or at least knew what everyone else was doing. Now four times that number will turn up for a meeting of just American physicists, and most of them will be strangers to each other. Why are they at the meetings? Some of them, no doubt, because of a deep interest in the structure of matter. But there are also some, I suspect, who are attracted by the fact that physics has become fashionable and by the possibility of being offered a lucrative industrial job. In the days of the lodge, physicists were automatically called 'obscure' in popular publications. Now the adjective, even for the most obscure of us, is 'prominent.' "

Goudsmit's present position in the world of physics enables him to observe, and contribute to, the general tumult from many angles. As chairman of the Physics Department at Brookhaven, a post he has held since 1950, he suffers daily from many of the administrative headaches that have shattered the serenity of his calling. The job entails, among other things, hiring and firing personnel, organizing scientific projects, and sitting in as a member of a committee that decides how the nine million dollars annually allotted to the Laboratory by its parent organization, the United States Atomic Energy Commission, is to be spent. As senior scientist at Brookhaven, he is in a position to take an active part in purely scientific research and to keep abreast of the latest developments and trends in that field. Another help to him in this respect is his editorship of the *Physical Review,* to which he was elected in 1951 by the members of the American Physical Society, which sponsors the publication. (The *Review* has a circulation of eighty-five hundred and annually publishes about five thousand tightly printed pages of treatises.) In this capacity, Goudsmit, at the head of a group of outstanding physicists who act as first readers, each in his own special line, passes on practically everything that goes into the journal. His public has a high opinion of his editorial talents. "The *Review* has improved noticeably since Sam took over," Bacher said not long ago. "The job must be pretty taxing at times, but it's effort well spent. After all, the quality of research everywhere is influenced by the quality of the *Review.*"

Goudsmit is an author as well as an editor. Since his student days at the University of Leyden, he has written, alone or in collaboration, two technical books, *The Structure of Line Spectra* and *Atomic Energy States,* and one that is not so technical, *Alsos,* as well as approximately a hundred papers for the *Review* and other scientific journals. Many of his papers have been significant contributions to the advance of physical science, and one of them, at least in the opinion of two Nobel Prize winners—Rabi and Dr.

Enrico Fermi, of the University of Chicago—has been of fundamental importance. This describes the discovery made in 1925 by Goudsmit and another Hollander, Dr. George Uhlenbeck, who is now professor of physics at the University of Michigan, that electrons, far from being static, as had been presumed up to then, are constantly spinning. The discovery cleared up a good many questions about the structure of atoms. "It was a tremendous feat," Rabi says. "Why those two men never received a Nobel Prize for it will always remain a mystery to me."

Alsos, Goudsmit's one nontechnical work, which he wrote in 1947, is an account of a wartime experience that he feels was fantastic for a man of his background but perhaps no more so than a lot of other things physicists have found themselves doing in recent years. In the spring of 1944, General Leslie R. Groves, who was then in charge of this country's efforts to produce atomic bombs, picked Goudsmit to serve as the uniformed civilian head of a highly secret mission to Europe whose object was to find out what progress German physicists were making along the same lines. Fortunately for the Allies, as the mission discovered at some peril, the Germans were not trying to produce atomic bombs, but, of course, nobody knew that then. As a matter of fact, the scientific community here, many of whose members had learned their physics from distinguished German enemies, was generally convinced that its accomplishments were lagging at least two years behind those of the Reich. Some of the scientists working in Chicago, which was at that time the heart of our atomic-bomb research, grew so jittery about the likelihood of a German atomic attack that they moved their families away from the city. As it turned out, the Germans were directing their efforts to building a uranium pile, which they hoped to use either as a source of power or as an explosive weapon to drop on an Allied target. Uranium piles, however, are as big and heavy as a concrete warehouse, and even had the Germans succeeded in building one, its value as a weapon would have hinged on the remote possibility of figuring out a means of transporting it to a target. By the end of the war the Germans were no farther along in their research than the Allies had been in 1943, when they started trying to put an atomic bomb together. In large part, according to Goudsmit, this stupendous failure of the Reich's physicists, whose ranks included men of the highest ability, was the fault of political meddling. "Science should be left to scientists, but the Nazis insisted on appointing loyal party hacks to important administrative posts," he says. "It was a case with them of holding on to power at all costs. It is not true that totalitarianism proceeds with matchless efficiency or that democracy is necessarily fumbling and inept."

Goudsmit claims to be unable to understand why General Groves selected him for the German assignment, which a number of high government officials regarded as one of the Allies' most important Intelligence missions. Some months after he had agreed to undertake it, he was handed a folder of papers listing the qualifications of several individuals who had been recommended to him as possible assistants. As he was shuffling them about on his desk, a memorandum that had somehow got mixed in with them fell to the floor. He picked it up and read, "Dr. Samuel A. Goudsmit. Has some valuable assets, some liabilities." His liabilities, he says, occurred to him right off, but he was far from sure about his assets. It seems likely, though, that General Groves made his choice on the basis of far more detailed information than was contained in that cryptic memorandum, for Goudsmit's abilities and temperament were already well known to the military. Early in 1941, he had left the University of Michigan and, after a few months at Harvard, had joined the Radiation Laboratory, a secret radar-research project at the Massachusetts Institute of Technology, in Cambridge, as editor of secret documents and acting head of a group investigating the theory of radar. This was the first time he had strayed from the insularity of academic life, and it ultimately taught him how to get along easily with an assortment of more or less worldly people. "It was a strange laboratory," he says. "I had to work with lawyers, engineers, administrators, security operatives, writers, and a charming husband-and-wife team of artists who were on leave from the Walt Disney studios to illustrate handbooks that explained our project to certain generals." In recalling this period, Goudsmit's wife, Jeanne, remarked not long ago, "Before we went to Cambridge, Sam found the ways of even chemists a little hard to understand." After Goudsmit had spent two years at M.I.T., his horizon was further broadened when, in the summer of 1943, the Radiation Laboratory sent him to England to find out why Royal Air Force crews were satisfied with their radar apparatus and American fliers using practically the same equipment were not. This involved interviewing scores of crews. Goudsmit lived with them in their barracks at various airfields, spent short leaves with them, drank with them. And he found the answer: The Americans were using the wrong kind of planes for the type of radar they were using. The American Eighth Air Force, which was then this nation's principal striking arm in England, was equipped with high-flying strategic bombers, but the radar instruments in the planes were better suited to low-flying tactical craft. Goudsmit then consulted another physicist from the Radiation Laboratory, Dr. Lauriston C. Marshall, who had been sent to England to help set up a similar laboratory there, and the two men presented the facts at a meeting of high-ranking Air Force officers held in a Tudor mansion headquarters outside London and presided over by General Carl Spaatz. A couple of times during recesses, Goudsmit heard himself referred to in the corridors as "the long-haired Joe." "It was the closest I've ever come to feeling like inorganic matter," he has since said. Goudsmit went back to M.I.T., and the radar equipment in question was presently shifted to the low-flying tactical planes of the Ninth Air Force, which had followed the Eighth to England.

It was shortly after his return to the United States that Goudsmit was tapped by General Groves for the rather more arduous, if on the whole less fruitful, task of finding out what the Nazi scientists were up to. The mission, for which Goudsmit was later awarded the Medal of Freedom and the Order of the British Empire, was called Alsos. This was a Hellenization of General Groves' last name and was chosen by the Army as a form of camouflage, apparently on the theory that Americans know Greek and Europeans don't. Only six members of the mission, which, at its peak, numbered about a hundred, were atomic scientists; the rest were military men, women clerical workers stationed in a rear-area headquarters, and several scientists who, while they didn't know a great deal about atoms, were distinguished specialists in other fields and were taken along as another means of throwing the enemy off the scent. There is some question in Goudsmit's mind as to whether the Alsos insigne—a white Greek lower-case "A" pierced by a bolt of red lightning—did much to help preserve secrecy, but anyway there it was, with orders to stencil it on the mission's vehicles and other equipment. "I suppose it represented power, might—the great atom itself," he says. "Life in those days sometimes seemed to consist mostly of fathoming the United States Army."

Tight-lipped and furtive, the Alsos people arrived at an airport near Cherbourg and headed for Paris in a caravan of jeeps and trucks. Once there, they began asking around for Dr. Frédéric Joliot-Curie, the famous French physicist, and this, of course, tipped people off to the nature of their errand. "Complete strangers—French and American—began coming up to us and confidentially offering their assistance," Goudsmit says. "They'd assure us that they knew our work was ultra-secret and that they wouldn't breathe a word to anybody. So after a while we began to relax. It got so that if we needed special co-operation of some sort—say, for cutting red tape to get at documents or prisoners—we'd just whisper to the right general or the right sergeant, 'Atom bomb.' It always worked."

Goudsmit and the five atomic scientists assigned to him felt that their primary objective was to find Dr. Werner Heisenberg, who was Germany's outstanding physicist and one of Goudsmit's oldest friends. "No one but Professor Heisenberg could be the brains of a German uranium project, and every physicist throughout the world knew that," Goudsmit later wrote in *Alsos*. The Pentagon, however, favored action on a wider front, arguing that Hitler might have entrusted atomic-bomb research to Germans Goudsmit had never heard of. He went to some pains to explain to Washington that while the Nazi political leaders might have developed almost overnight, there was no chance of anyone's having eclipsed Heisenberg as a physicist in the comparatively brief space of time since the two scientists had last been in touch with each other. "The military men in Alsos would probably have preferred to work with more conventional Intelligence agents," Goudsmit says amiably. "Sometimes both sides had a distinct feeling of being stuck with each other."

There were numerous instances of this difference of approach to the problem. The mission was barely under way when its Pentagon advisers forwarded a laboriously prepared report on a German scientist who had traveled extensively in the United States just before Pearl Harbor and in whom it was felt Goudsmit might be interested.

"The report was all right, I suppose, as far as it went," Goudsmit says. "It told us that he liked beer, didn't care for American women, and had had German measles. It might have told us a lot more if it had gone into the matter of what kind of questions he asked our scientists." A Regular Army colonel who had been assigned to direct whatever military maneuvers Alsos might be called upon to execute became impatient at Goudsmit's lack of the spirit of adventure. One day, Goudsmit learned that the colonel had put some Alsos officers and men through a special course of training in preparation for making a parachute raid on a German laboratory that Goudsmit had reason to believe was of little importance. "His plan was to seize the files and kidnap the scientists working there," he says. "He was quite crestfallen when I sat down with him and made him see that nothing in that particular laboratory was worth one sprained ankle."

Sometimes it was the colonel who had to explain the facts of life to Goudsmit. For instance, there was the morning when word reached Alsos that Heisenberg was spending a few days in a town in Switzerland. Goudsmit wanted to join him there. Sounding out the colonel on the idea, he explained in detail what old friends he and Heisenberg were; the German had visited him in Holland way back in the 'twenties and, until Germany invaded Poland, had regularly spent his summers with the Goudsmits in Michigan. Such old friends, Goudsmit told the colonel, would naturally have a lot to talk about when they met, and almost inevitably the subject of physics would come up. While it was to be assumed that Heisenberg would discuss such matters warily, he nevertheless might say enough to give Goudsmit a lead on what headway the Germans were making in atomic research. "When I was all through," Goudsmit says, "the colonel smiled and asked me, 'And while he's giving you a lead on them, why wouldn't you be giving him a lead on us?' Frankly, I'd been so excited at the prospect of talking to Heisenberg again that I hadn't thought of it that way."

When the Americans reached the Rhine, in September 1944, some of the Alsos men waded out into the river under enemy fire and collected samples of water. These were shipped to Washington to be tested for radioactivity, on the theory that the Germans might be using the Rhine to cool a uranium pile. Just before the shipment went off, an officer considerately inserted a bottle of French wine—an excellent Roussillon—for his friends back in the Pentagon. "Test this for activity, too," he wrote on the label. A few days later, Alsos received a Top Secret Action radiogram reading, "Water negative. Wine shows activity. Send more. Action." Goudsmit, concluding that Washington was simply entering into the spirit of things, tossed the message aside. That was a mistake. The message was soon followed by another, irately demanding an explanation of Alsos' failure to comply with orders. It developed that some abstemious and literal-minded officer in the Pentagon *had* had the wine tested for radioactivity. The test had proved mildly positive, and the officer, who was unaware of the fact that many wines are slightly, though harmlessly, radioactive, owing to the composition of the soil where the grapes are grown, had jumped to the conclusion that Alsos was on the track of something big. Before matters could be straightened out, Goudsmit, not wishing to run the risk of ignoring orders a second time, dispatched one of his atomic scientists —Major Russell A. Fisher, who had been a student of his at Michigan and is now chairman of the physics department at Northwestern University—to forage for more samples of wine. "I instructed Fisher not to be stingy with the confidential funds," Goudsmit recalls. The Major's tour of southern France was a triumph. Wherever he appeared, he was fêted with radioactive wine by French vintners, who assumed that he was taking advantage of his Army status to build up postwar business relations with French exporters. He rejoined the mission with a large and representative collection of Rhône wines, samples of grapes and soils, and vials of water taken from various small French rivers. "His bibulous wanderings must have given him courage," Goudsmit says. "The report he sent Washington after that trip was so outspoken on the subject of rear-echelon interference that from then on the Pentagon cut its efforts to direct us by remote control to an absolute minimum."

With the capture of Strasbourg in November 1944 four German scientists fell into Alsos' hands. They were uncommunicative, and, former colleagues though they were, Goudsmit ordered them interned, but their files, which were found in a laboratory at the University of Strasbourg, contained information showing that while the Nazis had a uranium project under way, its progress to date was inconsequential. Heisenberg, the papers revealed, was working in a German village called Hechingen, and his laboratory there, which was the Reich's closest approach to an Oak Ridge, took up only one wing of a small textile factory. Goudsmit's elation at this news is recorded in *Alsos,* in which he quotes himself as having exclaimed to another member of his mission, "Isn't it wonderful that the Germans have no atomic bomb? Now we won't have to use ours."

As Alsos pushed on into Germany, the seizing of more physicists, laboratories, and documents corroborated the evidence at Strasbourg. Still, as long as Heisenberg remained at large there could be no certainty. Shortly before the troops reached Hechingen, in April 1945, high American and British Intelligence officers came from Washington and London to be in on the kill. When the Alsos forces burst into Heisenberg's office, all they found there was a large framed photograph on the wall, showing its missing occupant and Goudsmit. The picture had been taken in 1939, while the two were enjoying their last summer together in Michigan. "The military men laughed about that photograph," Goudsmit says. "But they were also puzzled. I could have helped them out, I suppose, but that didn't seem quite the moment to explain about the lodge."

Heisenberg, who had abandoned his poorly equipped laboratory and sought refuge in the Bavarian Redoubt, was found near Munich a few days later, and taken to Heidelberg, where Goudsmit was waiting for him. "It was impossible for me not to greet my old friend warmly," Goudsmit says. "Purely on impulse, I asked him, 'Wouldn't you like to come to America now and work with us?' And he replied, 'No. Germany needs me. If you and your American colleagues want to learn about the uranium problem, I'll be glad to show you the results of our researches. But you will have to come to my laboratory.' "

On August 6, 1945, Goudsmit was poking about alone among the ruins of Himmler's headquarters in Berlin when an American officer hurried up to him and said that a special plane was waiting at the Tempelhof Airport to take him to Frankfurt, where Alsos then had its headquarters. The pair raced through Berlin in a jeep with screaming sirens, were waved through the Tempelhof gate without formalities, drove out onto the field, and stopped beside the plane, whose propellers were already turning. "I climbed from the jeep into the plane, the door slammed shut, the motors roared, and we were off," Goudsmit records in his book. "It was just like the movies."

In Frankfurt, Goudsmit found a two-week supply of fresh laundry waiting for him, but, welcome surprise though that was, it seemed unlikely to him that he had been rushed from Berlin simply to enjoy it. He asked the colonel what was up, but the colonel, who was ordinarily communicative enough, on this occasion evasively muttered something about somebody or other who might or might not arrive from Washington. Goudsmit spent the evening in an associate's apartment chatting with a group of Alsos people he hadn't seen in months, and shortly before midnight he drove one of them, a secretary, to the hotel where she was billeted. The lobby was empty except for a bored sergeant on duty at the desk, who was listening to a dance band on a portable radio. As Goudsmit was saying good night to the secretary, an announcer broke in on the dance band with a special bulletin: An atomic bomb had been dropped on Hiroshima. "That was the reason they'd shanghaied me out of Berlin," Goudsmit says. "The city wasn't zoned off yet, and our military thought that when the Russians heard the news, they might kidnap me. Well, anyway, the music came back on the radio, and the secretary started asking me all sorts of questions about atoms. I answered calmly, but I didn't feel calm. I was angry that the military should have been in a position to keep me in the dark about so momentous an event involving my science. But, standing in that lobby in Frankfurt, I realized that much more of the same thing was in store for physicists in the years ahead. And I realized, too, that the days of the lodge were over."

GOUDSMIT got his first tantalizing whiff of physics at the age of eleven. Alone and bored one afternoon, in his parents' comfortable, middle-class house in The Hague, where he was born, he flipped open a textbook of elementary physics that belonged to his older sister, and hit upon a passage describing how the science of spectroscopic phenomena had proved that the stars are composed of the same elements as the earth. "Hydrogen in the sun and iron in the Big Dipper made Heaven seem cozy and attainable," he says. At that time, however, physics did not occur to him as an eventual vocation. Millinery did. His mother owned a fashionable hat shop called Au Louvre, on the Prinsestraat, in The Hague, and from the time he was ten she consulted him regularly before deciding on new models for her clientele. "That one ought to have a flower instead of a feather," the boy would say, and more often than not his mother and her designers would agree that he was right. "I found the talk of styles and Paris entrancing," Goudsmit recalls. "Even now, when I think of Parisian streets and buildings, I can hear my mother's voice telling me about them. And then there was the excitement of guessing six months in advance what kind of hats Dutch ladies would want next. Both the risk and the romance of the business appealed to me greatly."

Goudsmit was in his last year of high school when his mother had to abandon Au Louvre, because of poor health. His father, Isaac, was a prosperous wholesale dealer in bathroom fixtures, but this business did not interest the boy at all. His only impressive grades at school were in science and mathematics, so, in 1919, for lack of any other signpost, he enrolled as a physics student at the University of Leyden, ten miles from The Hague. He began his studies with misgivings. His first love was still millinery, and he felt that in his case physics could lead only to a lacklustre career of high-school teaching; he didn't think he was up to meeting the stiff requirements for a professorship in some European university, which was then about as far as a physicist could hope to get. At Leyden, though, his reluctant embrace of physics soon turned to devotion, as he came under the influence of the late Paul Ehrenfest, a professor of international prominence. A less astute teacher might not have become aware of Goudsmit's talents, for they were of an unorthodox nature. Unlike most students of physics, he seemed to base his thinking on empirical hunches rather than on logical and analytical grounds, and he possessed an almost uncanny intuition, comparable perhaps to his ability to forecast Dutch ladies' taste in hats. "Sam always had a fanciful imagination," Dr. Walter F. Colby, director of Intelligence for the Atomic Energy Commission, who was responsible for bringing Goudsmit to this country, has said; and Dr. George Uhlenbeck, a fellow-student of Goudsmit's at Leyden and at present a professor at the University of Michigan, once told a friend, "As physicists go, Sam was never a conspicuously reflective man, but he had, and has, an amazing talent for taking random data and giving them direction. He's a wizard at cryptograms, and it's not hard to understand why." Rabi has also noticed this maverick strain in his make-up. "Sam has a sixth sense when it comes to bringing order to jumbled facts," he says. "He thinks like a detective. He *is* a detective."

Actually, Goudsmit would have the jump on the next man should he ever want to become a detective in the ordinary sense of the word. While studying at Leyden, he had a job on the side for a while as a research assistant at the University of Amsterdam, where he heard that the local police chemist was giving a course in detective techniques. He signed up for it, and for eight months learned how to compare fingerprints, spot forgeries with ultraviolet light, and analyze various types of stains, such as those made by blood and grease. "Taking that course was one of the most sensible things I ever did," Goudsmit says. "I learned a detective's attitude toward the evaluation of evidence. It's been extremely helpful in my work." And, blandly ignoring the tributes paid to his intuitive powers, he adds, "People usually go too much by intuition, without judging what's in front of them."

While at Leyden, Goudsmit also joined the Christian Huygens Society, a student discussion group. The members took turns giving half-hour talks on various cultural topics. Goudsmit's topic was always the same—the structure of the atom, and this caused a falling off of attendance at the meetings he addressed. The society's president finally asked him to find something else to talk about. Goudsmit was baffled. He felt that all he knew was the atom. Determined not to let the president down, he enrolled in a course in Egyptology. When he appeared in the classroom on the opening day of the semester, he found he was the only student there. "Three make a lecture—God, teacher, and student," the professor, an ancient, kindly gentleman began, intoning a Latin proverb, and Goudsmit was embarked on the study of Egyptology. He stayed with the course two years and, with an alacrity that brought joy to the heart of his lonely teacher, learned to decipher hieroglyphics. The professor was eager for him to go into this subject more deeply, but instead Goudsmit turned to collecting scarabs. "The professor considered that vulgar, but the reality of the scarabs made me feel closer to Egypt than the printed hieroglyphics I'd been working on," Goudsmit says. "It's odd that I've never been there, but it's not because I haven't tried. Some years ago, I attempted to set up a cosmic-ray experiment in which the Pyramids would be used as absorbers. I wanted to put Geiger counters both inside and outside them to gauge the rays' powers of penetration. But the project fell through. Another time, while I was teaching at Harvard, I made friends with an Egyptian student of mine, and he said that when he got home his first act would be to get the University of Cairo to invite me there as a lecturer. I gave him an A in the course, and then the scoundrel went and married an American girl and settled in Boston."

Under Ehrenfest's direction, Goudsmit made excellent progress at the University of Leyden. His second year there, when he was only eighteen, he produced a treatise, based on his own research, that dealt with the spectroscopy of alkali doublets. "A most presumptuous display of self-confidence but a highly creditable paper," Uhlenbeck has said of this early effort. Other papers followed, and they were climaxed in the summer of 1925, two years before Goudsmit received his Ph.D., by one he prepared with Uhlenbeck, describing their discovery of the electron spin, a contribution of fundamental importance to the quantum theory; without it the magnetic properties of matter cannot be adequately explained. The electron spin has since become so taken for granted in physics that students today are inclined to believe it was revealed in Genesis, but at the time it was what physicists needed to clear up an enormous number of riddles involving the structure of the atom. More than one winner of a Nobel Prize has drawn heavily on the findings of the two young Leyden scholars in working out the contribution to science that earned him the award.

With the publication of the electron-spin theory, both its authors were established as important physicists. Goudsmit was invited to attend discussions at the Institute for Theoretical Physics, in Copenhagen, which was headed by the eminent Dr. Niels Bohr, and he was subsequently awarded a Rockefeller Fellowship, which he used to study in Germany; while there, he joined forces with Dr.

Ernst Back, a German scientist, and the two men succeeded in measuring the spin of the atomic nucleus, the first time this had ever been done. In 1926, Colby, who was touring the Continent as a talent scout for the University of Michigan's Physics Department, visited Leyden and, on Ehrenfest's recommendation, signed up Goudsmit and Uhlenbeck as instructors. Goudsmit was engaged to Jeanne Logher, a former designer in his mother's shop, and he felt that the relatively high teaching salaries offered in the United States were a factor that a young man who was about to assume domestic responsibilities was in no position to ignore. Moreover, the opportunities for academic advancement were considerably greater in America than in Europe. The idea, however, had its drawbacks. For one thing, he hated to leave Ehrenfest. For another, he hated to leave Europe and its "string-and-sealing-wax era." Ehrenfest minimized both objections. "I'd advise you to go," he said to Goudsmit. "American physics may disappoint you at first, but the science is building up there. Always watch the slope of the graph. It's not where a thing is at the moment that counts but where it's going." In the summer of 1927, Goudsmit, now a married man, moved with his bride to Ann Arbor.

At Michigan, some of the time Goudsmit was accustomed to devote to research was taken up by the unfamiliar task of teaching, but he found that this did not make him nearly as unhappy as he had feared. In fact, he soon came to look upon teaching as a welcome new aspect of his career. In his spare hours, he continued his study of the atomic structure, writing numerous papers and two books on the subject, but, valuable as his findings were, none were as spectacular as the spin theory. This did not surprise him. On the eve of the spin theory's publication, Ehrenfest had warned him that just such a letdown was likely to follow, and in 1931, while Goudsmit, then twenty-nine, was delivering a guest lecture at the Sorbonne, he referred to himself, more or less facetiously, as a "has-been." He has since elaborated on this phenomenon. "As a physicist's career goes, it was to be expected," he says. "A scientist can do useful work all his life, but if he is to carry learning one big step forward, he usually does so before he is thirty. Youth has the quality of being radical, in the literal sense of the word—of going to the root. In science, as in other fields, youth seems to be the time when one is driven to examine the roots—the basic assumptions of everything that has previously been accepted. Obviously, if one hits on something through this approach, it may well be outstanding. After a scientist passes his creative peak, it seems to me the most useful thing he can do is teach the status quo to youngsters, who may then attack it with all their irreverent curiosity and so perhaps arrive at fresh knowledge. Teaching gives older scientists the same satisfaction as parenthood—the sense of self-renewal."

This fairly abstract satisfaction was not the only one that Goudsmit derived from teaching. Somewhat to his astonishment, he discovered that he also enjoyed the homely, day-to-day routine of academic life. He liked the company of his students outside the classroom as well as in it. Friday nights, he held open house for them, with his wife acting as hostess. "They'd bring their dates, and the girls and I would fix pancakes and later wash the dishes together," Mrs. Goudsmit recalls. Goudsmit's first candidate for a Ph.D., Robert F. Bacher, who later became a member of the Atomic Energy Commission, remembers that during his final year at the university he spent three hours or more every day simply hashing things over with his teacher. "We talked not only about physics but about Egyptology and life in general," Bacher has since said. "I've observed a great deal of teaching in the more than twenty years since I left Michigan, and I believe Sam is probably one of the two or three best lecturers in the profession." Goudsmit's ways in the classroom were far from formal, if a report of an episode at Columbia, where he taught a summer-school class shortly after the war, is any indication. According to Rabi, who, no matter what the season, is usually busy in his laboratory on Morningside Heights, Goudsmit was proctoring an examination one suffocating August afternoon when, glancing out the window, he saw an ice-cream vender in the street below. Silently invoking the honor system, Goudsmit left the room. Ten minutes later, he returned with thirty popsicles and put one on each of his perspiring students' desks.

Goudsmit has some fairly strong feelings about the teaching of physics. He thinks, for one thing, that the textbooks most teachers use stress applied science over theory to an appalling degree. More than once he has heard a teacher tell students that diligence in laboratory work will make them handy at repairing mechanical gadgets at home. He summed up his opinion of this approach to the subject during a symposium at Harvard in 1950: "I can only say that I have taught elementary, intermediate, and advanced laboratory work to undergraduates and graduates for many years and . . . I still am unable to do anything helpful around the house." Goudsmit feels that even when teachers do stress theory they tend to resort to homespun analogies that are misleading; in discussing radio waves, for example, a teacher will usually draw a wavy line on the blackboard and mention the surface of the ocean, although actually radio waves and water waves have nothing in common. "To some teachers an atom is always a ball," he says. "In the winter it's a basketball, in the spring it's a baseball, and the rest of the time it's a ping-pong ball. The atom is no more explained by such images than the idea of God is by a picture of an old man with a long beard sitting on a cloud."

Some years ago, a student of Goudsmit's at the University of Michigan wrote a letter in which he made an earnest attempt to give a friend of his an idea of his teacher's classroom technique:

> Dr. Goudsmit started his lecture today with the usual serio-levity with which he approaches his almost futile effort to impart even a cursory grasp of physics to dull engineers. He made the routine cracks about the inefficacy of the "prehistoric" demonstration apparatus, and wandered playfully around the darkened lecture room snatching spectra, which were being produced by a machine on the lecture table, with a small screen held in his hand. Presently, however, he became serious and began to talk about atomic theory. His accent thickened slightly, and his voice became a bit louder. He spoke with a trace of negligent reverence of those colleagues of his who had contributed vastly to the great mass of modern scientific knowledge—Bohr, Einstein, and the like. His enthusiasm mounted as he explained how new concepts evolved into satisfactory theories with the help of classical physical manipulations. Philosophically, he discussed the pitfalls man has encountered in trying to resolve the most basic puzzles of nature in terms of "wire models and ping-pong balls" and with great humility he accepted man's impotency and insignificance. He was eloquent! When the bell rang, he stopped abruptly in the middle of a thought, as though awakened from a trance, smiled wryly at the stupid dolts pulling on their coats, and disappeared through the door at the rear of the lecture platform.

The fact of the matter is that, unfortunately, few scientific concepts are reminiscent of wire models, ping-pong balls, or anything in everyday life, and Goudsmit is pretty much resigned to the belief that it will probably be a long, long time before the general public begins to get so much as a glimmer of what the physicists who influence their destiny are talking about. He feels, however, that this is no valid reason for the tendency—more noticeable in the past, perhaps, but still in evidence—for scientists to live apart from other people. As an example of this tendency, he recalls the time he drove down to Princeton in the winter of 1948 to visit his old friend Uhlenbeck, who had spent the preceding six months or so at the Institute for Advanced Study there. After discussing physics for a few hours in Uhlenbeck's quarters, the two men went over to the Institute's lounge for tea and sat down at a table no more than a yard away from one at which Goudsmit thought he recognized T. S. Eliot, the poet and dramatist. "George started talking physics where we had left off a few minutes before," Goudsmit says. "But I broke in and asked him if the fellow at the next table wasn't Eliot. He said it was, and that Eliot had been at the Institute for the past two months, working on a play. The two hadn't even nodded to each other when we went in, and I thought that was strange. 'Haven't you and he ever met?' I asked George, and he looked mildly surprised and said no, they hadn't. There was nothing unusual about that, he assured me, since the scientists at the Institute and the people studying arts there rarely mingled, and he pointed to several tables in the lounge at which scientists were clustered and then to some others at which there were only people in the humanities. What a wretched situation it was, I thought, that two men of such enormous curiosity as George and Eliot could spend a couple of months in the same small community and never even get around to passing the time of day."

In the summer of 1938, while traveling in Europe on a Guggenheim Fellowship, Goudsmit returned to the Netherlands, where the University of Amsterdam offered him the professorship he had once thought he was incapable of attaining. The offer was tempting, but by then he felt too firmly established in the United States to make the switch. He was a full professor of three years' standing at Michigan, and he had a comfortable house in Ann Arbor and a five-year-old daughter, Esther, who was already beginning to acquire American ways. Esther, now a junior at Smith, looks back happily on her childhood in Michigan. "There were always people in the house—either students or scientists," she says. "I. I. [Rabi] and Uncle Enrico [Fermi] and all the others would sit around in a circle, discussing and discussing. I never understood what they were talking about, of course, but I felt sure they did, because they all seemed like such fine men."

The excursion to the Netherlands gave Goudsmit his last opportunity to visit his parents. The next time he entered his family's house in The Hague, he was the uniformed civilian head of Alsos. In the summer of 1945, after beating his way across France and into Germany, Goudsmit made a side trip to The Hague, but he knew when he parked his dusty jeep outside the family house that he would not find his father and mother there, for he had learned from captured German records that, being Jews, they had been gassed two years earlier in a Nazi concentration camp. The house was a shambles. Everything made of wood—doors, walls, moldings—had been torn down and burned as fuel during the Occupation. "Climbing into the little room where I had spent so many hours of my life," Goudsmit wrote in *Alsos,* "I found a few scattered papers, among them my high-school report cards that my parents had saved so carefully through all these years. If I closed my eyes, I could see the house as it used to look . . . Here was the glassed-in porch which was my mother's favorite breakfast nook. There was the corner where the piano always stood. Over there had been my bookcase . . . The little garden in back of the house looked sadly neglected. Only the lilac tree was still standing."

After four years of war service, most of it secret and technical, Goudsmit found the prospect of resuming his placid existence at Michigan hardly satisfying. His realization that he did not want to go back there came to him on the evening of December 10, 1945, while he was having dinner on a train with Dr. David Dennison, an old friend and colleague of his at Ann Arbor, whom he had not seen since 1941. The two men, both of whom had errands in Washington, had boarded the train at Trenton after attending a party given at Princeton in honor of Wolfgang Pauli, who had just received the Nobel Prize for his Exclusion Principle. As they sat in the dining car, Goudsmit was enjoying the reunion immensely when Dennison, who was chatting about faculty doings at Michigan, happened to remark that he had some good news for him—Goudsmit was going to be granted a wish he had made in 1937. In the spring of that year, Goudsmit, who was spending most of his time in research and was teaching only a few graduate students, had told the head of the Physics Department that if and when the opportunity arose he would like to devote himself solely to teaching elementary courses to undergraduates. His feeling at the time was that he was done for as a research man because he hadn't an adequate mathematical background, and that teaching first-year physics was the next-best thing to retirement, which he couldn't afford. Now, eight years later, Dennison was telling him that the opportunity he had asked for was awaiting him. To his amazement, Goudsmit realized suddenly that he no longer wanted it. "I can see in retrospect how childish it was of me, but that evening I found myself wondering how David could think I would possibly be interested in teaching undergraduates at a Midwestern university," he says. "I'd returned only recently from overseas, and I suppose I hadn't yet got things back into their proper perspective. Anyway, I had the feeling that it was my duty to take an active part in scientific developments in order to—yes, at the time I perhaps even meant it literally—to help save the world. I had the illusion then of—well, of having grown considerably. I felt caught up in the violent upsurge of everything associated with physics that had followed Hiroshima, and I wanted to be more closely associated with it than seemed possible on a university campus. In a modified way, I still feel the same about a physicist's obligation to society, but in 1945 I went overboard on the subject."

It took Goudsmit some time to figure out how to translate his rather vague feelings about obligation into some form of positive action. He wasn't even sure that his decision on the diner had been a sound one, and, while groping for a solution to his problem, he joined the faculty of Northwestern University, in Evanston, Illinois, in the hope that a change of scene might revive his interest in academic life. But after a year of it he was still, in his word, "restless." In the spring of 1948, he received an offer to join the staff at Brookhaven as senior scientist and, after some soul-searching, accepted it, for there, he hoped, he could not only continue his research and teaching but would have a hand in the elaborate scientific enterprises that were sprouting up all over the nation. "It was a straddling maneuver, my coming to Brookhaven," he has since said. "I imagined that it would spare me the decision of choosing between the old and the new." It might be thought that he swung both feet on the side of the new when, in 1950, he became chairman of Brookhaven's Physics Department, and thus assumed a heavy burden of administrative worries, but in theory, at least, he is still straddling, for he has not relinquished his post as senior scientist, which offers vast opportunities for pure research—if he only had the time.

In taking on his additional duties, Goudsmit was, of course, well aware that he would have to give up much time that he would like to devote to research, but by then he was convinced that in view of the current trends in science he could do no less. The military was moving in on the physicist. Government and industry were investing huge sums of money in the profession. Decisions affecting the whole future course of physics were being made by men who in many cases were not the best qualified to make them. Some of these men had never got beyond teaching science to high-school students, and others weren't scientists at all. Then, too, Goudsmit had observed that certain excellent physicists were proving themselves first-rate administrators—instituting efficient research techniques in their organizations, cutting through red tape whenever it threatened to hamper the scientists working under them, and discreetly handling senators with an itch to pry into what goes on in government laboratories. "That interested me," Goudsmit says. "It seemed to demonstrate that there might be an art to administering, that one might learn to guide without commanding. I now know that this is true, but I also know that many researchers who haven't yet come around to seeing it that way are taking an intellectually snobbish attitude toward administering that isn't helping the situation any. It's the same sort of snobbery that makes young physicists feel they won't get ahead unless they use the title of 'Doctor.' As if titles meant anything—except when it comes to airline-reservation clerks. They're the only ones I use my Ph.D. on. It guarantees me a seat, because they always figure I'm a physician dashing off on an emergency call."

The friendliness Goudsmit displayed toward his students during his teaching days was not, as is sometimes the case, a calculated pedagogic device for charming them into an interest in his subject;

his geniality is as definite a part of his nature as his intuitiveness, and it helps to make him something of an exception among physicists. He had not been at Brookhaven long when a reactor expert paid a call on him and, upon leaving his office, was heard to exclaim in astonishment to a colleague in the corridor, "That fellow Goudsmit! He talks physics, but he talks a lot of other things, too. Gives you the feeling that we've been infiltrated by a layman." Mrs. Mariette Kuper, who is executive assistant to the director of Brookhaven, feels much the same way. The wife of Dr. J. B. H. Kuper, who is chairman of the institution's Department of Instrumentation and Health Physics, she regards physicists as pleasant and human enough, on the whole, but rather like members of a religious order. "They go around talking their special language, like monks in India," she says. "Sam talks the language the rest of us talk." Mrs. Regina Brown, who is Goudsmit's administrative secretary, has found working for him an unusual experience. "I'd heard he was an important scientist, and that made me kind of nervous when I started out," she recently said. "I got a real surprise during my first few days on the job. While I was getting acquainted with the files in the office, I found several transcripts of technical addresses he had delivered, and saw that the recording stenographer had typed in the word 'laughter' in parentheses after a good many of the sentences. I could hardly believe my eyes. Most physicists are just walking brains, but he's different. He's more interested in people. A lot of the young men around here—and the olders ones, too—come to him for advice about their personal problems. They ask me if Mr. Anthony or the Great White Father can see them, and he somehow makes time for them." Dr. Edward O. Salant, a well-known cosmic-ray man of Brookhaven, puts it differently. "Sam's rather peculiar for a physicist," he says. "Most of us are just as sensitive as he is, but to inorganic matter rather than to people and their private worries. Our work isn't concerned with life. It doesn't involve us with the sort of emotions that physicians and people in business see so much of, so if there's anything to Shaw's claim that man becomes like his work, it's only natural for us to be pretty inept when we're confronted with human problems. I envy Sam, in a way, but personally I regard the world as essentially a convenient platform for a cosmotron."

As for Goudsmit himself, he is unaware that his outlook differs much from that of other physicists. He believes that physicists are no less capable of experiencing human emotions than any other group, but he concedes that what stirs their emotions may be rather different. As he sees it, achievement arouses affection in a physicist, and he cites as an example his own feeling toward a notoriously bad-mannered but exceedingly brilliant scientist. "He's a mean, caustic, and boorish man," Goudsmit says. "I once dined with him in a restaurant and he hounded the waiter until the poor fellow got so nervous he dropped his tray, and that made my friend howl with glee. To most people, he would be *persona non grata*. To me, he is a man who has solved difficult scientific problems, and in my home, he is welcome."

In Goudsmit's dual capacity at Brookhaven, he is constantly plagued by the feeling that no matter what he is doing at any given moment, he ought to be doing something else. "Before the bomb, contemplation was the physicist's stock in trade," he says. "It's a luxury now." His only moments of calm come in the early morning, before the day's problems begin. He tries to leave his home, a stucco house in Sayville, in time to reach his office ahead of the rest of the staff, so that he can have a few minutes of solitary reflection to strengthen him for the long hours ahead. He makes the half-hour trip to Brookhaven in an aging Oldsmobile, and finds the drive exhilarating. "It gives me the virtuous illusion that I'm exercising," he says. The sight of armed guards at the entrance to the institution is slightly disturbing, he admits, but once they have let him by, he forgets them as he looks about at the neatly laid-out grounds and finds solace in the reminiscent names of its thoroughfares—Princeton Street, Cornell Avenue, Columbia Street. If, as he nears Building 109, a plain, one-story wooden structure in which he and his assistants have their headquarters, he finds the adjacent parking space empty, he is cheered. "No good mornings to say, no telephone bells ringing or typewriters banging," he explains. Entering 109, he makes his way down a short, still corridor, and, unlocking its door, lets himself into his unpretentious office. At this point, he takes a deep, satisfied breath and feels ready to tackle the day's work. But at the thought of work his energy and confidence die. "At that instant, my day begins to disintegrate," he says. "I don't know where to start. All sorts of projects crowd into my head. The morning has fooled me again. A moment before, my office seemed a citadel, but now it has become a trap—a maze with countless passageways that I must explore all at once."

A blackboard that stands in front of Goudsmit's desk—all physicists think with chalk—does nothing to restore his peace of mind. Its upper right-hand corner, where he has scrawled the day's schedule, is crammed with disparate commitments that make his head swim. By way of an antidote, he is likely to tell himself that this may be one of the days when two physicists who are engaged in improving a mass spectrometer that he conceived in broad outline, in 1948, will burst into his office with the news that they have ironed another wrinkle out of their working model. Goudsmit has told them that, regardless of what he is doing, they are to break in on him the minute they have any progress to report. "That spectrometer is one of the few projects I'm involved in nowadays that give me the feeling I'm a scientist," he says. When the spectrometer is finally ready for use, it will be more compact than and one-tenth as expensive as any other model, and, what is more important, it will weigh heavy atoms with greater accuracy. While Goudsmit prefers to think of his spectrometer as an instrument that will be primarily useful in basic research, he is not oblivious to the fact that an industrial engineer who recently visited Brookhaven expressed the belief that it may prove valuable in refining oil and analyzing gases. The possibility of a substantial reward from industry, much as he could use it, confuses him. "Money and engineering have diverted us to the point where I don't know if we're gadgeteers or scientists," he says. "There are easily three times as many physicists now as there were before the war, but only ten per cent of them are in the fields where important discoveries are made. The bomb showed so-called practical men that physicists aren't necessarily vague long-hairs, and now they won't let us alone."

Sooner or later, of course, Goudsmit has to turn his attention back to his blackboard. On a typical day, one of the notations on it may remind him that he has called a meeting of the group leaders in his department for three that afternoon. He does not expect it to be as exhausting an administrative session as the one at which the nine million dollars that the Atomic Energy Commission appropriates to Brookhaven every year is budgeted, but touchy considerations are bound to arise. Some extra money has been allocated to the Physics Department, and the heads of the ten branches of the department—High Energy Physics, Nuclear Properties, Solid States Studies, and so on—will have a lot to say about how it should be apportioned. It will be up to Goudsmit, as chairman of the department, to make the final decisions and fend off the brickbats of the men who feel that they didn't get a fair share. This is a position most administrators find themselves in from time to time, and Goudsmit does not enjoy it, but then, as he often points out, he never did think that he would wholeheartedly enjoy being an administrator.

Goudsmit's cherished solitude ends when one of his two secretaries comes in and puts the morning's mail and a cup of coffee on his desk. The coffee cup, a gift from his staff, has a whip painted on its side—a little intramural joke testifying to his easygoing nature as a boss. Sipping his coffee as he goes through his mail, Goudsmit may find a couple of pieces of particular interest. One may be a research paper from his old friend Fermi, submitted to him as the editor of the *Physical Review,* the semimonthly publication of the American Physical Society. Although Goudsmit has a board of distinguished scientists and a clerical staff of four to assist him in editing the *Review,* the job could consume his entire working day if he allowed it to, and sometimes it seems to him that he has enough to do without it. But this morning the job is a joy, for it gives him the opportunity to be one of the first to read the results of Fermi's newest research.

The other item of interest in the mail may be a long memorandum from the Navy describing in detail the educational backgrounds of four outstanding young engineering officers who have been selected to study nuclear physics under Goudsmit at the Massachusetts Institute of Technology, where he gives a four-week course each year. Its aim is to prepare officers for later training in nuclear engineering, which, it is expected, will eventually enable them to direct the operation of submarines run by atomic energy. "I try to wean them away from the engineering handbooks they've been raised on," Goudsmit says. "Those manuals are anathema to a physicist. They're answer books without questions. The principal spur to scientific thinking is doubt about the answers and a desire to remove that doubt, so I try to teach them the questions and make them wonder if the old answers are really the right ones. Well, they're bright, eager young men, but so far I can't say that they have become exactly weighed down by doubts. But perhaps that's all for the best. I've put in for a dive on the first atomic submarine, and if I get to go along, I sincerely trust there won't be any doubt about surfacing."

Fortified by his coffee, Goudsmit tackles the blackboard again, but at this moment his telephone may ring. Possibly the call is from an Intelligence official in Washington who wants to discuss the advisability of letting a certain German physicist work on an American atomic project. Goudsmit's experience in Germany during the war has made him an authority on such matters. Assuring the government man that he will call back, he opens the combination lock of a cabinet near his desk and plows through his files for the necessary information. The files are full of documents he accumulated in the course of the Alsos mission—Himmler's dossier on underground laboratories, for instance, which was found in Munich, and Goering's budget for atomic research, a souvenir of Göttingen. Frequently while he is rummaging about in the drawers, he lingers over another accumulation—a box containing the hundred or so scarabs that he has collected since his Leyden days. One of his favorite pieces of Egyptology is a worn clay figure of a pregnant hippopotamus, representing Toueris, the goddess of fertility, and as he runs a thumb over its smooth back, he may turn to gaze at lithographs on the wall that show the Temple of Karnak and people drinking tea on the terrace at Shepheard's. "I love my scarabs because they remind me that there is a life beyond the world of physics," he says.

After Goudsmit has called Washington back, a secretary may place on his desk a bulky security report, its cover stamped "CONFIDENTIAL" in large red letters, that concerns a candidate for a physicist's job with the Atomic Energy Commission. Goudsmit is a member of the three-man Personnel Security Board for the Commission's New York district, which checks on scientists against whom security charges have been made. The reports submitted to the board are exhaustive, and Goudsmit generally finds that reading them takes more time than they are worth. "So many of them fall into the category of men who have an in-law who has, or had, Leftist connections," he says. "Frankly, after three years on the job I've just about concluded that the screening process is far less likely to catch a Fuchs than to hurt many innocents. That man Fuchs! Harmful as he was to the free nations, he was even more harmful to science. So many travel restrictions now keep scientists of different countries from getting together to talk science—the science of nature's secrets, I mean, not governments' secrets. We need each other's ideas or our research will run dry."

At last, Goudsmit takes a good stern look at the blackboard, and notes that a brand-new physics Ph.D. who would like to work at Brookhaven is due in exactly three minutes. He has allowed the young candidate half an hour, which, he realizes, may be excessive. It won't be if the applicant is the diffident sort of man who is hard to get to know but who may well have the makings of a valuable scientist. On the other hand, if he turns out to be one of those smooth and garrulous opportunists who a generation ago would have scorned the idea of struggling along with string and sealing wax but who now regard physics as the coming thing, Goudsmit will find the half hour far too long. The chances are, though, that the young man will not fit exactly into either classification but will be the mystifying composite of visionary scientist and well-adjusted citizen that the universities are turning out nowadays, and that Goudsmit finds intensely difficult to relate to anything in his previous experience. In the corridor outside he can hear the secretary and the Ph.D. approaching, and, rising from his chair, he spends his last seconds of privacy rearranging the cast of his mind in order to present the proper front. "At times like that, I wish that I felt sick," he says. "Just sick enough, that is, to go home and go to bed and do some serious thinking about my mass spectrometer—or even sort out my scarabs—while the Long Island fog closes in around my bedroom windows. But then the door to my office opens, and there's no escape."

CHAPTER 16 | JULY, 1956

I KNEW EXACTLY WHY

PHYSICISTS ARE now so widely regarded as a remote and menacing breed of intellectual that it may seem incongruous to suggest that these latter-day Merlins, endlessly experimenting with radiation, can themselves be burned by the strange, inextinguishable fire they have learned to create. But the fact is that they can be burned, and have been. Exposed to radiation, they are every bit as vulnerable as the people of Hiroshima, or the Japanese sailors who unwittingly went fishing for tuna along the rim of the fallout area surrounding Eniwetok in 1956. So far, in the United States, eleven physicists have been casualties of radiation. One of these, a Los Alamos researcher, met his death, in 1946, when he saved the lives of several colleagues by pulling apart with his bare hands two chunks of uranium that were producing an uncontrolled chain reaction. The ten others, working in various universities around the country, were injured when neutrons, the type of atomic particle that most readily penetrates matter, entered their eyes. Although in each instance the fusillade of neutrons was relatively light, it was nonetheless pernicious, for the eye is uniquely susceptible to cellular damage. Unlike the other parts of the body, it is unable to slough off and replace dead cells; instead, the cells gradually accumulate until cataracts are formed, and then surgery becomes necessary. Since neutron-induced cataracts differ from the familiar cataracts that frequently afflict elderly people, the physicists' injuries gave rise to unusual surgical problems, but all ten men have had their vision at least partly restored (one lost an eye and several have to wear powerful spectacles) and all are back in the laboratory, working, in most cases, with the same kind of machine that brought on their cataracts.

Not long ago, I looked up a member of this group—Dr. Lloyd Smith, a theoretical physicist whose eyes were injured by a cyclotron during the Second World War. I wanted to hear his account of his peculiar modern accident, and I wanted to find out whether he had coped with his ordeal any differently from the way a layman might have. I was also curious to learn whether the darkening of his sight had produced any change in his attitude toward his work. Smith, a quiet-spoken, thoughtful man of thirty-four, is spending a year at the Brookhaven National Laboratory, in Upton, Long Island, where he is helping to design the synchrotron—a particle accelerator, or atom-smashing machine, that is due to be completed in the near future and will be the largest in this country. He is on leave of absence from the University of California, in Berkeley, and before coming to Brookhaven he had a hand in designing that university's bevatron, which currently holds the American atom-smashing championship. As might be expected, he has not only a high degree of intelligence but a taste for objectivity and precision, and although his words sometimes convey a certain intensity of feeling, he always chooses them carefully and speaks in a cool, measured voice. He is not, however, above making an occasional statement that, by his standards, is far from precise. "I may be more upset by that cataract business than I appear to be," he told me, and then appeared somewhat abashed at having advanced so obviously undemonstrable a proposition.

Smith is a thin man, not quite six feet tall, with brown hair parted haphazardly on one side. His eyes are blue-green. They stare at one, magnified and transfixing, through large, thick bifocals. Without these glasses, he can make out only vague silhouettes of people and objects; even with them, his peripheral vision is fuzzy, which means that he has to face directly whatever he wishes to see. In general, Smith says, his poor sight has not hampered his work, and although the bevatron is about six hundred times as powerful as the cyclotron that damaged his eyes, and the synchrotron is to be five times as powerful as the bevatron, he is not worried about a repetition of his accident. "The art of protection has been greatly refined since the war," he explains, without bitterness. "Mishaps of the sort I experienced are now extremely unlikely."

Early one evening last month, I drove out to Smith's home, in the village of Brookhaven, twelve miles from the National Laboratory and a couple of hundred yards from Great South Bay. Smith and his wife, the former Marianne Freundlich, and their three children live in a modest frame house, designed for summer occupancy, which they have rented, furnished, for their year in the East. It was dusk when I arrived, and not far from the house, in a wind-swept field of brown grass, I could see a weathered picnic table. The living-room furniture was simple and rather rickety, and Mrs. Smith, a tall, spirited brunette, who came to the door with her husband to greet me, made a point of directing me to a dependable chair. She had once been a physicist herself, I knew, and then had switched to mathematics—she and her husband met at the University of Illinois, in Urbana, where they were fellow-students—but since the birth of their third child she had been devoting practically all her time to the family. The children, she informed me, would not be in our way; Peter, six, and Winnie, four, were spending the night with friends, and Lloyd, eighteen months, was asleep. Explaining the banishment of her brood, she told me she didn't want to miss anything that was said, for she herself had never heard her husband try to sum up his experience. She sat down diagonally across the room from me, on a chair near a small piano; I noticed the sheet music for a Schubert violin-and-piano sonata on the music rack. "Lloyd's the pianist," she said, following my gaze, "and I'm the violinist." Smith sat on a sofa opposite me, and after turning his head to glance at his wife he launched into his account.

In June of 1943, Smith said, he had just received his Master's degree in physics from the University of Illinois when he first saw the cyclotron that eventually injured him. It was a brand-new, hundred-thousand-dollar machine that could accelerate particles of matter to one-tenth of the speed of light, and it was one of the chief reasons that he decided to continue his studies at Illinois. "There probably weren't more than a dozen cyclotrons in the country at the time," he told me. "All of us in the Physics Department were proud to have one of them, and I was delighted to get a chance to work on it."

The cyclotron, Smith went on, was housed in a squat, yellowish laboratory building, just off the campus, that had once been a repair garage. The machine was a formidable contraption—eight feet high, eight feet wide, and twelve feet long—and its main theatre of action was a cylindrical vacuum chamber, four feet in diameter, that was located in the center of the apparatus. Inside the chamber, heavy-hydrogen nuclei, or deuterons, were whirled at ever-increasing velocity in ever-widening circles, until at length they collided with the target—some substance whose atoms the physicists wanted to break up. A small glass porthole provided a view into the chamber; looking through it, Smith said, one could sometimes see a hazy, bluish glow, which marked the path of the fast-moving deuterons.

When the target was hit, Smith said, atomic particles were dislodged, and among these particles were neutrons. Neutrons penetrate glass, stone, and metal with ease, but water tends to slow them down, and tanks of water, about the height of the machine and ten feet wide, surrounded the cyclotron at Urbana. Sometimes, though, the physicists worked inside this protective fence, and it was then that they took the risk of being exposed to neutrons. When a neutron crashes into one of the many billions of hydrogen nuclei in our bodies, Smith explained, there is apt to be a cellular disturbance, but as long as the dosage of neutrons, which, incidentally, are in the atmosphere all the time, is only moderate, most cells can recover easily. In 1943, the principal means of checking up on a person who had been exposed to radiation was a blood count. If the red-cell count fell off appreciably, a serious exposure might have occurred. "A physics instructor used to test us once a month," Smith recalled. "He made the counts under a microscope we had around, and he got to be pretty good at sticking our ear lobes." The trouble with the test was that it disclosed only the degree to which the whole body had been exposed, Smith said; a mild exposure that might not affect the rest of the body at all could injure the eye, and injure it badly.

Near one end of the garage was a fair-sized room that was equipped with a large panel of dials and flashing bulbs—something like what you see in the cockpit of an airplane, Smith remarked. This was a remote-control apparatus for operating the cyclotron. Beyond the control room were some other rooms, in which half a dozen graduate students, including Smith, checked and repaired the parts of the cyclotron, under the supervision of Dr. P. G. Kruger, the head of the

Physics Department, and Dr. Gerhardt Groetzinger, another physics professor. Smith worked on the cyclotron itself more than any of the other students did. "My reward for being something of a fair-haired boy," he told me ruefully. Kruger and Groetzinger, the men who rewarded him, were also to develop cataracts. The three of them would often spend entire nights in the laboratory. "New cyclotrons are balky things," Smith said. "They have to be broken in, like horses. They won't budge all day, and then at ten o'clock at night they're liable to start perking up. That's your big chance to familiarize yourself with the machine and its behavior, so you stay with it into the small hours. Eventually, it peters out again, by which time, of course, you've petered out yourself."

"Lloyd worked Sundays, too," Mrs. Smith said. "I used to tell him he should be taking me to the movies, instead. I was always worried about his work. You can't smell or feel or see that radiation. You never know what it's up to."

Groetzinger, Kruger, and Smith went on familiarizing themselves with their cyclotron for two years, and dutifully reported to the physics instructor once a month for a blood count. Whenever they could, they worked at the panel, but often the cyclotron would not respond to remote control. It would refuse to whirl particles around the way it was supposed to. Then its would-be masters had to leave their controls and make adjustments on the machine itself, flipping a lever or switch here, turning a knob there, inserting a probe. "And if we were really stumped, we'd look through the porthole to see what might be wrong inside," Smith said. "When the machine was unusually temperamental, I might look through it ten times a day. How well I came to know that blue glow! We had to get up close to the porthole, and the closer we got, the more neutrons were getting into our eyes. Not that we realized what was happening. There was never any pain. I must have looked through that glass a couple of hundred times. Not all those looks injured me, but some did, and I'll never know which ones. All I'll ever know is that there were days between June, 1943, and September, 1945, when I was damaging my eyes permanently."

One afternoon in September, 1946, Smith, who was by then a fellow of the University of Chicago's Institute for Nuclear Studies, decided he had better visit an oculist. He had had his eyes tested the previous spring in Columbus, Ohio, where he had gone to take his doctorate at Ohio State, and on that occasion he had done nearly as well as usual with the eye chart; the oculist had prescribed lenses only a little stronger than the ones that Smith, who had been slightly nearsighted since boyhood, was then using. He was reluctant to take the time for another visit to an oculist, he told me, for he was extremely busy that fall. His research at the Institute was absorbing, and congenial as well; he was again working with Groetzinger, who had also joined the Institute. His social life, too, was a full one. Chicago was his home town, and he spent his free time with relatives and old friends. And as often as he could, he went down to Urbana, a hundred and thirty miles away, to see Miss Freundlich, who was completing her doctoral thesis there. At any rate, Smith did consult an oculist—a reputable practitioner, who gave him a new prescription that was a trifle stronger than the last. Five months later, in February, 1947, he was in still another oculist's office, hopefully accepting still another prescription. "Something strange was happening to my sight," Smith said, "and I finally came to suspect that it had nothing to do with glasses. Back in Columbus, I had become aware of little floating things in my field of vision, but I was told that everyone sees them, to a certain extent. So that didn't bother me much. What followed did bother me, though—a splotchy bending of light. I seemed to be looking at things through a dirty, scratched-up window. I could see a blackboard or a book properly if I wasn't in a glare of sunlight, but if I was, there would be this slightly opaque glass. At first, the distortion was so subtle that I couldn't tell whether there was something wrong with my eyes or whether objects actually were the way I saw them. I'd turn my head at different angles, but the window was always there, and it kept getting dirtier. By the time I moved on to Chicago, I was finding it hard to resolve lights. The headlights of an approaching car would blur together. I was glad I didn't know how to drive. Lights always had halos—pretty ones, with rainbow colors and crystal-like patterns. On a clear night, I could count on a ring around the moon."

A few weeks after Smith's visit to the third oculist, he felt he needed yet another examination, and this time he went to the eye clinic at the Billings Hospital of the University of Chicago, just a few blocks from the Institute. As soon as he walked in, he told me, he felt that if his condition could be diagnosed anywhere, this was the place. "It was a university clinic, and research was in the air," he said. The man who examined him—an interne about his own age—not only looked at his eyes but questioned him closely about his work over the past few years. Then the interne, remembering something he had read recently, went out and fetched a book from the hospital library. He read Smith a passage about cataracts brought on by massive X-ray treatment in advanced cases of brain tumor. "My difficulties now made sense," Smith went on. "I had incipient radiation cataracts, and Illinois was where I'd got them. This possibility had never crossed my mind. There was surgery for the cataracts, the interne said, but that was for the future; my eyes first had to get considerably worse. He was very tolerant about the oculists I'd been to. How could they have been expected to look for cataracts in a man of twenty-five? The interne left the room again, and this time he returned with a senior ophthalmologist—a dogmatic middle-aged woman. I guess he wanted to show off his discovery. The woman told me I would have to give up physics—period. My lips must have tightened, but I didn't say anything. She couldn't have known what that meant to me. I still compose imaginary speeches to her."

Smith went back to the Institute and told the news to Groetzinger, who had yet to experience his own symptoms. For a while, Smith had trouble concentrating on his work—the first time this had ever happened to him, he said—but presently, as he grew accustomed to the diagnosis and his eyes seemed to be holding their own, his interest revived sufficiently for him to be offered a renewal of his fellowship. An invitation to work on the University of California bevatron came through at about the same time, however, and Smith decided to try his hand at that. Miss Freundlich applied for and got a job as a mathematics instructor at the same school, and the two made plans to go West as newlyweds. They were married in June, 1947. Not until the night before the wedding did Smith tell his fiancée about his injury. "It wasn't easy for Lloyd," Mrs. Smith recalled. "He said to me, 'There's something I have to tell you. I may go blind. I have radiation cataracts, but there's supposed to be an operation for them.' I reminded him that financially, anyway, we wouldn't be too badly fixed.

After all, I had a Ph.D., too, and if necessary, I could support him. I saw to it that we didn't dwell on the cataracts. It would have been inappropriate. We were supposed to be in a cheerful frame of mind. We were young, we were about to be married, and we were going to a part of the country neither of us knew. I proposed that we buy a used car and drive to Berkeley, and I told Lloyd he would have to pay for it out of his savings, because I had squandered mine on nylon stockings. Well, we bought the car, and even though I did all the driving, I saw lots of things along the way that Lloyd didn't. I'd always mention them. I wanted Lloyd to face up to the situation. I didn't want any taboo subjects coming between us."

In Berkeley, the couple rented a small apartment and went about their jobs. Although Smith could handle his work smoothly enough at first, he told his immediate superior, Dr. Robert Serber, about his developing cataracts, and Serber put him in touch with Dr. Frederick Cordes, the chief ophthalmologist at the University of California Hospital, in San Francisco. Once again, Smith found himself hailed as an interesting case, and in the next three years, during which he often saw Dr. Cordes and other eye men, he learned enough ophthalmology to share some of their clinical excitement. "You know, very few really new situations ever come an eye man's way," Smith said sympathetically. The doctors knew about radiation cataracts, but only the kind caused by X-ray; neutron-induced cataracts were something they had never encountered before. Moreover, Smith's youth raised certain new operative problems; it was for senile cataracts that procedures were well established. But, as the interne in Chicago had said, surgery would come later; Dr. Cordes agreed that Smith's vision had not yet deteriorated sufficiently to justify it. "Conservative methods," Smith said. In the meantime, though, the medical carpet was out for him. Whenever he appeared at the hospital, specialists and internes clustered around him, peering at his eyes, and on one occasion a technical artist drew a "portrait" of his right eye—the poorer one—for a medical journal. And when the time for the operation should arrive, Smith was assured, the University of Illinois would pay for everything, including a private room. "I had apparently been injured under the best of circumstances," he said. "I wouldn't have come off half as well if I had been a Hiroshima casualty. Not that I merited comparison. I had been exposed to an occupational hazard, not victimized by a war. Physics was something I had taken up deliberately. It was my career."

In the summer of 1948, the Smiths vacationed in the Canadian Rockies, and as they explored the mountains, it became plain that Smith's vision had deteriorated a good deal; his inability to make out scenic beauties was far more pronounced than it had been during their trip to California. As a matter of fact, Mrs. Smith observed, the move to the West had been fortunate, for the novelty of the place helped distract her husband. A visit to Dr. Cordes was an excuse for making a night of it in San Francisco, trying out new restaurants and wandering along unfamiliar streets. A picnic at the seashore was another treat for her husband, who had been reared in the Midwest. But his dependence on such diversions, Mrs. Smith said, was a sore point with him. "Of course, scientists like to relax, the same as anyone else, but only if they know they can go back to work and work as hard as they choose," she explained. "If a scientist can't do that, something vital is missing from his life, and he takes very little pleasure in an outing or a weekend. Christmas Eve becomes just an ordinary night for him."

By November, Smith continued, his eyes were so clouded over that he was spending most of his time at home. Sometimes his wife took him for a drive along the shore or, if her teaching schedule permitted, went to the movies with him right after lunch, when the theatres were apt to be pretty empty and he could pick out a seat that would allow him a good view of the screen. He couldn't read music and had to give up the piano, and before long he couldn't read anything without the help of a magnifying glass. The laboratory blackboard—the physicist's scratch-pad—held only indecipherable blurs for him. In the evening, his wife read him articles from technical journals. "Lloyd was avid for the latest news of the universe," she told me, and added wryly, "I suspect the universe wasn't quite as interested in the latest news of him."

"Of course it wasn't," Smith said, with a smile. "Person A may care about what's happening to Person B, but you can bet that the universe doesn't."

One night shortly before Christmas, though Smith didn't know it,

Drew Pearson broadcast the news that several atomic scientists were going blind as a result of exposure to radiation. The next morning, the Smiths were awakened early by a loud rapping on their door. When Smith opened it, he found a newspaper photographer outside, camera cocked.

"What do you want my picture for?" Smith asked.

"You're one of those atomic scientists, aren't you?" the photographer replied as a flash bulb went off.

That afternoon, peering through a magnifying glass, Smith saw his picture on the front page of a San Francisco paper. The local press soon began issuing occasional bulletins on Smith's condition, and strangers took to phoning him and writing him letters. Some of them exhorted him to turn to religion, claiming that his failing sight was retribution for the raids on Japan. Two women proposed marriage, and an Alaskan farm wife recommended that he pour a bucket of lye over his eyes—a measure, she said, that had cured her horse of blindness.

As a result of the publicity the injured scientists were given, the National Research Council, a private agency that advises the government on scientific matters, called a meeting in Washington in January, 1949, to consider the phenomenon of neutron-induced cataracts. Smith and five other injured physicists attended, along with a number of ophthalmologists. Mrs. Smith made the trip with her husband, and accompanied him to the daily meetings of the Cataract Conference, as it was informally called, which were held in a Washington hotel suite. Only one other casualty required an escort—a young physicist from the Carnegie Institution, in Washington, who, Smith told me, was in worse shape than he was. This man's escort was a distinguished ophthalmologist, who had recently operated on his left eye; the surgery had cost the physicist his eye, and the surgeon had been penitently guiding him around ever since. (The physicist's right eye was later operated on successfully.) Groetzinger and Kruger, Smith's Illinois colleagues, were among the injured physicists at the conference, and so were men from the University of Pittsburgh and the Carnegie Institute of Technology. The sessions, Smith said, weren't as sombre as one might suppose. Liquor and food were provided to lend them a festive air, but, I gathered, the men derived their real stimulation from dealing with the business at hand. "We wanted to get the facts straight," Smith told me. "We wanted to find out what had happened." Each injured man gave his own case history, attempting to estimate the amount of radiation he had been exposed to. "Groetzinger, Kruger, and I worked out our estimates separately," Smith said. "We didn't want to take the risk of influencing each other's story." Later, "subjective notes," more speculative in nature, were called for, and Smith, Groetzinger, and the Carnegie Institution man, as the most severely injured of the six, pooled their impressions for a small group of medical men. The conference reached the conclusion that similar injuries must have occurred in Japan, and Dr. Philip S. Owen, an officer of the National Research Council, said that he would urge the United States Atomic Bomb Casualty Commission to look into that possibility. The talk never languished, Smith told me, and at the final session it was unanimously voted to hold a Cataract Conference every year.

In April, 1949, the doctors at the University of California Hospital decided that the time had come for surgery on Smith's right eye, and he entered the hospital the night before the operation. Nearly six years had elapsed since his eyes were damaged, and by that time, he said, he had learned a good deal about his ophthalmological situation and had a very clear idea of what the doctors would be up to when they had him on the operating table. "Anything a doctor knows, a physicist can learn," Mrs. Smith put in matter-of-factly. Then, too, Smith continued, he was a specialist in radiation, and, of course, radiation was at the bottom of his trouble. All this knowledge, he was sure, gave him an advantage over the average preoperative patient. "Lying in the hospital that night, I wondered how my imaginary Hiroshimian would have felt in my place," he said. "He would have been mystified, I decided, and panicky. He would have known only that something had dropped out of the sky and had made him go slowly blind. He wouldn't have known why, and he wouldn't have known what to expect next. I did. I knew exactly why, and, unlike the Hiroshimian, I didn't have to worry that my hair would fall out in tufts, or anything like that. I could put boundaries around my injury. I knew that only my eyes were affected. If war should come, we scientists might die the same as anyone else, but at least we would understand exactly what was causing our death."

"It is a strict discipline, this trying to be detached and logical all the time," Mrs. Smith interposed. "It can protect, as Lloyd says, but it is a fragile flower. It may crumble at any moment, and if it does, someone like Lloyd is lost."

Smith assured me that he hadn't been altogether detached that first night in the hospital. "I was logical, all right, but there was a component of depression in my attitude, too," he said, in his measured way. "That made for a strange mixture. Perhaps the failure of the operation on the Carnegie Institution man had something to do with it."

Smith's operation went off smoothly. Afterward, he remained in the hospital for ten days, his eyes bandaged and his head braced by two sandbags to prevent hemorrhage. Then Mrs. Smith drove him home. His eyes were still bandaged, and the bandages were not taken off for another ten days. As a result of the operation, Smith's restored eye could admit light but could not focus, and a special powerful lens had to do the focussing for him. For the next two months, following Dr. Cordes' instructions, Smith diligently exercised his eye and got accustomed to the lens through which it would henceforth see. His left eye still had to be operated on, but while he was waiting to reënter the hospital, there were plenty of things he could do. He could work on a blackboard, he could read at almost his normal rate, and he could play the piano. He could even learn to drive a car, as he discovered when Mrs. Smith, who was expecting her first child and was worried about her own forthcoming trip to the hospital, persuaded him to take driving lessons. One afternoon, the instructor asked Smith why he had been so long getting around to driving, and Smith mentioned his cataract difficulties, among other things. "Oh, you're that scientist who's been in the papers," the instructor said. "My wife cried when she read about you."

It wasn't until September, after Peter's birth, that the Smiths were able to celebrate the upswing in their fortunes. "We went off camping in the Sierras for two weeks," Smith told me. "I could see a whole lot more than I had seen in the Canadian Rockies. I wanted to see everything, but I had to keep bobbing my head, because of my limited peripheral vision. I had to look up for low branches that might knock my glasses off and I had to look down for roots that might trip me. Still, I could see trees and bushes, the colors and shapes of rocks, the immense sky—even a hawk wheeling overhead. I didn't give a thought to the dynamics of flight. All that mattered was that I could see the world. I felt like a free man."

Smith has had the use of both eyes since April, 1950, when his left eye was successfully operated on, and now he would just as soon forget that his accident ever occurred. As it happens, though, there are reminders—the continuing Cataract Conferences, for one. At the 1950 meeting, he learned that the Atomic Bomb Casualty Commission had found more than a hundred Japanese with neutron-induced cataracts and that medical help was to be provided for them. During that conference, the chairman of the Physics Department at Carnegie Tech, a fellow-casualty, invited him to teach there; he accepted, and spent two years in Pittsburgh. In 1952, with two children now, the Smiths went back to Berkeley, and Mrs. Smith took the children to meet Dr. Cordes. "Just Person A dropping in on Person B," she said. When the weather turns warm, Smith told me, he is reminded that his swimming days are over; it would make him too uneasy to enter the water without his glasses. Children in the street sometimes stare boldly at his large bifocals, and now and then, forgetting to face directly where he is going, he bumps humiliatingly into a door or a filing cabinet.

Smith, who had been talking with unusual deliberateness, suddenly took off his glasses. His eyes darted and blinked as they tried to locate me. They looked extraordinarily small and strangely denuded. I hadn't realized that his glasses had been steadily reflecting the light of a floor lamp. "I can see you," he said, finally. "I make you out in about twenty striations—vertical and horizontal. They smear into one fuzzy image." He put his glasses back on.

At large scientific gatherings, Smith continued, speaking more quickly, he is conscious of a certain notoriety; sooner or later, a new acquaintance is almost sure to ask him, "You had that business with a cyclotron, didn't you?" Smith does not consider this question tactless. "My colleagues know that neutrons are a part of the general picture," he said. "They probably regard my injury as a cultural event, and they can well imagine themselves wearing my spectacles. Still, I don't care for the question. My work is what counts, and that's what I want to be known for. Even when my sight was at its worst, I never doubted that I would go back to my work, and the matter of how supposedly ennobling the scientific spirit is had nothing to do with it. What else could I do? To someone like me—and I don't deserve any special credit for it—the desire for knowledge is a fact of life."

Happily for Smith, he is snowed under with work at Brookhaven these days, and unexpected duties have been descending on him from other quarters as well. A few months ago, he flew to Berkeley to look into some bevatron problems; after that, he went to Geneva as one of the American delegates to an international conference on high-energy physics; right now, he is finishing up a paper on particle accelerators for the *Handbuch der Physik,* a German encyclopedia. As for the synchrotron, he said, it was coming along fine, and early the next morning he was going to show it to a group of visiting British scientists from Harwell.

I rose to go, and after I had shaken hands with Mrs. Smith, her husband walked me out to my car. The weathered picnic table was a black mass in the night. Above us was the universe—a deep sky, brilliant with stars. Smith looked up at it in silence for a while—long enough to make me wonder what he was seeing. Then, having looked his fill, he turned to me and said, "It's a beautiful night, isn't it?"

Not only scientists were affected by the advent of the atom. It shaped the lives of laymen, too, in ways that in terms of the past were sometimes recognizable and sometimes extraordinary. To some, it signified little more than the creation of jobs and prosperity. To others, it heralded the appearance of strange objects in the sky—a plausible addition to the many implausible feats of science. The abstruseness of nucleonics notwithstanding, the public's involvement in the scientific renaissance rapidly grew more varied and pronounced, most pronounced perhaps in the atom's home territory—the mines, the plants, the testing grounds.

BOMBS AWAY!

CERTAINLY ONE of the most exciting moments of a recent atomic-bomb test at Yucca Flat, Nevada—in which an atomic bomb was used for the first time as part of a tactical troop maneuver—occurred forty-two seconds before the detonation, when Dr. Gaelen Felt, a thin young scientist who had been briefing three hundred or so of us reporters, public officials and civil-defense people—assembled at the foot of an ugly, boulder-encrusted knoll overlooking a section of the Nevada desert, calmly announced over the public-address system, "Bombs away!" By that time, having heeded Dr. Felt's warning of eighteen seconds before, we were all staring blindly into special goggles approximately ten times as opaque as ordinary sunglasses. In the blackness, various images absorbed during the past hour of waiting were still fresh enough to be remembered clearly: the smooth, sandy miles of Yucca Flat, the dried-out salt lake where the target area was; a helicopter, which was going to take up a radiological-survey team twenty minutes after the burst, landing at the edge of the desert basin, not far from the observers' hill; the almost cloudless morning sky, streaked with the vapor trails, thirty-two thousand feet up, left by the B-50 that was carrying the bomb, as it made practice runs over the target; the bustle accompanying the deployment of the spectators and participants—the observers ten miles from the target; fifteen hundred troops, whom the bomb would theoretically help capture a hostile strong point, in trenches and foxholes four miles from the target; and, well ahead of the troops, serving as advance elements against the invisible enemy, sixteen hundred mice and twenty-four anesthetized pigs, who would wake up late that afternoon in a near-by laboratory, to find curious biologists examining them.

After Dr. Felt's "Bombs away!," however, a new and apocryphal image abruptly intruded itself in my mind—a free-falling atomic bomb (an unclassified model, I suspect). When Dr. Felt shouted "Zero!," a light that turned the world to sun engulfed my goggles. Simultaneously, I was startled by a jet of heat licking at me. (A scientist told me later that the temperature of the air had momentarily risen from eighty-three degrees to a hundred and forty, which was not surprising, because the temperature of the bomb's blast was nearly two million degrees.) Dr. Felt had advised us to count off three seconds before removing our goggles, and I heard myself doing so aloud. As I pulled mine off, Dr. Felt told us not to move, that a shock wave was approaching. A few seconds later, a sharp, jarring thunderclap struck down at our hill from the sunny sky, and Dr. Felt was through with his warnings for the day. My first relatively unworried look at the target area filled me with a guilty aestheticism. Beautiful peach, violet, and pink streamers, produced by the combining of nitrogen and oxygen, had been left behind by the so-called ball of fire, a spherical caldron, nine hundred feet in diameter, that was churning upward. Below the ball of fire, in hopeless pursuit, was a column of dust, five thousand feet high, that had been sucked out of Yucca Flat. Five minutes after the burst, Dr. Felt announced that the atomic cloud had attained a height of thirty-five thousand feet. Not far from where I was standing, a radio broadcaster, barking like a coxswain into his microphone, fastened onto the word "mushroom" and couldn't seem to let go. The man next to me, Merril Eisenbud, a radiation-monitoring expert who was not involved with the test, disagreed sharply with the broadcaster. "That's no mushroom—that's a Portuguese man-of-war," he said. "Look at those ice tentacles coming down from the cloud." The broadcaster finally shifted to "an enormous, enormous cloud," "a cataract of white waves," and "a glowing mass of energy," but Eisenbud still wasn't satisfied. "Sounds terrific," he said. "Wish I'd seen it."

The smell of burning sagebrush had long since reached our hill, and now, in the distance on Yucca Flat, I could make out several distinct fires. Airplanes and Army vehicles, left there to test the weapon's effect on them, were smoldering. A small first-aid shack three miles from the target—far enough to have been considered "safe"—was sending up black smoke. The helicopter with the radiological-survey team took off, and a short while later a second helicopter came spinning toward us and landed directly in front of our hill. From it emerged a lieutenant general, who strode past us halfway up the knoll, turned around, and delivered a talk. He had been up forward with the troops, he said, and the boys had made jokes immediately before and after the explosion. The weapon, he declared, had to be regarded as so much firepower. From a tactical point of view, he went on clinically, the day's bomb had been too big, because it had prevented the troops from advancing quickly enough. "We learned in the war that you have to follow close behind your firepower to capture your objective," he said.

After he finished speaking, I looked for the atomic cloud, but it had floated off and was now indistinguishable from other white flecks in the sky. Eisenbud couldn't pick it out, either. Whichever fleck it was, he informed me, it would drift south, then northeast. "It should be over northern Mexico by tonight," he said authoritatively. "Five days from now, thoroughly dissipated, it'll be over New York, and we'll have nothing more to worry about."

Spectacular and frightening as the burst had been, I left the proving ground with a troubling sense of detachment about the whole demonstration. Comparing notes with some of the other observers, I found that I was not alone. We agreed that we could blame this disturbing reaction, at least in part, on our safe vantage point, but the feeling persisted that the weapon had not seemed quite as terrible as we had anticipated. Back in Las Vegas, later that day, I mentioned this to the director of the test, Dr. Alvin C. Graves, a blue-eyed physicist of forty-two, whose vision is gradually deteriorating as the result of a radiation accident six years ago at the Los Alamos Scientific Laboratory, in New Mexico. Dr. Graves, who is an active churchman in Los Alamos, told me that he had had this feeling in the past himself, and had often worried about it; he added, with a smile, that it was elusive enough for him to go right on stewing over. A certain degree of detachment was appropriate, he believed. He didn't think people ought to be panicked by the mere existence of the bomb, the way they were in 1946. It was a fact of life, he said, and had to be lived with, like a heart condition. On the other hand, the weapon was too formidable to allow for very much detachment. Of course, he said, getting back to the morning's detonation, we had watched a test, not an attack on a city. The bomb had generated more energy than those used at Hiroshima, Nagasaki, and Bikini. We would never know how many people might have been killed by its neutrons or gamma rays; no buildings had been toppled by winds traveling at several hundred miles an hour. The desert was fireproofed with sand, but a city would have been a holocaust. Dr. Graves said that he and his colleagues had no way of measuring such hypothetical calamities, although on a few occasions, both in Nevada and at Eniwetok, they had tried to do so, in a limited way, by erecting more or less standard structures on which to test the weapon's effects. There had been times when, despite the expense it would have entailed, they had seriously considered building a model of a large city and then bombing it. The idea had been discarded because of the impossibility of arriving at any precise answers. "There aren't any two cities alike," he explained. "There aren't even two buildings alike. Each of them is different from the rest, just as each man's body is."

The detonation of the bomb—the sixteenth exploded in the United States—was, naturally, the reason for the descent on Las Vegas of governors, mayors, civil-defense officials, and newspapermen, but the event was preceded by three days of activities that in some cases were hardly conducive to thinking of the bomb as either an intellectual achievement or a stupendous menace. The night before the test, at a lavish cocktail party given by the Flamingo Hotel, the out-of-town observers were inducted into the Ancient and Honorable Society of Atom-Bomb Watchers, Las Vegal Local No. 1. A builder by the name of Hal B. Hayes flew in from Los Angeles and called a press conference to announce that he had developed a bombproof house featuring egg-shaped shutters to protect the windows. The Governor of Nevada, welcoming visitors, said that among his constituents the previous explosions on Yucca Flat hadn't caused "any more commotion than someone winning a jackpot in Las Vegas."

On the whole, though, thanks to the planning of the Atomic Energy Commission, the three days were spent quite purposefully. The better part of one day was taken up with a series of lectures delivered in the Las Vegas City Hall auditorium by scientists associated with the test. The men were extremely informative, as would be expected, but their uncertainties were occasionally more impressive than their facts. Dr. Norris Bradbury, the Director of the Los Alamos Scientific Laboratory, in making the point that it was difficult to foretell how a particular nuclear device would behave, disclosed that the Alamogordo explosion in 1945 had proved to be twice as powerful as anticipated. Another expert said that the larger weapons were being tested at Eniwetok rather than in the United States "because we don't want to take any chances." When the president of the Sandia Corporation, the ordnance-engineering firm operated by Western Electric for the Atomic Energy Commission, was asked from the floor to compare the physical damage produced by small and large explosions, he replied, "We may get more damage from small releases than large ones. Shock waves are rather unpredictable things." Dr. Everett F. Cox, an authority on blast effects, concluded his address by saying, "The A.E.C. agencies have been fortunate in that no damage has been done so far by shocks that have traveled through the ozonosphere. Damage can be done by ozonosphere shocks, as the Pacific Fleet learned in 1931, when gun practice off Catalina Island broke windows in Bakersfield. We are continuing our investigations to learn more about ozonosphere shocks and so be better able to predict where they will strike." Lieutenant Colonel J. B. Hartgering, a doctor of medicine specializing in radiological safety, after assuring the observers that the radioactive atomic cloud was unlikely to pass over the spot where they would be stationed and shower them with particles, added, "However, wind and weather conditions are always unpredictable. In case of a sudden shift in the target-area winds, or the occurrence of something unforeseen, all arrangements have been made for an orderly evacuation. Explicit instructions will be given over the public-address system."

In addition to attending the lectures, we visited a near-by airfield used by elements of the 4925th Test Group (Atomic), the unit whose planes drop the bombs and also sample the atomic clouds and then track them for six hundred miles, in order to warn off pilots of other aircraft, who might mistake drifting radioactivity for an ordinary cloud. While I was at the airbase, a very young-looking pilot sounded me out on an idea he and his fellows had been kicking around. "We're considering painting a little white cloud on our planes for each of our test missions," he said. "What do you think?"

We also toured the proving ground, where the prize attraction turned out to be an air-conditioned underground bunker filled with oscilloscopes and other electronic equipment for recording data during a burst. The bunker, which was well within the destructive range of the target area, has a concrete ceiling that is six feet thick and covered with twelve feet of earth topped by macadam. Its walls, also concrete, are four feet thick. Its entrance, which is labyrinthine, is protected by a two-inch hollow steel door, filled with lead, that weighs three tons. I asked Roy A. Norman, a technician who was showing us around, if he thought a man could survive in the bunker during a test. "He might, but I wouldn't want to be the fellow," he said. "I'd go nuts waiting for the instruments to start clicking with timing signals just before the shot. I wouldn't want to be leaning against a wall after the shot, not unless I wanted my head bashed against it by a shock wave. And I'd be awfully wary about coming out, no matter who telephoned me it was all right."

Of the various officials I talked with during the tours and between lectures, none awaited the impending test more eagerly than the civil-defense people. "We're counting heavily on this bomb," one of them told me. "It's a tough job selling accident insurance." Another thought that the explosion would greatly boost the morale of his organization but regretted that only seventy-five invitations had been allotted to its members. "Some of our volunteers are sore as hell at us," he said. "You can't blame them. This shot is going to be something to talk about for a long, long time."

Eight hours after the detonation, a hundred troops who had been in the foxholes and trenches that morning were marched into the City Hall auditorium. They were ranged against the walls in groups, by states, for the convenience of newspapermen interested in local stories. Almost instantly, the barnlike structure was alive with the din of feature stories. I wandered down one of the aisles, listening to snatches of the interviews, and found that the atomic G.I. sounded very much like his counterpart of a few years ago. An Arizona boy had prayed. A chipper California man said that he'd take the atomic bomb any day over those German 88s he'd known in Sicily. An Illinois corporal said that he'd drawn a stranger as his foxhole mate, but that after the hot earthquake they'd experienced together he was sure they'd be buddies for life. A very young blond New York City corporal wanted the reporter talking to him to do him a favor. "My name is Geiger, Vincent Geiger," he said, "and all the fellows in my company keep asking me if my father's the guy who invented that counter. I would appreciate it if you wrote that he isn't." The most hopeful, though unconsciously hopeful, words I heard were uttered by a New Mexican, an earnest, swarthy private first class named Evaristo Hernandez. "I passed up my furlough to be in on this test," he told his interviewer. "I figured I might never have another chance to see an atom bomb."

A day or so later, I ran into Dr. Graves at the local offices of the Atomic Energy Commission. He had only a minute to spare, and he spent it talking some more about detachment. Perhaps what had dismayed me and the others on leaving the proving ground, he said, hadn't been indifference about the bomb but an awareness that our imaginations had limits. That, he assured me, smiling, had been a trait of human beings for a long time. It certainly applied to him, and he knew the exact pressure measurements of each bomb that was being exploded. "I can give precise answers to precise questions about the weapon," he said, "but what all of us want are precise answers to vague questions. We want to know what to do about the bomb—what will happen to our homes? How can I answer this? Just ask me precise questions."

BLACKJACK AND FLASHES

THE PROVING GROUND at Yucca Flat, where I witnessed the detonation, is probably the only atomic-energy installation in the United States that tallies to any great extent with the layman's conception of such projects. The other manifestations of the thriving new industry —factories producing radioactive fuels, piles cooking fissionable materials, laboratories housing novel research equipment, and so on—have thus far turned out to be eerily silent and generally as well-behaved as a hosiery mill. At Yucca Flat, sixty-five miles northwest of Las Vegas, in the desert of southern Nevada, there is a bit of action. Neither the tight security watch that is maintained over the government-owned proving ground nor the distance between it and Las Vegas, where I spent considerable time both before and after attending the shot at Yucca Flat, has prevented taxpayers in the vicinity from getting at least a sketchy idea of the nature of the product they are helping to finance. On numerous occasions since the proving ground was started in the winter of 1951, a piercing flash of light, many times the intensity of the sun's, has burst over the proving ground in the very early morning, momentarily transforming a gloomy Nevada dawn to a dazzling noon. The same light, pale and diminished, has been seen simultaneously as far away as San Diego, on the Pacific Coast, and Kalispell, Montana—three hundred and fifty and a thousand miles, respectively, from the proving ground. The atomic clouds, with their unearthly hues, that accompany nuclear detonations have been plainly visible from Las Vegas, and sound, in the form of shock waves, has hurtled into this mecca of gamblers, divorcees, and elopers, cracking hotel walls and demolishing restaurant china. Merchants have seen the panes of their display windows shattered and strewn on the sidewalk. After one detonation, the owners of Allen & Hanson, a haberdashery, placed a barrel filled with plateglass fragments outside their shop and posted a sign over it: "ATOM BOMB SOUVENIRS—FREE!" Within an hour, the barrel was empty. At last reports, five hundred sixty-two people in this region have collected damages from the government, amounting to nearly fifty thousand dollars, and additional claims are pending. The detonation of one bomb broke a vase in Modesto, California, five hundred miles from the testing area.

Thanks to their new neighbor, Las Vegans have picked up a little physics. When they see an atomic flash in the sky, they immediately consult their watches, for they have learned that it takes the ensuing shock wave about seven minutes to reach their town from the proving ground. They know, too, that the low-pressure wave that follows a shock wave does not push windows in but sucks them out, and that the best thing to do to escape damage from both waves is to open a window or door. Despite all the rainless lightning and thunder the Las Vegans have been subjected to, it is possible to find among their other reactions a certain pride in their proximity to the proving ground. "It annoys me to read about some statesman saying that the *world* is living with the atomic bomb," a local divorce lawyer told me. "Damn it, it's not the world. It's Las Vegas."

Late in 1950, when word got around that the government was planning to detonate atomic bombs in the desert near Las Vegas, the news was greeted with as much enthusiasm as would have greeted the news that gambling, the principal local industry, had been legalized in California, the state from which the town draws its most prodigal players. The general feeling was that the near-by bombing range would scare visitors away, disastrously upsetting the local economy. In its own peculiar way, Las Vegas, at the time, was doing quite well. It had become so popular as a divorce center that some of its more optimistic inhabitants were looking forward to the day when it would pull even with Reno in that respect. An increasing number of couples from southern California, too impatient to bother with the blood tests required by their own state, were eloping to Las Vegas, to be married in such chapels as the Hitching Post, Gretna Green, and the Wee Kirk o' the Heather. (A typical sign outside one of these chapels reads, "ORGAN MUSIC—FLOWERS—PHOTOGRAPHS—IMMEDIATELY!") But while it would be bad enough to lose the marriage-and-divorce trade, Las Vegans were concerned above all lest the proving ground impair their town's standing as the gambling capital of the only state in the Union where gambling is legal. The gambling business in Las Vegas was flourishing. Western Air Lines was providing non-stop service for players from Los Angeles, three hundred miles away, and gambling members of the affluent movie crowd were showing up with gratifying regularity. Along the Strip—a short stretch of Highway 91, about two miles south of the center of town, that is flanked by the more elaborate hotel-casinos—the revenue from gambling was substantial enough to enable hosts to favor their patrons with lagniappe. Leading entertainers, such as Josephine Baker, Jimmy Durante, and Joe E. Lewis, could be seen going through their routines in hotel night clubs where there was never a cover or minimum charge, and the same hotels strove to outdo one another in the magnificence of the fare they provided on their so-called chuckwagons—buffets at which, from midnight to eight in the morning, the customers could help themselves to all they wanted for a mere dollar and a half. "If a man loses enough money, we'll even pay his fare back home," a stick man at the Thunderbird told me. "It's a wonderful town, all right! Where else can a fellow gamble all day, get drunk, go to sleep, get up at four in the morning, and find plenty of company when he walks into the lobby?"

On January 11, 1951, the government officially confirmed the reports of its plans to build the proving ground, and shortly thereafter the Las Vegas Chamber of Commerce printed up some publicity releases intended to allay the qualms of future visitors. One showed a girl sporting an Atomic Hairdo, the product of a Las Vegas beauty parlor. Another heralded the Atomic Cocktail, invented by a bartender in one of the hotels here, and consisting of equal parts of vodka, brandy, and champagne, with a dash of sherry. In a third, a girl wearing a Bikini suit was brandishing a Geiger counter as she checked the beard of a grizzled desert prospector for radioactivity. "The angle was to get people to think the explosions wouldn't be anything more than a gag," a Chamber of Commerce official explained to me.

During the early days of the proving ground, I was told, the heads of two or three of the casinos tentatively discussed some rather special civil-defense plans. "We were afraid the bombs might shake the tables so hard that the dice would be tipped over and the roulette balls would bounce out of one number into another," one of them recalled. "We thought we might have to post signs warning players that in such an event the house man's ruling, as always, would be final." Such precautions were subsequently found to be unnecessary, and they would have been unavailing anyway on the one occasion when the physicists out at the proving ground did disturb Las Vegas gamblers. That was in November, 1951, when a plate-glass window near a crap game in the El Cortez Hotel was broken by a shock wave. The players turned briefly to see what had happened and, when they got back to their game, found that the pot was shy twenty dollars.

As word of what was in store for Las Vegas spread, motoring tourists began making it a point to stop there long enough to shop for merchandise, which, they calmly explained, they wanted not for utility but as mementos of a town that archeologists would in all probability soon be exploring. "It got to be pretty grim," a salesman at the local Sears, Roebuck store said to me. "One morning during those last days of waiting, an elderly lady from Los Angeles came in and told me to hurry up and sell her two shirts, that her husband was waiting outside in the car with the motor running. She said she wanted to hand them down to her grandsons, as heirlooms that had come from Las Vegas just before it was wiped off the face of the earth."

To add to the general apprehension, it began to appear that the Commission had decided not to make known in advance the hour, or even the day, when its bombs were to be exploded (a policy it later discarded). Provoked by this, some Las Vegans, upon learning that the local office of the Civil Aeronautics Authority would be responsible for clearing air lanes near the proving ground several hours prior to a detonation, took to calling that office daily, pretending to be pilots of private or commercial planes and asking for the latest reports. Others called the Bonanza Air Lines, in Las Vegas, to inquire whether its Reno-bound flights, which would be halted by the C.A.A. when a shot was impending, were leaving on schedule. The movements of known scientists staying at Las Vegas hotels were carefully observed by bellhops and guests. "It got so that, besides worrying about gambling takes, we were worrying about our own skins," a hotel manager told me.

The members of the Atomic Energy Commission, being quite unconcerned about either the marriage-and-divorce business or the comings and goings of gamblers, proceeded unhesitatingly with their project, convinced that they had chosen a site that was ideal for their purpose. To be sure, the Commission already had a proving ground at Eniwetok, out in the Pacific, but that was five thousand miles from its weapons headquarters, at Los Alamos, New Mexico. While the isolation Eniwetok affords was—and still is—considered advisable for the testing of certain bombs, the A.E.C. people felt that the majority of shots, to use the trade term, could be safely run off closer to home. Ralph Carlyle Smith, the Assistant Director of the Los Alamos Scientific Laboratory, enumerated for me some of the considerations that prompted them to establish the Nevada proving ground. "It's a terrible waste of valuable time to have our scientists spend all those days traveling to and from Eniwetok," he said. "Since the island is hardly within commuting distance of New Mexico, whenever they go there, they stay there—for six months or so, without their families or any of the amenities of life. And it's a nuisance to have to keep the island free of pests by continually spraying it from the air. Screens are useless there. The corrosion caused by that tropical climate is something fierce. I've seen buildings practically disintegrate before my eyes. Apart from all this, it's important for us to be near our laboratories, with their instruments. Some of the radioactive samples that have to be analyzed are extremely short-lived."

The Nevada site, which, as at least one of the blasts has proved, is within hearing distance of Los Alamos, had several things besides its handiness to recommend it, Smith went on. Consisting of six hundred and forty square miles of unpopulated land, it was looked upon as large enough to accommodate experiments with most kinds of atomic weapons. By the time radiation resulting from the explosions reached the nearest inhabited places, the A.E.C. figured, it would be sufficiently dissipated to cause no ill effects. (The A.E.C. also figured that if radiation in lethal strength *should* drift toward populated areas, there would be ample time to alert and evacuate the threatened citizens.) Furthermore, it was felt that delays caused by the weather would be fewer in the equable desert climate than in most other parts of the United States. Because rain tends to concentrate radiation, the desert's scant rainfall was regarded as an asset. So was the circumstance that strong winds, capable of carrying radioactive matter quickly to populated areas, are rare in this part of Nevada. And the almost daily clear blue skies over the desert would simplify the task of Air Force crews charged with precision bombing and with the tracking and sampling of atomic clouds. Moreover, the tract was already owned by the government (it had been bought during the war for an Air Force bombing range), so it would cost the Commission nothing. Finally, Las Vegas was considered both near enough to and far enough away from the proving ground—near enough for supplies to be delivered to the freight yards of the Union Pacific Railroad, on the town's outskirts, and for its population, of twenty-five thousand, to furnish the labor needed for constructing and maintaining the proving ground, and far enough away to insure the isolation required for reasons not only of safety but of security. "Out on the desert, anything that moves, animal or human, is an event," Smith said. "It can be seen for miles."

On January 26, 1951, the Commission let it be known that two nights earlier there had been a "dry run" to test the proving ground's communications and other facilities. At this point, the atmosphere of suspense in Las Vegas became almost unbearable, but it was dispelled at dawn the next day by an incredibly brilliant flash and, seven minutes later, a whacking blast that left a trail of broken glass from downtown Las Vegas clear out to the Strip. Operation Ranger—the name the A.E.C. gave its first series of tests—was under way. Most of the residents were awakened by tumbling window shades and shaking walls; some of them were tossed out of bed. Nobody was hurt, but one of the town's two daily newspapers, the *Review-Journal,* indulged its readers' dire expectations with the front-page headline "VEGANS ATOMIZED." All that day, there was worried speculation as to whether this might be only a tame curtain-raiser, but on the following morning a second shot came off and turned out to be no worse, and the atomized Vegans began to take their obstreperous neighbor in stride. Some of them expressed their relief by filing damage claims, of varying validity. Several home-owners declared that the shock waves had cracked the walls of their houses, but in more than one instance investigators found an accumulation of dust and cobwebs in the fissures. Others wanted reparations for broken water pipes, a few of which had obviously been corroding for years. The government was asked to provide new roofs to replace roofs that had been patched and repatched. A rancher in an area where no shock wave had struck charged that his chimney had been shaken loose and his house set on fire. A hermit living miles from town complained that his farm implements had been stolen "in the general excitement."

Operation Ranger consisted of five shots, which occurred on an average of one every forty-eight hours. Out along the Strip, the gamblers and divorcees took to throwing what became known as dawn parties—drinking and singing sessions that began after midnight and ended, if there was a shot that morning, with the sight of the flash or, if there was no shot, by just petering out around breakfast time. The Desert Inn's Sky Room, a glass-enclosed cocktail lounge with a sweeping panoramic view, was an especially popular spot for dawn parties. "It was a wonderful place for what the customers wanted," a waitress there told me. "They could sit around and listen to our piano player and look out the big windows and see the pretty hotel fountain and the guests swimming in the pool and the traffic speeding by on Highway 91, and then, just when they were starting to get tired, the A-bomb." The patrons at bars without views had to keep on their toes. As a bartender in one of these places recalled one afternoon, "Some fellow who'd been sitting around with his girl all night would suddenly look at his watch and say, 'Guess it's time for the bomb.' They'd grab their drinks and dash out, and then the rest of the crowd would follow them. After the damn thing went off, they'd all disappear, but by that time we'd have done more business than if we had television out here."

One night early in February, at the proving ground, Carroll L. Tyler, the Test Manager, and Dr. Graves, the Test Director, received a weather report from their meteorologists that led them to postpone a shot originally scheduled for the coming dawn. The two officials drove back to Las Vegas, arriving at their hotel—it was the Last Frontier, and they were well known there—at about three in the morning. Before turning in, they decided to breakfast in the hotel's Gay Nineties Bar, which was jammed with the usual dawn-party set. They had hardly sat down when they had the place to themselves and a hotel official was at their table pleading with them never to stop by there at that time again. "He said that we should have gone right upstairs and that he'd have been delighted to present us with breakfast in our rooms," Tyler recalls.

The townspeople didn't go in for dawn parties. They had less turbulent ways of greeting the unnatural daylight that was breaking spasmodically over their community. "Around five-thirty in the morning, the lights would start going on in my neighborhood," I was told by Doris Leighton, who is an administrative assistant at the Nevada Construction Company, a contracting firm. "Some of us would come out on our porches with cups of coffee and wait there. We'd be wearing heavy wrappers, because those winter mornings were quite nippy, you know. Sometimes husbands would back their cars out of the garage and into the street to get a better view. They'd let the motor run until the car was warm, and then their families would come out and join them. I used to see parents pinching small children and playing games with them to keep them awake. I guess they wanted to make sure their kids would see history in the making. People all looked expectant, but in different ways. Some, you could see, were afraid. Others smiled and acted nonchalant."

"There was one dawn test I saw from a rooftop, and I'll never forget it," Mrs. Donald Lukens, the wife of a Las Vegas journalist, told me. "When I could see again after the blinding, terrifying flash, I was looking at the sun. It was just coming up over the mountains.

The sun, you know, isn't always kind to us here in the desert, but at that moment it seemed like an old friend. It made me feel safe."

Operation Ranger came to an end with a shot at dawn on February 6, 1951. The following October, the second series—Operation Buster-Jangle, seven shots—started up. During Operation Buster-Jangle, Las Vegans displayed little of their earlier skittishness. Less worried now about their own skins, they showed a tendency to regard the proving ground as a good thing. Many heads of families were holding down steady, well-paying jobs with the Commission, and, far from scaring visitors away, the experiments, and the resulting publicity, were actually attracting more. To the joy of the shopkeepers, many of the new visitors turned out to be of a different breed from the accustomed ones who passed up the town in favor of the Strip and spent their time and money out there. Now Las Vegas was besieged by people who cared little about room service and gambling; they bought their own groceries, and cooked them in trailers or motels. They were not interested in getting married or divorced; they simply wanted to be on hand for an explosion. When a detonation was in prospect (by this time the Commission was disclosing its plans), they got into their autos and, along with numbers of Las Vegans, headed for Mount Charleston, a forty-two-hundred-foot vantage point about fifty miles southeast of the test area. "Bumper to bumper, just like a ball game," an attendant at a gas station along the way said in describing the cavalcade.

Meanwhile, business at the big hotels was excellent, too. "I don't know exactly how much the bomb had to do with it, but around shot time the play in our casino seemed to go up and the drinking got heavier," I was told by Wilbur Clark, the head of the Desert Inn. "The curious thing was that guests would drive here from Los Angeles to see a shot and then not bother to look at it. I'd instruct my pitmen to let the players at their tables know when it was about time for the flash, but the players would go right on with their games."

A shot that took place on the morning of November 1st, sent Las Vegas its most jolting shock. Over two hundred damage claims were filed as a result—a record number at the time. "That was another time we had an especially good take on gambling," Clark recalled. "Same for liquor. Hell, I took an extra drink myself."

Most of the shots of the second series went off between 7 and 8 A.M., instead of at dawn, but that was no bar to dawn parties. One of the parties turned out to have nothing to celebrate, but everybody there had a fine time just the same. "That was quite a night," Ted Mossman, the pianist at the Sky Room, told me one evening. "Standing room only. They were drinking like fish. Some of them had cameras for photographing the flash—a thing they couldn't have done even if they'd been sober. It's too bright. Everyone wanted to sing. They requested all the old numbers—'Margie,' 'The Sidewalks of New York,' 'Bye, Bye, Blackbird,' 'Put Your Arms Around Me, Honey.' They sang as if they were on a ship and it was going down—loud, desperate voices. After a while, I couldn't take it any more, so I improvised some boogie-woogie that I called 'The Atom-Bomb Bounce.' I kept playing it and playing it, until I thought my fingers would fall off. Seven o'clock in the morning, we get word there's been a circuit failure out at the proving ground and the bomb's called off. The crowd took the news fine. They all started betting when the next bomb would be exploded—the week, the day of the week, the hour of the day."

By no means everyone in Las Vegas and its environs has become resigned to the Commission's activities. Certainly no one can blame a rancher by the name of Carroll, whose water hole was found to be dangerously close to the test area, if he is inclined to bridle at the mere mention of the A.E.C. Carroll had already had to move his herds once, back in 1945, when the Manhattan District requisitioned his grazing land in New Mexico for the first atom-bomb test. When the authorities informed him he would have to move a second time, and why, it was almost too much for him. "Oh, Lord, no, not again!" he cried out as he grasped the significance of the deputation that had come to wait upon him. Some of the A.E.C.'s security guards turned cowhand for a day to help drive Carroll's cattle to a new range, but that did little to assuage the rancher's exasperation.

Among the other people who wish the government had located its proving ground elsewhere, some are convinced that a variety of melancholy events are attributable to the explosions. There is a tendency among people who have recently been afflicted with any disease to blame it on the bomb. Governor Charles Russell, of Nevada, told me that one Las Vegan had written to warn him that if the explosions weren't discontinued soon, the minds of southern Nevadans would be addled by the tremendous light and sound waves. The Governor also said that he knows of an old prospector who is living in perpetual dread lest his small outcropping be hit by a bomb. A woman in California has telephoned the Governor several times to express her conviction, in the face of his repeated denials, that federal prisoners are deliberately being exposed to the weapon's radiation, "like the mice and goats on Bikini." The experiments were widely regarded as responsible for the winter's abnormal severity in northern Nevada in 1952. During one particularly cold spell, nine manganese miners, whose work was being hampered by snow and ice, petitioned Governor Russell to put a stop to the detonations, and he, in turn, asked some meteorologists at the University of Nevada to look into the matter. They assured him that, far from being localized, the bad weather conditions prevailed throughout Montana and the Dakotas, and, as far as they knew, had nothing to do with the bombs.

Still, the Governor said, every now and then, while reading his mail, he finds himself wondering who is right—the nuclear physicists or his correspondents. "The whole field of atomic energy is so new," he went on. "Perhaps the scientists will eventually come around to agreeing with the beliefs of some of the people who write to me. But no matter who's right, it's exciting to think that the submarginal land of the proving ground is furthering science and helping national defense," the Governor added. "We had long ago written off that terrain as wasteland, and today it's blooming with atoms."

After a third series of shots had come and gone, the predominant attitude in Las Vegas toward the proving ground was one of casualness. In fact, that series, which ended in June 1952, was generally dismissed as having been something of a dud. There were eight shots, and none of them gave the town more than a mild tremor. Only twenty-odd damage claims were filed. The townspeople didn't bother to climb up on their rooftops to sight billowing atomic clouds, and dawn parties went out of style. "Bigger bombs, that's what we're waiting for," said one night-club proprietor. "Americans have to have their kicks." The local A.E.C. offices, according to Marjorie Allen, a secretary there, received several complaints that the third series was a let-down. "After one of our shots, we got a phone call from a sweet old man who had heard about this grousing and was afraid we were taking it to heart," Miss Allen went on. "He just wanted to let us know that he'd been fishing out at Lake Mead at the time of the shot and that the shock wave had come in nice and strong there."

Many Las Vegans had become nostalgic connoisseurs, pining for the days of the unannounced, robust dawn shots of Operation Ranger. "Good bangs, and so pretty coming at sunrise like they did" is the way one veteran recalled the early tests. Others, less aesthetically inclined, fondly remembered the concussive quality of the November 1st shot. One day during the third series, Joe McClain, a columnist for the *Review-Journal,* which once had Las Vegans atomized, used his space to accuse the A.E.C. of "gypping its public."

> Time was when a nuclear detonation took place, people knew about it [McClain wrote] . . . People seemed to enjoy the show. But the good old days of Operation Ranger have passed. The scientists, to speak loosely, seem to have a little more control on the old fireball . . . Yesterday afternoon we had several calls wondering when "the A-bomb was going off." The people were real sore when they learned it already had been detonated. We think it might be good for the town's spirit if the scientists would send a few effects down Vegas way. Just to keep people happy.

At present, Las Vegas is a shrill, restless resort town. While this is as true when tests are not in progress as when they are, Chamber of Commerce officials and hotel people attribute the community's present condition in large part to the publicity that the proving ground has given it. "We're in the throes of acute prosperity," one hotel man informed me. "Before the proving ground, people just heard that this was a wide-open town. Now that we're next door to the atom bomb, they really believe it." The pangs of prosperity are especially perceptible to visitors trying to book rooms in Strip hotels. Even when one of them is successful in making a reservation, his triumph may not last if the degree of his gambling isn't sufficiently impressive. While I was visiting Las Vegas, an acquaintance of mine who was staying at one of the larger hotels was hailed by a desk clerk as he passed through the lobby, and brusquely asked to give up his room. The guest took the matter up with a managerial assistant, who simply said, "We've got a ten-thousand-dollar player waiting for that room. What do you think keeps the doors open?" The guest packed up and left. At another hotel, an Eastern scientist, just arrived in Las Vegas for the first time, felt that he was on the verge of landing a room when, spotting some crapshooters in the lobby, he was reminded of a mathematical technique known in scientific circles as the Monte Carlo method and used by physicists to estimate the odds on such eventualities as a neutron's escaping from a pile or causing fission. He started discoursing on this to the desk clerk, whose face at once took on a bored expression. "I informed him that I preferred gambling with the Monte Carlo method, a rather ingenious form of nuclear craps," the scientist told me later. "The next thing I knew, he was informing *me* that he had a lot of mail to sort—and no rooms."

Some of the scientists, however, are on occasion quite willing to indulge in the more conventional forms of gambling. The evening following a shot, when the strain under which they have been working eases up for a while, they are likely to be far less interested in computing nuclear odds by the Monte Carlo method than in letting off steam by the accepted Las Vegas method. At such times, a number of them are to be seen playing blackjack in the casino of the Last Frontier. There they while away the evening at the green baize tables, sipping highballs and chain-smoking. They weigh the purchase of a card with as much concentration as if they were pondering a problem in nucleonics, and become too absorbed to take notice of the crowd around them—townspeople who, having watched the hotel's night-club show for the price of a cup of coffee, are killing a few dollars at the slot machines; divorcees in long evening dresses, cheerfully rolling dice; shrewd-faced Hollywood figures at the roulette wheels; impecunious soldiers ordered to Nevada for atomic maneuvers, who play blackjack vicariously by staring at the cards in the gambler's hands. Finally, soothed by the unpredictability of the cards, the scientists go off to their rooms. On such evenings, when the scientists are at the Last Frontier and it may be taken for granted that no atomic bomb will explode in the desolate wilderness to the northwest, Las Vegas, for all the heavy play at its tables, seems less of a gambling town than usual.

CHAPTER 19 | MARCH, 1953

THE COMING THING

WHILE AMERICA'S SUPPLY of nuclear weapons may be the largest in the world, the same cannot be said of its known deposits of uranium, that essential raw material from which the bombs, as well as more salutary applications of atomic energy, are manufactured. Indeed, a large part of the radioactive material that is going into American atomic piles comes from the Shinkolobwe mine in the Belgian Congo. Canada, thanks to extensive deposits at Great Bear Lake, in the Northwest Territories, is also providing the United States with many tons of uranium. Another of the world's important sources of uranium is the Erzgebirge region in Saxony and Czechoslovakia, but that, unfortunately for us, is under Soviet control. While America's supplies are adequate at present, the Atomic Energy Commission has felt from the start that the United States ought to develop its own uranium deposits with the utmost speed in order to make itself as little dependent as possible on foreign sources. Any number of unpleasant contingencies might disrupt the steady flow of ore from abroad; a Congo dictator might emerge to make hash of the Commission's atomic planning, or Canada might expand its nuclear research to a point where it would feel justified in holding back the greater part of its uranium for its own use. And, of course, no one knows how the outbreak of another world war might affect America's uranium imports.

Since 1948 the Commission, as a result of this edgy feeling, has been urging American prospectors to make an exhaustive search for uranium at home. By way of inducement, the government is paying a far better price for uranium than private industry did before the war, when uranium was used primarily for such amiable non-essential purposes as coloring pottery and tinting false teeth. (The Commission now strictly limits the amount of uranium that the nation's manufacturers may use for non-military purposes.) Mine-owners are being paid double for their first ten thousand pounds of uranium oxide—the chemical compound in terms of which the uranium content of the ore is assayed—to get them digging. These and similar incentives have started a uranium rush of some magnitude. Indians are roaming the desolate western canyons in search of rock formations bearing the yellow markings that indicate deposits; having spent their lives in this wild region and being free of preconceived ideas about geology, the Indians have proved particularly adept at finding uranium in unlikely rock formations. Veteran prospectors, who until recently were panning streams for gold, are now concentrating on uranium. Amateur prospectors have bought themselves Geiger counters and are taking to the hills in their spare time. (There are several models, each of which employs one or more of three ways of showing that its owner is on the right track—flashing lights, a dial indicator, and a clicking mechanism with earphones attached; the Super Sniffer, a $49.50 job turned out by the Nuclear Chemical & Instrument Corporation, in Chicago, is a popular beginners' model that both clicks and lights up.) It is not uncommon for families in some of the Western states, in which uranium seems to exist more abundantly than elsewhere, to take along their counters, together with their thermos bottles, when they set out for a day in the country. A year ago, an archeologically-minded North Dakota couple were looking for pictographs when their counter, which they had taken with them as a matter of routine, set up a feverish clicking that led them to a find that turned out to be far more rewarding, in a material sense, than any pictograph they may have missed in their excitement. An Arizona plumber underwent a comparable experience. After a luckless day of fishing in a small reservoir, he was trudging back to his car with his rod and his counter when, casually slipping on his earphones and flicking the switch, he, too, heard the rapid clicking. The next day, he returned to the spot with pick and shovel, started digging, and came upon an extensive deposit of uranium. A dentist in Grand Junction, Colorado, has learned that one way to distract patients whose teeth he is about to drill is to tell them how smoothly the drilling operations in a small uranium mine he owns across the state line in Utah are coming along.

While, thanks to the Commission's efforts, uranium is being discovered in a number of areas widely scattered throughout the country, the great bulk of what the United States is now mining domestically comes out of the Colorado Plateau—a region that has lured prospectors ever since the West was settled. The plateau, which has an area of a hundred and thirty thousand square miles, spreads out in all directions from the point where Colorado, Utah, Arizona, and New Mexico meet and includes some of the most rugged terrain in the United States—grim, seemingly limitless expanses of desert sand and forbidding ranges of sheer, snow-capped mountains, some of whose so far unscaled heights are tantalizingly believed to be studded with uranium. The plateau has its roads, but they are few, narrow, tortuous, and unpaved. It is for the most part a trackless as well as a waterless waste, and the living conditions of the men hacking away at its rocky fastnesses are exceedingly primitive.

It was Dr. Phillip L. Merritt, the assistant director for exploration of the Commission's Division of Raw Materials, which has offices in New York, who arranged for me to travel by car and rail through this geologist's dreamland, mostly in the company of a couple of notably well-informed officials, so that I could see how operations are progressing in America's biggest uranium field. The starting point of my trip was to be Grand Junction, a town of fourteen thousand people, where the Commission maintains an operations office, and Dr. Merritt gave me the names of several geologists to look up there. Upon my arrival at the Grand Junction headquarters, situated in a two-story building near the Gunnison River, I asked my way of a man I encountered just inside the door, and found I was talking to one of them—Mike Reinhardt, a stocky, middle-aged fellow who is a Commission staff geologist. "We've been expecting you," he said. "Welcome to the great outdoors. I don't see how anyone lives in New York." As we walked down a corridor, he informed me that my guide for the first part of the trip, to the Navajo reservation in

Arizona, would be Dr. Robert J. Wright, the assistant chief geologist; when we reached Indian country, I would be taken in tow by Jack Leonard, one of the Commission's liaison men with the Navajos. Reinhardt showed me into Wright's office, which was empty at the moment. We sat down to wait for Wright, and Reinhardt gave me some pointers about my forthcoming journey.

The first thing Reinhardt told me was that I shouldn't expect to find the uranium miners primarily motivated, as they toiled away, by any brightly burning concern over the international situation. "Uranium is strictly a living to them, and not an easy one, either," he said. The ore they mine, he went on, has to contain at least one-tenth of one per cent of uranium to qualify for purchase by the government; anything less requires too much processing to make it economically worth while. He pointed out that while many laymen are under the impression that there isn't much uranium in the world, that's far from being the case. It occurs in many common types of rock and, for that matter, in sea water and most drinking water, but generally in such minute quantities that the outlay for machinery and chemicals would not be justified.

Of course, Reinhardt continued, there are grades of ore far richer than those ordinarily found on the plateau. "A mineralized tree, now, there's a real find," he said. "I mean one in which geological processes have replaced the original vegetable tissues with uranium. The uranium content of such a tree sometimes runs to fifteen or twenty per cent. Two of them, I believe, once netted a miner a total of a quarter of a million dollars." These arboreal bonanzas, which are estimated to be around a hundred and twenty million years old, are the result of tremendous geological changes, Reinhardt explained. The first of these was the Triassic period, an arid era that lasted twenty million years. This was followed by the equally long Jurassic period, when the sea covered much of western North America, among other areas. Then, eighty million years ago, the Laramide Revolution, perhaps the earth's greatest upheaval, took place. It was the Laramide's violence, Reinhardt said, that molded the Andes and the Rockies and also twisted the Colorado Plateau into what he termed "its weird, contorted uplift."

By and large, Reinhardt added, the ore thus far discovered on the plateau hasn't been nearly as good as the ore received from the Belgian Congo. This is because the African uranium is found in veins—exceptionally rich ones, too—of pitchblende, a mineral that contains the element in a purer, more concentrated form than does carnotite, the mineral in which most of it is found in the United States. Unlike pitchblende, which runs in narrow, more or less vertical veins, carnotite frequently spreads out horizontally on surface rock, or rimrock—a fact that has caused uranium prospecting on the plateau to become known colloquially as "walking the rim."

Suggesting that we look at some ore specimens, Reinhardt led me to a table at one end of Wright's office, on which was a collection of mineral fragments, along with a Geiger counter. Reinhardt handed me a small chunk of rough black rock, which, for its size, was extremely heavy. "From the Congo—pitchblende," he said. "As you can see, black as pitch, which accounts for its name." He took the pitchblende from me, hefted it fondly for a moment, and then gave me a piece of carnotite to hold. It was a bright mustard yellow, and much lighter in weight than the pitchblende. As I gripped it, a bit of it crumbled in my hand. "Carnotite's quite friable," Reinhardt said. "In the pure state, uranium is steel gray, but it always comes mixed up with one or more other metals—copper, silver, cobalt, nickel, lead, vanadium. Prospectors on the plateau used to go after carnotite for its vanadium, but now that the word's out that there's a good uranium market, the vanadium, important as it is, has become more or less incidental." He picked up the Geiger counter and switched it on, holding it close to the specimens on the table. The instrument flashed its tiny bulbs like an agitated pinball machine as it measured the amount of radiation of various ores. "Well, that's what it's all about," Reinhardt said, and switched the counter off.

The drive for uranium was coming along fairly well, Reinhardt told me as we resumed our seats. He said that he was not permitted to give out production figures but that the rate at present is several times what it was when the government's prospecting program was initiated in 1948. He had an idea that the rate would pick up even more as time went on and the prospectors got the hang of modern ways of searching for uranium. A few of the prospectors, he added, were successful professional men who had come to the plateau from big cities to escape civilization, and occasionally it took them a while to settle down to the job at hand. "They enjoy poking around on a mesa, where there's no one within ten miles and they haven't any appointments to keep or any other obligations," Reinhardt said. "That's one of the joys of prospecting, all right, but a bigger one is finding something, and usually it doesn't take them long to realize that." He went on to say that prospectors of the old school seem to have as hard a time as they have traditionally had in holding on to the money they earn, and told me about one old-timer who had recently got hold of six hundred dollars. Returning in his jalopy to his home town, a plateau settlement with a population of fifty, where he owed money to half the inhabitants, the prospector got out, hailed a youngster, handed him the six hundred dollars, and told him to trail him down the middle of the town's one street. In each doorway stood a highly vocal creditor, and at each dunning the prospector would call grandly over his shoulder "Pay the man!" and the lad would peel off the proper number of bills. By the time that brief stroll was over, the old-timer had hardly enough money left to buy a drink.

Reinhardt said he thought his own contingent of geologists was setting a good example for the independent prospectors. There were thirty-nine of these geologists, many just out of college, swarming all over the plateau, and they represented a new kind of prospector, versed in geology and skilled in the use of technical equipment. "They never make a move without a Geiger counter," Reinhardt said. "One of those counters weighs fifteen pounds in the morning and feels like a ton by nightfall, and there are still some prospectors who won't use them. They consider them new-fangled contraptions, and just look for the color of the rock, as they did when they went after copper and so on in the old days." Most of his geologists have made at least one strike, Reinhardt said, but for them it's all in the day's work. Their job is to scout for areas that look promising enough to be investigated further. They're what might be called prospectors' prospectors. They receive no extra pay for their discoveries and no royalties on whatever uranium is extracted from their finds. Whenever preliminary drilling on a site of theirs indicates that it is worth developing, the government leases the prospective mine to a private operator. So far, Reinhardt said, the cost of the drilling has been offset by the money the government has received for the leases.

The Commission's geologists do some of their prospecting in light planes equipped with extremely sensitive counters. (No radium paint is used on the dials of the planes' instruments lest the counters be led astray.) The planes skim the mountainsides, and whenever one of their counters detects radiation, a geologist accompanying the pilot bombs the spot with bags of flour to mark it for the scouting parties who will later approach it on foot. Most of the prospecting, however, is done by jeep or on horseback. Reinhardt was pleased with the way the young geologists have adapted themselves to the rigors of life on the plateau. "That's something that has little to do with a college degree," he said. "The majority of them have been used to soft living at home and in Ivy League schools. They may have majored in geology at college, but until they get here their knowledge of it is pretty theoretical. Fortunately, their interest in the subject seems to keep them going during those first few tough months out on the plateau, when survival rather than exploration is their chief worry." The country is so treacherous, Reinhardt said, that he insists his geologists always work in pairs. That turned out to be a well-founded precaution on at least one occasion, when a young Yale man, who had only recently arrived on the scene, fell off a ledge and started to roll down a rocky slope toward a sheer precipice. His partner, a University of California graduate, was standing a few feet from him, and grabbed him just in time.

"They soon catch on," Reinhardt continued, with some pride. "Before long, they're covering fifteen miles a day in deep-canyon country and snaking jeeps out of quicksand with no more trouble than they used to have changing a tire. They tramp through country where it's pretty certain no white man has ever been before and probably very few Indians. Still, you never can be sure. Every now and then, just when a couple of our boys are patting each other on the back and telling themselves that they're the first human beings ever to reach some all but inaccessible spot, they come on the name 'Wetherill' scratched on a rock, and that really takes the wind out of their sails." He went on to explain that during the latter part of the nineteenth century and the early years of this one there were four

Wetherill brothers—Richard, John, Alfred, and Clayton—who spent a good deal of their time scouting for Indian ruins on the Colorado Plateau and who had a habit, disconcerting to latter-day would-be pioneers, of leaving behind incontestable evidence of their wanderings. "It's a letdown for our fellows," Reinhardt said. "They get all the way into the worst kind of remote country and what do they find? A message from one of Kilroy's predecessors."

Reinhardt was embarking on a philosophic soliloquy about how New Yorkers would benefit in body and soul if they moved West and started looking for uranium when Dr. Wright entered the office. He is a youthful, prematurely bald Ohioan, who was formerly an assistant professor of geology at St. Lawrence University, in Canton, New York. He seemed harried and distracted, and after quickly arranging to pick me up next morning at my hotel, he turned to a pile of correspondence on his desk. "Paper work, paper work!" he said grimly. "Geologists were never meant to be indoors."

When I climbed into Wright's Ford sedan the following morning, I found him a changed man. "Nice to be getting out of this headquarters town," he said jovially, stepping on the accelerator. "We probably won't be stopping anywhere for lunch, so I brought along a few sandwiches. Better have a last look at the metropolis. You won't see anything like it for the next few days." Presently, as he guided the car up a spiraling road into wild, mountainous country, he began exuberantly greeting each geological formation we passed as if it were an old friend. "The Morrison Salt Wash!" he exclaimed as an eroded mass of rock, perhaps a thousand feet high, came into view. "That's a sedimentary Jurassic rock." Twenty minutes later, after we swung around a hairpin turn, Wright delightedly introduced me to the Brushy Basin, a sloping series of mudstone ledges. Then the sight of another geological masterpiece filled him with such pleasure that he stopped the car for two or three minutes to contemplate it. This was a manifestation of the Dakota Formation, which is a hundred million years old.

After his joy at being outdoors again had subsided, Wright, settling down to the grind of negotiating the rough, serpentine road, outlined my itinerary. I would be proceeding in a general southwesterly direction, he said, and the trip, which would take four days, would enable me to have a look at the two principal types of uranium areas on the plateau. One was the old-established mining region, where metals of various kinds had been dug out of the ground for over a century; we were traveling through that country now. The other was the region where the Indians were making their uranium finds, most of it in Arizona, but some of it extending well into New Mexico, as far as the town of Grants, which, Wright said, would be my last stop. At Grants, I would meet Paddy Martinez, a part-Mexican, part-Navajo sheepherder who had astounded geologists by discovering a tremendous uranium deposit in a limestone formation called the Todilto, on Haystack Mountain, twenty miles west of the town. "We were taught at school that uranium was extremely unlikely to occur in sedimentary rock of the limestone type, like the Todilto," Wright said. "I'm glad Paddy didn't take the same courses. The Indians have gone looking for carnotite figuring they might find it anywhere, and they've proved to be the program's secret weapon." He went on to say that Jack Leonard, who was to be my guide for part of the second half of the journey, had a downright gift for getting the Navajos interested in prospecting. "I wish I could drive on to Grants myself," Wright told me. "But there's always that paper work waiting for me back in Grand Junction. Anyway, I'll have a couple of days away from the office."

Three hours out of Grand Junction, we came upon the first settlement along our route—a pretty hamlet called Gateway, which has a population of sixty-five and lies in a canyon beside a small stream. Here was also the first water of any consequence we had encountered. Stands of poplar and cottonwood trees surrounded the village—signs of fertility that were almost startling after the stark, treeless country through which we had been driving all morning.

In a matter of seconds, we had passed through Gateway and were back in the mute wilderness of the plateau. After a few miles, we came to a steep downgrade where the road seemed to me to get much narrower, but that impression may very well have been caused by the fact that pressing in on Wright's side was an enormous, wall-like mountain and on my side, with perhaps two feet to spare, was the edge of a cliff that dropped precipitously several hundred feet to the silvery surface of a turbulent river. For ten minutes, Wright drove on gingerly, his jaws tense and his arms rigid, and then the mountains fell back on one side and the cliff on the other, and no parkway ever looked as gratifyingly broad to me as our road did at that moment. The mountains on either side of us now loomed taller and had sharper contours than the ones we had been driving through earlier. Wright, whenever he could, scanned them attentively. "There's a mine!" he said at last. "That's what I've been looking for." He slowed the car to a crawl and pointed out a small, blackish indentation near a dirty-white summit some five hundred feet above us. "It's impossible to tell from this distance whether there's anybody working up there," he went on. "All I hope is that they're not ten-day miners—men who quit after ten days or so and don't come back again till they've spent their money. Some of them do that in the privately owned mines. With those who are leasing from the government, of course, it's a different matter." Wright gave the mine another look and shook his head. "I still find it hard to believe that those measly black spots have anything to do with atomic bombs," he said. "Why, most of them are hardly any bigger than gopher holes, and usually no more than two to six men are needed to work them. Maybe a couple of hundred of them in all, on the whole plateau, with funny names like Buzzards' Roost and I Don't Know and Main Street. And that's the whole extent of one of the most important mining operations in the world! Oh, well, you never can tell how you'll get your uranium." As the car gathered speed, he added, "Did you ever know that the ore that made our first bombs possible came out of a Staten Island warehouse? It was stored there by a Belgian, a man named Edgar Sengier, who was the managing director of the Katanga mines in the Congo. Sengier didn't have anything specific in mind when he stored it there—certainly not the bomb. He was simply playing a hunch. He figured the Nazis would overrun Europe, so he shipped several tons of pitchblende to the United States, just on the chance that it might come in handy in some way or other against the Germans. The stuff lay there on Staten Island from 1940 until 1943, when the Manhattan District people, who were badly in need of it, heard about it and got hold of it. Sengier was awarded a Medal of Merit for his hunch. I guess it was one of the real breaks of the war."

Two hours out of Gateway, driving smoothly along on high ground, we looked down on the mill town of Uravan, which is owned by the United States Vanadium Company and is bisected by the San Miguel River, a stream that is rusty from the mine refuse that has been dumped into it for decades. The mill, the town's reason for being, was perched astride a hill, and we could hear crushed ore tumbling down an enclosed chute to the drying ovens. In the years just after the war, Wright said, Uravan had been well on the way to becoming a ghost town, because there were few orders for either of the products—uranium and vanadium—for which it was named, but then the government's intensified search for domestic uranium brought it prosperity. Now it is a purposeful-looking, if drab, community. "Population eight hundred, three telephones," Wright said. "One's in the general store, another's in the company's office, and the third's in the superintendent's home."

We turned in to a narrow side road to search for more gopher holes. After an hour, during which we ate our sandwiches as we drove, we had located two, but no one was around at either. "Guess they've made enough money for this month," Wright said irritably. A few minutes before four o'clock, which is quitting time in most of the mines, we arrived at one called Reserve Block 1. As soon as we got out of the car, a middle-aged derelict emerged from a make-shift shack and came shuffling toward us. "Living like a stinking coyote in this goddam country," he said. "I've worked as long as seventeen days in my time. I ain't no lousy ten-day miner." He turned in the direction of two men in their forties, who were standing some distance away in a welter of jackhammer drills, with an air compressor and a box of dynamite on one side of them and a narrow-gauge track supporting a small mine car on the other. "People!" he yelled to the pair, announcing us.

We approached the two men, the derelict trailing us valiantly. They were brothers, Cecil and Phil Bunker, to whom Reserve Block 1 had been leased by the Commission. Cecil, an earnest-looking man wearing a battered fedora, courteously said that he would have liked to show us through the mine but that we had arrived too late. Six men worked there, he explained, but the others had left for the day and he and his brother, following standard procedure at closing time, had just set off a charge of dynamite inside the shaft, creating fumes that would suffocate anybody who tried to enter. Their mine was producing nicely, he said, and he and Phil considered themselves lucky to be operating it; the Commission not only had discovered the mine but had given him and his brother a fair idea of how extensive the deposit was. "We should be busy here for maybe another couple of years," he said. "That's the kind of information it's darned valuable to have when you're mining uranium, because it's different from other kinds of mining. Sometimes when you're prospecting for uranium, you come across an outcrop that runs along for half a mile and you think you've got a real strike, but then you find there's nothing back of that yellow rim, and it's mined out in no time. It's a whole lot different from coal mining. Phil and I used to mine coal back home in Wilkes-Barre twenty years ago. We left there during the depression."

"Living like a stinking coyote," the derelict said again.

"He's our watchman," Cecil said in an apologetic tone.

"This is paradise compared to the way the miners are living in the back country," Phil said sternly, his eyes on the watchman. "Those guys are nowhere near towns the size of Uravan. They've got no machinery, like us—just wheelbarrows. And no beds—just sleeping bags." The watchman subsided, and Phil went on to say that another thing he and his brother liked about the uranium setup was the way the government guaranteed prices. "Now, lead, for instance," he began. He glanced at Cecil, and the two men laughed derisively. "Mining lead's like playing the stock market, the prices fluctuate so," Phil explained. "Then there's gold. Sure, gold's still pegged at thirty-five dollars an ounce, but, considering how costs have gone up and how hard it is to find the stuff, I'd say the price is pegged too low. We prospected for gold for years up around Victor, Colorado. No doubt about it, uranium's a much better deal nowadays. I guess the government won't ever get as much ore as it wants."

"I expect very few people know how much the government wants," Cecil said. "But they do say that this atomic energy is the coming thing."

"That's what we've heard," Phil said. "That's what makes me think we did right in quitting gold for uranium."

After we were back on the main road, Wright looked at his watch and said we'd have to keep driving steadily if we were to reach our first stopover point in time for a decent night's rest. That was Monticello, Utah, four hours away; there were no nearer overnight accommodations, he said. Halfway to Monticello, however, he relented when, thirsty and tired, we came upon a ramshackle store standing all alone on the edge of an immense plain. We went in and ordered Cokes. As we raised our bottles, the storekeeper, a beady-eyed middle-aged man, said to Wright, whom he obviously knew, "You want to see something?" Wright nodded, and the storekeeper went out back and returned with a jar of bright-yellow carnotite fragments, which he asked Wright to examine.

"They look pretty good," Wright said tentatively.

The storekeeper was delighted. "Darn right they do!" he said. "And there's plenty more where they came from. Man, this yellow runs on and on, and there's plenty back of the rim, too! I had a rough ride up the mountains in my jeep before I spotted it. But I'm not telling anyone else about it, leastwise after what happened a month ago." He gave us a conspiratorial smile. "A couple of fellows came into the store then for Cokes—just like you—and I showed them the jar," he continued. "They said they were oilmen from Oklahoma and they'd be back after they finished some business. I didn't tell them too much about where I found this stuff, but I figured they might be trying to get in ahead of me, so I went and posted a claim notice. I'm looking for a big boy who's not afraid to take a chance. I'll give him the land and take twenty per cent of the profits for myself, and I'm to be the manager and superintendent for five hundred a month. I've got something good, as sure as atomic energy is the coming thing."

As we drove away, Wright told me that the specimens looked promising but that he was skeptical about them because this part of the countryside had already been pretty thoroughly explored. "Good specimens are easy to come by on the plateau," he said. "People in these parts pass them around as souvenirs. Of course, if that fellow has really got something, the government would be glad to help him develop it, but I gather from talks I've had with him before that he doesn't want things that way and we can't force him to lead us to his find. What will happen, if he's not just enjoying a pipe dream, is that pretty soon this big boy of his will come back, or another one will show up, and put up the money. Then they'll start producing uranium ore, we'll start buying it, and everyone will be happy. Oh, well—anyway, we had our Cokes."

Now, far off in the distance, and for the rest of the waning day's journey, the jagged, snowy peaks of the La Sal Mountains, the tallest range we had yet seen, formed our vista. A blue haze lay over their ridges, a number of them more than twelve thousand feet high, and there was something vaguely inviting about them after the barren slopes that had flanked our route. At ten o'clock that night, the lights of Monticello shone below us, and Wright hurried the car downhill. When we reached level ground, we were on Highway 160, a paved road. "Feels slippery, doesn't it, after what we've been driving on all day?" Wright asked. "Well, here's our motel. Now for a bath."

Wright and I had only one objective the following day—to reach the Navajo trading post at Kayenta, Arizona, where I was to meet Leonard—but we were on the road early, and had time to make a short, unscheduled detour to a uranium mine operated by the Vanadium Corporation of America. This was a larger mine than Reserve Block 1, and looked out across a wide, swift-running stream toward some cliff-dwellers' ruins. Horses hitched to steel carts were being led into the mine entrance—a hole in the side of a mountain—and they came out again tugging loads of ore, which were transferred to trucks. From within the mine came the faint but industrious chatter of rock drills. The foreman, an alert-looking young man named Calvin Black, invited us to follow him inside. "We're finishing a mineralized tree," he said. "It's only three hundred feet in." He handed us helmets equipped with carbide lamps and told us to stick close behind him. The instant we passed the mouth of the mine, we were in a world of darkness. As my eyes became adjusted to it, I could make out several long, low-ceilinged corridors. Miners, their slanting silhouettes etched against the walls by their flickering lamps, pressed at the ends of the corridors with jackhammers whose din ricocheted through the passageways—an almost tangible sound.

Black led us down a corridor in which I could see no drillers, although, as we picked our way over its soft, uneven floor, I could hear the persistent noise of a jackhammer, coming from directly ahead and growing steadily louder. That, Black told us, was where the tree was being worked on. "We're drilling it from the opposite side," he said. "You can hear the drilling, all right, but you won't see any." When we reached the tree, Black detached the lamp from his helmet and held it close to the wall of the shaft. "There she is!" he shouted, above the racket of the jackhammer. The contours of the tree, which was horizontal, stood out plainly against the inky surface of the rest of the wall; a dirty yellow, it was about fifteen feet long and a foot wide. At the end where the tree's roots had been, the yellow ore spread out into several mottled strands. "She's a beauty!" Black shouted. "Sixty feet long when we found her!" Wright, peering through the gloom, nodded approvingly. Suddenly, the drill ceased its furious jabbing in the corridor beyond, and in the new stillness Black said, "I guess that means Pete's gone to lunch."

"If that tree had been growing annual rings all these years, there'd be ninety million of them," Wright said. "Dinosaurs probably nibbled off that tree."

I asked what kind of tree it had been. "It probably looked something like a palm," Wright replied. "It had no branches, and its leaves grew directly out of the top of its trunk—like a bouquet in a vase."

"Sure wish I owned her," Black said respectfully as we started making our way back to daylight. "She drives a Geiger counter wild. I'll bet we get six tons or more of really high-grade ore out of her."

Outside again, Black told us that once, while out prospecting, he had found a mineralized tree and cleared eighteen hundred dollars on it for only a few hours of labor. "Maybe I own a tree right now," he added. "I have six claims, but there's one in particular, about forty-five miles from my home town—Blanding, Utah—that I consider really promising. I haven't developed it yet, but I'm thinking about it pretty hard. I've got a good job here, but that tree we just looked at has made me a little restless. Uranium is all I've bothered with since I left high school five years ago, and I guess I've been lucky so far. I own ten thousand dollars' worth of mining equipment and a third interest in the Blanding Electric Company." He glanced at some of his fellow-miners who were eating lunch fifty feet away, on a ledge of rock. "Maybe they're restless, too," he said. "Every one of them has at least one claim somewhere. Come on over and say hello."

Black led us to the group and introduced me as a visitor from New York. "Say, you got any hot information on how to get rich mining?" a burly, sandy-haired miner asked me. The others roared with laughter.

"Feed your kids and keep your clothes on, that's all you can expect," a skinny, handsome man told him. "This mine's the end of the world."

"I've got two claims that I don't know what to do with," another man said. "I can't afford the equipment to develop them and I hate to sell out to the big companies and watch them clean up. There's no such thing as an independent miner."

"It ain't the companies," one of the others put in. "The government ought to pay better prices."

"All this damn griping!" said an older man, sitting off by himself. "Everybody knows mining's all we'll ever do the rest of our lives."

The remainder of the day's trip was uneventful. We soon passed through the Mormon village of Bluff, and after that for a while a desert spread out before us like a vast sandy beach, except that it was dotted here and there by the clustered leaves of yucca plants. A few miles farther on, there was a short stretch of Navajo sandstone—a prettily scalloped, reddish-brown rock, worn smooth by the winds. Still farther on, we saw a waterless river course that wound gracefully in and out among the bases of mesas that had been marvelously whorled by thousands of years of erosion. At about this point, we passed a sign, planted in the sand, that read, "DO NOT DUMP GARBAGE HERE."

Arriving in Kayenta late that night, we found that Leonard had already turned in and had left word with the proprietor of the trading post there that he'd like me to meet him at his jeep station wagon out back at six-thirty the following morning. "Jack's car has two coyote tails hanging from the radiator cap," the proprietor said. "You can't miss it." I told Wright as we walked to our rooms that there was no need for him to get up that early, and that I would introduce myself to Leonard. Then I thanked him for all he had done for me, and we said good night and goodbye.

Even at six-thirty in the morning, I found it easy to like Leonard. An amiable, quiet-spoken, blue-eyed man of nearly forty, he had an unmistakable air of reliability about him that at once commanded respect. It was his reliability, in fact, that had necessitated our getting under way at such an early hour. As we set out in the jeep, Leonard explained that two Navajos, a father and son, were expecting him that morning at their home near Cameron, three hours away. They had a find for him to inspect, and he hadn't felt it wise to change the hour of the appointment. "If you give them reason to believe that you don't keep your word, they'll ignore you forever," Leonard told me. "That's because they've been rooked so often on the sale of their sheep's wool, silver jewelry, and rugs. Nobody likes to be rooked, but the average Navajo family—and that's usually seven or eight people—lives on about four hundred dollars a year, so a little rooking means a lot to them. Just let a small misunderstanding grow up between the Navajos and us and our whole prospecting program might be hamstrung in two weeks. That's about the length of time it takes for the word to be passed from one end of the reservation to the other." Of course, he went on, the geologists would still be out searching for uranium, but their knowledge of the reservation, which covers about twenty-five thousand square miles, didn't compare with that of the Navajos, for these Indians are nomadic by nature, and many of them travel from one region to another, following the seasons, in search of good grazing conditions for their sheep and horses. "Under the circumstances, it would be pretty hard for them *not* to get to know the country," Leonard added.

Luckily, Leonard said, the Navajos have been co-operating with the government. In 1951, at the outset of the program to enlist their aid, it was by no means a certainty that they would co-operate, for the government's Indian policies haven't always been acceptable to the Navajos, among other tribes. "The only way we could prove our sincerity was to pay well and treat them squarely," Leonard told me. He said that in the beginning he had driven his jeep up and down and back and forth over the reservation, spreading the news among the sixty-five thousand Navajos about what the Commission was planning to do. Using trading posts as headquarters, he had signed up a number of dependable-looking Navajos and sent them out into the field, paying them a dollar and twenty cents an hour and encouraging them to try to interest their fellow-tribesmen in the undertaking. If they, or any of their unsalaried companions, found anything worth developing, he assured them, they would enjoy the same benefits from it as the other prospectors, who may also explore the reservation, provided they get permission from the Bureau of Indian Affairs. "At the start, we counted heavily on the hired Navajo prospectors to set an example for their fellow-tribesmen," Leonard said. "They had the incentive of their hourly wage, and we figured that when we paid them their money, just as we'd promised, the others would see that we were on the level." Leonard had known it would be useless to try to get the Indians to use Geiger counters, so he had left samples of uranium ore at each trading post. "I'd tell them to bring in rock like the samples, and that I'd be back in two weeks to see how they'd made out," he went on. "Then I'd shove off for the next trading post, wondering if anyone had given a damn about what I'd said."

Leonard had been astonished at the results when he made his second round of the trading posts. "The word had certainly gone out," he said. "At each post, there'd be twenty or more Indians waiting for me with samples they'd found. The Navajos aren't prospectors by tradition, but they have remarkable memories and powers of observation. They'd studied the specimens I'd left behind and then gone straight to canyons and mesas where, over the years, as they moved about with their herds, they'd come across the yellow of uranium. In some cases, it had been more than twenty-five years since they'd last seen those deposits, but they hadn't forgotten them, or how to get to them. Not all of them were so co-operative, naturally. At one of the posts, I heard about a Navajo in the Carrizo Mountains who had been eating bits of uranium as a medicine most of his life. I looked him up, but he was no help. He said that the other Navajos could find uranium for me if they felt like it, but that he was content to watch his sheep and let his young wife take care of him. His medicine may not have helped him, but it certainly hadn't hurt him. He was ninety."

A gratifyingly high percentage of the finds reported by his Indian prospectors had paid off, Leonard said, and the Navajos are still bringing in specimens that warrant investigation by the Commission's geologists. One of the prospectors, Alfred Miles, has tipped the Commission off to an area that, according to Leonard, may prove to be just about the richest strike on the whole plateau. "To look at Alfred, you'd never think he had it in him," Leonard said. "He's a little old dried-up fellow of fifty-two, but he runs me to death out on those trails. He and I were two days on horseback getting to his big discovery. It would probably have taken our geologists ten years to spot the place. It was on a crazy mountain, all cut up and no pattern to it at all. When we got there, we scrambled over endless tricky ledges, a good deal of the time on all fours. We hadn't even bothered tying our horses when we left them. Hell, they didn't want to wander around and fall into a fifteen-hundred-foot canyon. We kept running into wonderful showings, one of them four feet wide. They'll start mining there as soon as a road is completed."

By now, Leonard said, the Commission's geologists have enough showings on file to keep them busy investigating for years to come, and his own job is beginning to become routine. "I just look at samples or sometimes, like this morning, at an outcrop," he told me. "If it's worth while, I let the geologists know about it. The main thing now is to keep the Navajos convinced that they're getting a square deal, which they are." I asked him if the Indians understood what all the commotion was about. "Well," he said, "some of them think the government is just collecting rocks. They tell me I ought to want red rocks, not yellow, because the red is easier to find and softer to dig. Others think it's *ola*—gold—because the ore is yellow. Most of them, though, connect our program with some kind of explosive. They ask me if it's like a gun and I say that it's more like blasting powder—that it could blast out rocks for miles around. They have their doubts about that, so then I try to describe a bomb —just any old bomb—but even that's a difficult idea for them to grasp. Of course, it's a whole lot easier with the Navajos who were in the last war. They know what an ordinary bomb is like. I tell them it's bigger than anything they saw in the Army and let it go at that."

The road to Cameron was smooth, and although the day was windless, we were moving along at a clip that made the coyote tails flap wildly on the radiator cap. Leonard looked at his watch. "We'll be all right," he said, and slowed down long enough to light a cigarette. I mentioned that Wright had told me Leonard had had a lot to do with the success of the program on the reservation. If that was so, Leonard replied, it was probably because he could speak Navajo. Very few white men can, for it is an extraordinarily difficult language. "During the war," he said, "I was in a Marine outfit with some Navajos in the South Pacific and we found that the language made an ideal unbreakable code." I learned that Leonard had been raised in the Southwest and had picked up Navajo by spending a great deal of time with members of the tribe; his home, where he lives with his wife and three sons, is in Farmington, New Mexico, where he formerly owned a trading post. His present job doesn't pay very well, he said, but, apart from that, he finds it extremely agreeable. "What I really like to see is the way the Navajos are gaining prestige all over the country because of their contribution to our uranium program," he said. "Maybe if Alfred and the others keep scrambling, the powers that be will let them have a few more hospitals and schools."

Toward midmorning, Leonard swung the jeep off the road and up on a hillock, where he parked it a few yards away from a Navajo hogan—a circular house built of adobe and logs. This was the home of the two prospectors he had promised to visit. The father, a wizened fellow named Charles Huskon, came out to greet us, and behind him I could see the building's one, communal room. It was windowless, and a wood fire, on which food was being cooked, was burning on its dirt floor, making the place quite smoky. Huskon was followed by his son Evans, a flabby-faced youth in his twenties. Another Huskon, a lad of nine or ten, romped up to us from the fields and said something in Navajo to Leonard, who replied by wiggling his ears. The boy was delighted. Charles Huskon informed me, in fair English, that Leonard was known among the Navajos as Loose Ears. A moment later, Mrs. Huskon, a heavyset woman whose fingers were festooned with turquoise rings, and a daughter in her late teens, who was dressed in pink and purple silk and held a baby in her arms, came out of the hogan. The women stood apart from us and watched intently as Huskon handed Leonard a battered Carnation milk can containing some rock fragments. Leonard examined them and said, "Let's see the place."

The two Huskon men piled into the jeep with us, and, at Huskon's direction, we drove west for twenty minutes along a narrow road. Then, for an hour, Leonard skillfully coaxed his jeep up and down a series of dunes, until we came to a halt at the top of a slope that descended a hundred feet or so to the bank of a creek, where we all got out. The only discernible sign of life was a lizard that lay sprawled like a patch of pale-green sand a scant few inches from the jeep's right front wheel. Huskon nodded to Leonard and then plunged nimbly down the slope. Evans followed clumsily; Leonard, although encumbered by a Geiger counter he had taken out of the back of the car, could have easily passed him but diplomatically refrained from doing so. I brought up the rear. We walked along the creek a few yards and then Huskon stopped and pointed to some yellow-and-black sandstone partly hidden under a ledge. Leonard switched on his counter and, holding it close to the formation, studied the dial. "More," Huskon said, pointing ahead. We followed the outcrop for thirty yards and then stopped again. I could make out a yellowish glint under the ledge for at least another thirty yards. "The counter shows only a fair degree of radioactivity, but there seems to be so much of the rock that it's worth digging into to see what's back of the rim," Leonard said to me. "I'm going to suggest that the Commission do some drilling here." He turned to Huskon and said something in Navajo, concluding, in English, "I have hope. We will see." Huskon nodded earnestly.

"What do you think this rock can be used for?" I asked Huskon.

He studied Leonard's face briefly and then replied, "It is what the white man wants."

We returned to the jeep, and Leonard, after driving the Huskons back to their hogan, saw to it that I got to Grants and Paddy Martinez on schedule by letting me off in Flagstaff a few minutes before a mail train with seats for a dozen passengers pulled out. I rode it for three hundred and fifty miles and spent the night at the Motel Milan in Grants.

Grants, I came to realize the next day, was all Paddy Martinez. The Indian sheepherder's discovery on Haystack Mountain three years earlier had completely changed the town's way of life. Before he spotted his yellow ore, local boosters, by way of trumpeting what was then Grants' big money crop, called their community the Carrot Capital; now they want it known as the Uranium City. (Miniature sacks of uranium-ore chips, with mailing tags marked "Guaranteed Radioactive and Harmless" attached, are now on sale in shops there for a quarter apiece.) In the old days, Grants prided itself not on its carrots alone but on being the only place of any size along the hundred and thirty-five miles of Highway 66 that connect the cities of Albuquerque and Gallup—a distinction that brought it an assortment of motels and gas stations, with a reptile house by the name of Cobra Gardens in the midst of them. Approaching the town, one still sees such signs as "PEACE PIPES, 98c," "CACTUS HANKIES," and "DID YOU KNOW THERE ARE 55 KINDS OF RATTLESNAKES?"

These ancient glories are now dimmed by the big-time operations that have followed upon Paddy Martinez's strike. Millions of dollars are being spent on mine development and further exploration of the region. A considerable part of this money has been invested by the Santa Fe Railroad, which, under a government land grant authorized decades ago to encourage railroad building in the West, has turned out to be the legal owner of the mineral rights on the land where the uranium was found. The deposits of ore involved in Operation Haystack, as the Santa Fe has named its project, have proved extensive enough to justify the construction of a plant just outside Grants, which the Anaconda Copper Mining Company is building at a cost of three and a half million dollars. Anaconda has also signed a prospecting contract with the Laguna tribe of Indians, whose reservation is about eight miles from Grants, and is now putting up a housing development for its plant personnel. I learned most of this in the course of a talk I had with Carroll Gunderson, president of the Grants State Bank. Gunderson was mayor of Grants when, in the summer of 1950, Paddy—as Gunderson, and everybody else, calls him—brought him some samples of ore from Haystack Mountain, and after examining them he took them to a group of geologists from the Colorado School of Mines who happened to be in the vicinity conducting an experiment for the Defense Department. They were profoundly impressed.

Nearly everyone I talked to in Grants had a definite point of view about Paddy. A Commission geologist was pleased but deflated by what Paddy had found on Haystack—one of the largest uranium deposits so far discovered in the United States. Paddy, he said, not only had flown in the face of academic geology by finding uranium in a limestone formation but had done so in a most humiliating manner. "What a ludicrous location!" the geologist said. "Haystack—a mountain in full view of a transcontinental highway that thousands of tourists drive over all year long. Now Paddy's name is turning up in geology journals, and to some people, I guess, we look pretty silly." A good deal of the talk about Paddy had to do with what he was getting out of his strike, but no one I ran into appeared to have gone to the trouble of asking Paddy himself. It was understood that he had been put on the Santa Fe payroll, some thought for life (he was almost sixty at the time of his find), at a salary the size of which seemed to be anybody's guess. I talked to Grants residents who declared that Paddy was losing out to what they darkly termed "the interests"; several of these people also felt that when the Santa Fe moved in on him he became the victim of a thoroughly obsolete law. Other residents believed that Paddy was cleaning up, and predicted that he would squander his sudden wealth. One man said it was obvious that Paddy was doing all right. "He's the only Indian around these parts whose hogan has windows," he pointed out.

Stopping by at Paddy's hogan, I found that he hardly knows what to make of his lot. He and some of his family were shearing sheep when I arrived, and he led me through a flock of sheep and loudly bleating lambs to a large burlap sack filled with new fleece, on which we found comfortable seats. A husky, swarthy man with a single tooth, Paddy was wearing Navy fatigues and a sombrero. His voice was low, rasping, and lugubrious as he told me that the whole Haystack business started one day in April 1950 when he ran out of cigarettes. "I don't remember the date, but it was lambing season," he said. "I was on horseback, going along a trail to the Rattlesnake Trading Post for the cigarettes, when I saw this little yellow spot under some rock. I got off and dug it out with a stick, because it reminded me of the time in 1947 when I bought a bus ticket in Grants at the Yucca Hotel. Three white men were talking about an ore called uranium and saying it was worth a lot of money. They were showing some of it to each other and I got a look at it. It was the same yellow stuff I was holding in my hand on that trail. Well, I got my cigarettes and came home and told my wife I'd found some kind of ore. She didn't believe me. The next day, I went out with a pick and hammer and walked west along the edge of this rock for a mile and a half and kept finding more and more. I got on my horse and went east for five miles and found more.

"I got lots of friends—Americans, Indians, Mexicans. But I didn't trust anybody except maybe Ed Harmon—he's a farmer—and Mr. Gunderson. I had the whole thing on my mind for a week. Then I went to Ed and I said to him, 'Ed, I found an ore they call uranium. Help me fill out the blanks for the claims.' Ed filled out sixteen blanks for me in Grants. After that, I took some samples to Gunderson, and he told me that some college men from Colorado said they were good. I didn't know what to do. Then a fellow over on Mount Taylor heard about the ore and he wanted to dig. I didn't trust him, but he came around nine or ten times, so finally I said to him, 'O.K., but you stay right here and dig, and nothing else.' Well, the next thing I knew, he'd done plenty else—he'd put in a claim for where I already had one. I got mad, and he went and told everyone about the place. There must have been a thousand cars on Haystack Mountain in the next ten days. Then it came out that the Santa Fe owned all my claims, and now they mail me a check for two hundred and fifty dollars every month."

The income has brought Paddy complications of a middle-class sort, I gathered. "I'm in debt," he told me, waving vaguely toward his windowed hogan. "My wife bought a sewing machine and now she wants a washing machine. I have about fifteen children, and for the first time in years I'm seeing every one of them at meals, now they know there's going to be something to eat." Plainly, life had been simpler for Paddy before he set out for those cigarettes three years earlier. Back then, he said, he hadn't known where his next dollar was coming from, but a man who only raised a few sheep wasn't expected to know a thing like that. He had also earned a little money recruiting harvesters for the carrot growers and picking carrots himself. "You get dirty picking carrots, but it's clean dirt," he said. "You don't even need water for it. You can just wipe it off on your pants. Now, this uranium, they tell me it's used for a powder for some kind of bomb. Carrots you can eat. I'll take carrots. This damn uranium—my friends don't like me the same any more. Some of them are jealous of me and the others are mad at me because I didn't tell them about what I'd found. They think if I had, they might be getting checks the same as me. But carrots—there are no secrets about carrots. You're in an open field. If you stop picking for a minute and look around, there are the others picking. You can see them and they can see you. Everybody knows what everybody else is doing."

CHAPTER 20 | APRIL, 1951

CAMELLIAS AND BOMBS

A FAR LESS mountainous and more ordered part of the United States than the Colorado Plateau is to be found in south central South Carolina where the first plant designed to further the production of the hydrogen bomb has been started on a three-hundred-square-mile tract of land surrounding the town of Ellenton. When I visited this once agricultural area, which borders the Savannah River, hundreds of graders, tractors, and bulldozers were noisily converting it to its new purpose. A four-lane highway, extending nineteen miles to North Augusta, South Carolina, had been built to accommodate first, the heavy traffic of the building phase and, later, that accompanying the operation of the factory and its laboratories. A large administration building, newly erected on what was part of a peanut farm, was being used as a headquarters by Atomic Energy Commission officials and the managerial and engineering representatives of the Explosives and Engineering Departments of the du Pont Company, which, as the government's dollar-for-the-whole-job contractor, was overseeing the construction of the plant, the cost of which was estimated at nine hundred million dollars. (It has since risen to one and a half billion dollars.) One-eighth of the seven thousand people who were living in the area when the government decided to condemn it (the local press called them "the D.P.s of W.W. III") had already made way for the weapon, moving, most of them, just beyond the perimeter of the budding reservation. Thanks to the appearance of four house movers, many of these D.P.s were still living in their homes, which for the most part are sharecropper shacks and modest farmhouses. The first of the house movers, a man by the name of Ralph South, set out for South Carolina from Ordway, Colorado, on November 28,

1950, the day the government announced the project. The house movers were also towing churches to new locations, and, under the supervision of Army engineers, about a hundred cemeteries were to be shifted, at government expense.

The remainder of the seven thousand residents were gradually being eased out by the expanding construction. The site was soon to be overrun by the work crews, and the entire pre-November 28th population, many of whose forebears settled there before the Revolution, established elsewhere. The tardier of the dispossessed were witnessing changes that they found only slightly less startling than they had found the announcement that they would have to leave. "A stranger used to mean a revenue agent after moonshiners," a tenant farmer remarked to me. "But this, it's made *us* the strangers." On Sundays, an average of a thousand visitors, out on rubberneck jaunts, had been driving into Ellenton (pop. 700), the largest town on the site, and piling out of their cars to inquire eagerly of the first native they came across, "Where are they making that bomb?" On weekdays, the lingering residents could count on seeing five thousand other outlanders, the complement of the construction force. Every day brought a new batch of migratory construction workers lumbering through Ellenton in trailers that bore the license plates of distant states. Many of them hoped to find jobs, having heard that, at its peak, the construction roster was to reach 35,000; by that time the farming community having vanished, newcomers would be newcomers only to project workers of senior standing. When these thousands of people were through with their job, the tall smokestacks of our most modern oven, the nuclear reactor, would tower above the vestiges of pastures and cotton plantations.

The plant that was being built by the Savannah River Operations Office, to use the project's singularly unspecific official name, was to be related to the hydrogen bomb in much the same way that the plants at Oak Ridge are related to the atomic bomb; that is, the weapon itself would not be assembled there but in some other part of the country. Only fuels required by a hydrogen bomb were to be made there. One is plutonium, which, if international tensions ever permit, can also be employed to create power for peacetime needs. Another, which has yet to be officially identified, is good for destruction and nothing else. Aside from these facts, the authorities of the Savannah River Operations Office would disclose nothing of a technical nature about their work, but even this scant information was enough, at the time it was revealed, to engender a widespread fear in near-by Aiken and Augusta, Georgia, as well as in smaller communities, that the construction of the plant might result in the Soviet Union's deciding to drop an atomic bomb on one of America's hydrogen bombs. This particular worry, according to one official of the Atomic Energy Commission, had been pretty well allayed by government speakers, who, in scores of addresses to local civic groups and fraternal orders, harped on the point that the bomb would not be put together in or near Ellenton. "Of course," the same official said to me, "the bomb will have to be assembled *somewhere,* but we'll let somebody else worry about that." The orators also gave assurances that the plant's radioactive fuels would not harm people living in the vicinity. "Now, about those fish in the Savannah River," George O. Robinson, the project's information officer, said at a Rotary meeting in Augusta. "A man catching them from the banks of the Savannah at its nearest point to the plant would have to eat eight pounds of them every day for the rest of his life before he would approach the radiation tolerance we'll allow our employees inside the factory." Mrs. Mattie Hall, an antique dealer in Aiken, told me that the mere arrival of the construction workers from other parts of the country had had as reassuring an effect on the population as all the government's carefully worded statements. "At first, everybody wanted to run away," she said. "Then we saw these fellows pouring in from every state and we changed our minds. We decided that living here couldn't really be so dangerous if all these men were coming in with their families. Maybe they won't stay on when the plant is built and starts to operate, but it doesn't seem likely they'd have brought their families with them unless they planned to stay. By now, we've convinced ourselves that the plant's going to be protected all day long by Air Force planes and that we'll all be just terribly safe."

Most of the people with homes near the site were uncertain about how the project would affect their way of life. A number of the businessmen, however, were definitely enthusiastic, for the plant was to be one of the largest industrial developments in the Southeast. "It's as if a hundred new industries were settling down in our fair city," Lester C. Moody, the secretary of the Augusta Chamber of Commerce, told me. "It's going to mean empire-building to us. Augusta is going to grow and grow and be prosperous. Of course, the folks around Ellenton are being inconvenienced, but you can't have progress with sentiment." Then he added majestically, "The hand that shuns the thorn can't have the rose."

The government, needless to say, was not primarily concerned with local inconvenience or prosperity in choosing its site. A committee spent four months examining likely sites in twenty-five states and, in all, considered over a hundred locations. "We almost located near Terre Haute and Paris, Texas," Curtis A. Nelson, the Atomic Energy Commission's project manager, told me, "but neither of these places could quite match the combination of factors here in South Carolina." Perhaps the most important factor was one that Nelson guardedly referred to as "technical considerations." "If I described them, I might be giving away the process we're planning to use," he said to me. The proximity to sources of power—the Savannah River and the Clark Hill hydroelectric dam—was another inducement, Nelson said. Interstate highways were at hand. So were two rail lines. Engineers studied the soil and found it suitable for the support of heavy buildings. There were no natural obstacles, such as mountains or dense forests, to slow up construction work. The closest atomic-energy installation was three hundred miles away, at Oak Ridge, and this fact appealed to the advocates of dispersal. The land, much of it uncultivated, was comparatively cheap and thinly populated. Only a small percentage of the two hundred thousand acres would actually be occupied by the plant and its laboratories, Nelson said, but it would be necessary to have a good deal of land around them to avoid what he called "possible hazards" to the surrounding countryside and to prevent unauthorized persons from getting near the installation. "There'll be plenty of space left over for the quail, deer, and wild turkeys," Nelson said. "They're not being asked to evacuate. It may even be possible to permit the South Carolina Wild Life Federation to plant food crops for them in a swampy section along the Savannah. If that works out, they'll probably be living in the world's best-guarded sanctuary."

In the course of a talk I had with Arthur Tackman, Nelson's assistant, I learned that a survey made by the Federal Housing Administration also had quite a lot to do with selecting the site. The survey had been undertaken to ascertain how well the towns near the area—primarily Augusta and Aiken—could absorb the influx of workers. The F.H.A. turned in an optimistic report on the availability of housing in these communities, on their schools and hospitals, and on the ability of local banks to lend money for building additional facilities. "Many people have asked why the plant isn't being built in an even more sparsely populated place," Tackman said. "I understand that President Truman himself asked that when he was shown our plans. But the Atomic Energy Commission has been putting a new policy into effect, and this made us locate within a few miles of fair-sized communities. Right here we've got one of the least populated spots in the United States that's near such communities and that meets our other requirements. The government doesn't want to set up any more government towns, like the ones at Oak Ridge, Los Alamos, and Hanford. They had to be built because everything was so secret during the war, but in general the government hates the headache of running government towns."

Augusta (pop. 71,000), one of the two towns on which the success of the government's anti-government policy was most dependent, was expected to play its part without undue difficulty. About Aiken (pop. 7,000), the other town, a lovely community and one of the horsiest winter resorts in America, there was, however, considerable speculation as to whether it would be "spoiled." Some of the wealthiest and oldest families in the United States were in the habit of spending the winters in their fine homes along Whiskey Road, the highway that, after passing through their neighborhood, continues, as Route 19, on to the government's development, fourteen miles away. Most of the town's broad avenues, bisected by island parks planted with pin oaks and magnolias, were still unpaved, out of consideration for the sensitivity of horses' hoofs. The Hitchcock Woods, an eleven-thousand-acre park where no automobiles were permitted, provided a highly attractive setting for riders. The horses of some of the nation's leading racing stables, the majority of which are owned by Northerners, wintered there. Many Derby winners have had their débuts at the annual Aiken Trials, on the beautifully laid-out Mile Track. Hunts helped to pass away the short winter days. Aiken was one of America's polo centers. For those of the winter residents who were not entirely engrossed with riding, one of the country's seven court-tennis courts was available at the Aiken Tennis Club, and for golfers there was the Palmetto Golf Club's superb course. "We know Aiken as a simple country town," S. A. Warner Baltazzi, a retired bank president, told me when I called on him at his Whiskey Road home.

Whether Aiken was to retain its simplicity hinged on the manner of its impending growth. Many townspeople feared that their community would lose its appeal as a resort town if it were invaded by large numbers of construction workers and plant employees. This would seriously upset Aiken's economy, which had long been firmly based on the winter colony. At the same time, the townspeople hoped to see their incomes increased by the spending of the new arrivals. "We shouldn't have to make a choice between the winter colony and the people the plant will bring here," one fairly agitated shopkeeper told me. "That can be avoided if the right people are attracted —scientists, engineers, government officials. The winter residents have their houses and stables here, and I know they want to stay, but will they if these construction workers trespass on their estates? They've got the money to lead a secluded life with, and if they can't find it here, they'll probably look for it elsewhere." Another Aikenite with whom I talked, Albert Howell, an editor of the Aiken *Standard & Review,* was less perturbed about the likelihood of the town's being swamped by construction workers. "They'll go to Augusta," he predicted confidently. "This town's too dull for them. No night clubs, no roadhouses. You can get liquor in South Carolina only between sunrise and sunset, and you have to buy it by the bottle and drink it in somebody's home. No bars. Their big Saturday night would be dismal. All they could do would be sit in a restaurant and drink beer until midnight, when the blue laws take over. But Augusta is wide open."

The winter residents with whom I talked seemed far less exercised about the construction workers than were the native Aikenites. (None of them talked of "riffraff," as several of the townspeople did.) Their principal concern was to preserve their agreeable privacy. Some intrusions, to be sure, had already occurred, but these were taken more or less in stride. For example, Gracefields, a seven-thousand-acre hunting preserve near Ellenton that was formerly leased by Mrs. W. R. Grace, of the shipping family, for shooting parties, had been acquired by the government as part of its site. "Oh, well, there's no point crying," Mrs. Grace assured me philosophically. "I've had a good time. The hydrogen bomb hasn't been the only surprise. This past winter, we had one of our coldest snaps and the camellias went. And, of course, in New York the Ritz-Carlton's come down. I lived there for eight years." One of the few kind words I heard for construction workers came from Terence Preece, one of the country's best polo players, who had been making his living by training ponies and promoting matches in Aiken and elsewhere. "Those I've seen so far are rabid polo fans," he said. "We've sold more dollar admissions this year than ever before."

The traffic on Whiskey Road had increased to the point where some horsemen, trying to cross it in order to enter the Hitchcock Woods, were annoyed by the delays and danger to them and their mounts. Those dowagers who liked to shop were inclined to wish the stores were less crowded. "So many new faces," one of them said to me. "It's bewildering." Ten trailer camps had been set up between Aiken and the site of the plant, with more to come, and although the fashionable district of the town was protected by zoning laws, the camps were not very far away and some of the old-timers found the informality of their new neighbors' homes disconcerting.

The feeling along Whiskey Road was that the hibernating grounds of the winter people would be left alone. "What would a construction worker want with court tennis or drag hunts?" asked one Northerner with whom I discussed the subject. "Maybe he's done some skeet shooting, but we go in for live pigeons at the Gun Club. Why, a day there would set the fellow back thirty dollars. A dollar a pigeon, you know, plus a ten-dollar sweepstakes, cartridges, and the rest. Let's suppose that someone from the trailer crowd was put up for the Palmetto. He'd have to fork out two hundred and forty dollars for a membership fee, and five dollars for greens fees whenever he played. You talk to people around here and they'll tell you that inheritance taxes are a hell of a lot worse nuisance than this hydrogen bomb." Mrs. C. Oliver Iselin, a handsome elderly lady who had been spending her winters in Aiken since she was a child, told me that she was rather looking forward to the arrival in Aiken of certain project employees. (She was in exuberant spirits, her trainer having just phoned her from the Jamaica track that one of her horses had won a race.) "I think the heads of departments would make interesting additions," she said. "There's a beautiful forty-four-acre section of my property on which I'm ready to let twenty-five of them build houses, provided the character of the property is preserved."

The winter resident who had undoubtedly made the happiest adjustment to the presence of the construction workers was Mr. Fitch Gilbert, an extremely affable Whiskey Road man of sixty-eight who owned a large tract of farmland adjoining the government site. Mr. Gilbert had opened a trailer camp on his property that would accommodate four hundred families. "My family is horsy, but I'm not," he told me. "I've tried a lot of things on that farm, winters, to keep busy—corn, wood, peanuts, cheese, cotton, cattle, and whatnot—but this trailer camp is the best thing yet. Four hundred families at eight dollars a week—why, that'll be more money than I've made in a long time. Some of my competitors are charging six dollars, but I'm not making my customers pay for electricity and I'm letting them have unlimited hot water. A plumber was telling me the other day that the one thing women want in a trailer camp is hot water. I may even throw in a few washing machines. I've named my camp Pine-Shade, to get over the idea that it doesn't sit out in the broiling sun, the way the others do. It's in a grove three hundred yards back from the road and only a mile from an artificial lake. My farmer put me on to the idea. I'm letting him run the camp's food store. He's been wanting to get ahead for a long time. Well, now he's getting ahead." Mr. Gilbert was absolutely certain there would be no exodus from Whiskey Road. "Hell, no!" he said. "We'll stay until we pass on."

While Aiken was waiting uneasily to see what the project would do to it, the project's effect on Ellenton and the requisitioned land around it was one of utter finality. The residents, quite naturally, were stunned by the fate that had been visited on them by the government. They couldn't understand why their community had to be the one spot in the United States to attract the Atomic Energy Commission for its new project. "This is the worst thing that's happened since Sherman marched through," a South Carolina congressman declared in an interview in the local press. A Negro sharecropper indignantly asked his employer, "Why doesn't the Klan do something about this?" It is not unusual in Bible Belt country to find wooden signs with crudely lettered religious exhortations posted along the highway. After the government's announcement, signs of a secular nature went up, such as:

IT IS HARD TO UNDERSTAND WHY OUR TOWN MUST BE DESTROYED TO MAKE A BOMB THAT WILL DESTROY SOMEONE ELSE'S TOWN THAT THEY LOVE AS MUCH AS WE LOVE OURS. BUT WE FEEL THAT THEY PICKED NOT JUST THE BEST SPOT IN THE U.S. BUT IN THE WORLD.

WE LOVE THESE DEAR HEARTS AND GENTLE PEOPLE WHO LIVE IN OUR HOME TOWN.

WE'RE LIKE THE BOLL WEEVIL—LOOKING FOR A HOME.

The Ellentonians' shock was all the greater because it was unexpected. For several weeks before the announcement, they had watched engineers set up drill rigs at various points to plumb the soil. They had no idea what was going on, and invented a variety of rumors: The engineers had been assigned to find a site for a glue factory, a cotton-goods factory, an aluminum plant; they were prospecting for oil, uranium, kaolin. Each of these rumors was greeted as good news, for while there was still some profitable bale-to-the-acre land near Ellenton, cotton, once the region's money crop, had long been on the decline, because of the boll weevil's destructiveness and the increasing shortage of farm labor. "We wanted an industry, but instead we all got drafted—men, women, and children," Judge P. H. Buckingham, the town's magistrate, told me. The government came forward with assurances to soften the blow: Department of Agriculture agents would assist farmers in finding fertile new acreage; Ellenton residents would be given first consideration for project jobs; assessors of their properties would take inflationary real-estate prices into account. Despite all such palliatives, a wild hope persisted that the edict would somehow be rescinded. The hope withered in December 1950, when Mr. Nelson and several of his colleagues appeared at a meeting in Ellenton to answer any questions that might be troubling the townspeople. A member of the audience asked whether Ellentonians would be given the opportunity to buy back their land if by some chance the project should ever be shut down. "We came here not just to build a war plant but to make things that can be used for peace," Mr. Nelson replied. "We plan to be with you a long time."

At the time of my visit, there was an almost lively, if muted, air of enterprise in and around Ellenton. The still-undisplaced residents, using whatever ingenuity they were endowed with, were contriving to make the best of their common accident. Merchants were looking over near-by towns for likely places to do business. Farmers were busy scouting for acreage; some had searched as far as two hundred miles away, but the majority were trying to stay close to Ellenton. A number of the older farmers had decided to retire, and most of their tenants and sharecroppers had applied for positions with the project. "If I get that job, it'll pay me more than I've ever made," one tenant farmer told me. "I want to be the chauffeur for a government official. I know a good fishing hole to take him to." Mike Cassels, the owner of the general store and the rich man of Ellenton, was spending many hours poring over plans for his new home, to be built on Whiskey Road, not far from Mrs. Iselin's place. "I can't figure the architect out," he said to me. "I told him I wanted a comfortable home, not an expensive one. The last time he was in to see me, I said to him, 'Make a couple of mistakes in those damned plans if you want, but get the price down.' " Probably the most time-consuming activity was the endless deliberating over the best price that could realistically be expected of the government agents when they got around to assessing a property. "In the last month or so," I was told by Hunter Kennedy, one of Mr. Nelson's assistants, "they've been hounding us to hurry up and make them an offer for their land. They're impatient to find out what the future has in store for them."

Anticipation of the assessor's visit, helpful as it was, had not entirely distracted the Ellentonians from their plight. There were too many cheerless reminders of the community's imminent disappearance for that—fields reverting to brush, houses in disrepair, empty shelves in the stores. The thing that most bothered the citizens was the uprooting of the aged. No one I talked to in Ellenton failed to mention this. "Nobody's worried about the old folks who are well off, but about how the sick and poor ones can possibly get along someplace else," said Dr. Fred C. Brinkley, who had been the town's physician and druggist since 1910. "Still, some of these old sharecroppers have been here right along for years and years, and I never heard anyone worrying much about them until now, when the town's breaking up. I think it's just that people are taking stock of the kind of place they made it while it was alive. Whenever anything dies, people wonder if they couldn't have treated it nicer."

CHAPTER 21 | SEPTEMBER, 1952

SOMETHING IN THE SKY

ONE TYPE OF aerial development, guided or unguided, planetary or interplanetary, whichever it may be, that Dr. von Braun and other space experts have so far not busied themselves with is the flying saucer. That continuing mystery is one that the U.S. Air Force has been pondering since midsummer of 1947. It was then—at a time when the Air Force was already concerned with such problems as the refinement of supersonic craft, the rigging up of radar networks, and its budgetary skirmishing with the Army and Navy—that it found itself confronted by this new and completely different headache. People in every section of the United States were seeing strange objects that streaked across the sky at tremendous speeds, and although these people, who included such practiced students of the heavens as airplane pilots, farmers, and the Lieutenant Governor of Idaho, were not able to identify the things they had seen, they were able to describe them vividly and unforgettably. The newspapers called the first of these puzzling objects a flying saucer, taking their cue from the man who reported having seen it and who described it as saucerlike, and the name stuck, although later people reported seeing things that looked like flying chromium hubcaps, flying dimes, flying teardrops, flying gaslights, flying ice-cream cones, and flying pie plates. As more and more curious things were seen in the skies, cautiously quizzical editorials began to appear in the papers, and the President and members of Congress received a deluge of letters demanding an explanation. Many of the letter writers had concluded that the objects, whatever they might be, were manned by Russians, and that as soon as their pilots had reconnoitered sufficiently, they would return loaded with atomic bombs. Others thought the earth was being visited by spaceships from another planet. Still others suspected that the U.S. Air Force was secretly testing some new form of aircraft. Everyone agreed, however, that it was up to the Air Force, as the custodian of the American welkin, to explain the flying objects and, if necessary, to repel them. The result was the launching by the Air Force, on January 22, 1948, of a special investigation—an investigation that, though it has reached numerous conclusions, is still under way and has yet to put the public mind at rest.

It appears that, aside from the hope of reassuring a jittery populace, the Air Force, in embarking upon this undertaking, had any or all of three things in mind. It may well have shared the civilian concern over what, if anything, the Russians might have to do with the reported phenomena, and it may even have felt that to insure a thoroughgoing investigation there was certainly no harm in assuming for the moment that the era of interplanetary travel had arrived and the earth had become an objective for journeys from elsewhere in the solar system. Or—and this would not necessarily exclude the first two considerations—the Air Force may have been setting up a smoke screen to protect, in the interest of national security, the secret of some experimental flying objects of its own that only a trusted few of its members knew about. Whatever the purpose, the investigation, with which I have been in touch from time to time, has seemingly been exhaustive. The Air Force personnel originally assigned to it was later augmented by astronomers, psychologists, physicists, meteorologists, physicians, and representatives of the F.B.I. The investigation, which soon became popularly known as Project Saucer, was first headed by Lieutenant General Benjamin W. Chidlaw, Commanding General of the Air Matériel Command, and its base was, and is, at Wright Field, Dayton, Ohio. The project's task turned out to involve a mixture of old-fashioned detection, scientific analysis, public relations, and the study of a widespread state of mind. In December 1949, after checking, over a period of two years, three hundred and seventy-five reports of intruders in the sky, the Air Force publicly called it quits, but Project Saucer was not actually disbanded. National security, the Air Force announced at the time, was not endangered. The flying saucers were apparitions, it said, all attributable either to a failure to recognize conventional objects, to hoaxes, or to a mild form of mass hysteria. The Air Force, however, did not let the matter rest there.

Not long after the apparent demise of Project Saucer, I had a talk in Washington with Brigadier General Ernest Moore, then chief of Air Force Intelligence, in the course of which he made four categorical statements that I felt sure he had made many times before. "First off," he said, "the Russians have nothing to do with these so-called saucers—I'll swear to that on a stack of Bibles, if you like. Second, we don't have any secret new types of aircraft that could have started all this commotion. Third, nobody, in our opinion, has spotted spaceships from some other planet. Fourth, everything our investigators learned has been made available to the public."

The first saucer incident occurred on the afternoon of June 24, 1947, when Kenneth Arnold, on a business trip for a Boise, Idaho, firm that makes fire-control equipment, was flying his private plane from Chehalis, Washington, to Yakima, Washington. The reflection of a bright flash on one wing caught his eye. He turned and, at a distance he thought was about twenty miles, saw what he took to be nine tailless aircraft heading toward Mount Rainier. "I could see their outlines quite plainly against the snow," Air Force Intelligence quoted him as saying. "They flew very close to the mountaintops, directly south to southeast, down the hogback of the range, flying like geese, in a diagonal, chainlike line, as if they were linked together . . . a chain of saucerlike things at least five miles long, swerving in and out of the high mountain peaks. They were flat . . . and so shiny that they reflected the sun like a mirror." Arnold said he watched the saucers for three minutes and estimated their speed at about twelve hundred miles an hour.

Air Force technicians, consulted by newspapermen, said that any object moving that fast would be invisible to the naked eye at Arnold's estimated distance. The press scoffed at Arnold's story, and he was resentful. "Even if I see a ten-story building flying through the air, I won't say a word about it," he declared, and when he got back to Boise he wrote a series of articles about his experience for a magazine called *Fate*.

No sooner were the skeptical newspaper accounts printed than dozens of people turned up with similar reports. Another resident of Boise spotted a disk over that city, "a half circle in shape, clinging to a cloud and just as bright and silvery-looking as a mirror caught in the rays of the sun." Lieutenant Governor Donald S. Whitehead, of Idaho, disclosed that one evening he had seen a comet-shaped object sailing over the western part of the state. It finally dipped below the horizon, he said. (Later on, the personnel of Project Saucer decided that the Lieutenant Governor had been looking at either Saturn or Mercury.) Four cops in Portland, Oregon, saw a group of disks "wobbling, disappearing, and reappearing."

Reports of other phenomena having been seen in the skies appeared in the papers almost daily. Two Army officers at Fort Richardson, Alaska, reported seeing a spherical object flying through the air at incredible speed and leaving no vapor trail; some fishermen off Newfoundland saw a series of aerial flashes, silver to reddish in color; a lady in Oregon watched a group of saucers spell out "P-E-P-S-I," and alerted her neighbors to the presence of foreign agents practicing a secret code in our skies; an Oklahoma City man saw a saucer "the bulk of six B-29s"; and a prospector in the Cascade Mountains of Oregon saw six saucers in a group, banking in the sun—"round, silent, and not flying in formation." On Independence Day, 1947, there were twelve reports of saucers in widely separated parts of the United States. One of these saucers, sighted at Trenton, New Jersey, was traced to a fireworks display. Dr. Paul Fitts, an Ohio State University psychologist who was for a time attached to Project Saucer, considered this crowded condition in the holiday skies the result of mass suggestibility, the same jumpy trait that caused Americans to see Zeppelins overhead during and after the First World War. "Our graphs show that saucer incidents always increase dramatically after publicity," he has since told me. "The sky, you know, has been a source of exciting visions from time immemorial, and its attraction is particularly strong in our jittery moments."

From the beginning, the officers in charge of Project Saucer recognized a peculiar difficulty in their assignment. "If you look out the window and see something, how can I prove or disprove what it was if I didn't see it and you can't tell me much about what you saw?" Major Jerre Boggs, who was then the chief liaison officer between Wright Field and the high command in Washington, asked me one day shortly after Project Saucer had presumably become a thing of the past. "It would be different if flying saucers were known to exist. Then we could have collected evidence indicating the degrees of probability that such things were sighted and the reason for their appearance at a given place. But it is impossible to prove, logically and with finality, a double negative—that is, that there are no flying saucers and that people have not seen flying saucers. The best we could do under the circumstances was to deduce, first, from the fact that it had not been proved, that saucers *had* been seen and, second, from the fact that reasonable theories could be advanced to explain away all the *reports* of seeing them, that probably nobody had seen them at all. The fewer the theoretical explanations and the less plausible they were, the more reason there was for suspecting people *had* seen saucers." The Major shook his head, and continued, "It's a difficult concept to grasp, but so was the job we were tackling."

I asked Major Boggs whether there was any way to account for the epidemic of reports of strange celestial objects. "Of course there is," he replied. "If you look up at the sky long enough, you can almost always make out something there that appears strange. And more people are looking up now than ever before. Kids don't count freight cars any more—they count airplanes. People who were trained in air observation during the war have gone right on observing. Also, the public hasn't forgotten that the atomic bomb was kept secret from it for three years. This time, people want to know what's cooking, so they look up." Major Boggs sighed. "Time was when people used to make a wish if they saw a shooting star. Now they telephone the Air Force."

Major Boggs and I pondered this unromantic age in silence for a moment. Then he turned briskly to the problems that had confronted the investigators. "The one tangible thing we had to work on was the fact that the sky is full of things," he said. "I can't even come close to estimating the number of commercial and military aircraft up there at any given moment. Then, there are more than five hundred outfits of one kind of another that release balloons from time to time. These range from simple weather balloons, no larger than a volleyball, to complicated clusters of balloons, as big as a house, for radar soundings or cosmic-ray research. At night, balloons always have trailing lights. In addition to all those balloons, there are advertising blimps, the sweeping beams of searchlights and air-lane beacons, clouds that reflect the sun and other sources of light, clouds scudding by the moon, and pieces of paper that are swirled aloft from the street by the wind. And, of course, birds, kites, St. Elmo's fire, meteors, comets, lightning, and fireballs—or, if you prefer, bolides, which are bits of interplanetary matter, with trajectories that sometimes seem to parallel the surface of the earth, trail a wisp of flame, and disintegrate with a flash when they hit the earth's dense atmosphere."

The officers in command of Project Saucer began by breaking this aerial hodgepodge down into its principal divisions, Major Boggs told me. Then they started looking for clues to what people had actually seen when they thought they were seeing flying saucers. Dr. J. Allen Hynek, the head of the Emerson McMillin Observatory, at Ohio State University, was called in to consider objects that might be of astral origin. The United States Weather Bureau, the Air Weather Service, and various other scientific setups, among them the Electronics Laboratory of the Cambridge Field Station, at Cambridge, Massachusetts, were asked to study the reports of sightings to determine whether any of their balloons were responsible. Airline schedules and flight charts of military aircraft were studied. In this work, Project Saucer had the assistance of the personnel attached to the Air Matériel Command laboratories at Wright Field. These included specialists in aerodynamics and propulsion—men who might be able to ascertain whether what were described as the maneuverings of a saucer might not really be the movements of an airplane or balloon. Wright Field physicians who had had experience with the limitations and idiosyncrasies of human beings in the air were also available for consultation, as were all kinds of engineers, in case any material evidence turned up. All told, at one time or another, some two hundred people were engaged on Project Saucer. It was agreed among them that they would not pool their ideas. "We didn't want them influencing each other," one officer explained to me. "We had enough suggestibility on our hands as it was."

Practical jokers, precocious children, publicity seekers, and mentally unbalanced people were among those who saw saucers, or said they did, but those who reported seeing them also included men whose reliability was such that if they had claimed to have seen flying gorillas, Project Saucer would have taken them seriously. Two of these were Captain C. S. Chiles and Pilot John B. Whitted, experienced Eastern Air Lines pilots. At 3 a.m. on July 24, 1948, these men, flying a passenger plane at five thousand feet near Montgomery, Alabama, saw something that the newspapers later called a "space ship." Chiles and Whitted didn't call it that. They said it was a "wingless aircraft," a hundred feet long, cigar-shaped, with a diameter about twice that of the fuselage of a B-29, and was moving a third faster than a jet plane. It seemed to have a row of windows above a globular cabin that suggested a pilot's compartment. The interior of the cabin was extraordinarily bright—as bright as a magnesium flare—and along its sides was a less brilliant glow, which looked like "a blue fluorescent factory light." The exhaust of the object seemed to be an orange-red flame. "We saw no occupants," Chiles said. "We saw it at the same time and asked each other, 'What in the world is this?' Whatever it was, it flashed down toward us and we veered to the left. It veered to its left and passed us about seven hundred feet to our right, and above us. Then, as if the pilot had seen us and wanted to avoid us, it pulled up with a tremendous burst of flame from the rear and zoomed into the clouds, its prop wash or jet wash rocking our DC-3." The only passenger in the plane who was not asleep at the time said he had seen the same thing the two pilots saw.

An hour before the two pilots and the wakeful passenger saw whatever they saw, ground observers at the Robins Air Force Base, at Macon, Georgia, nearly two hundred miles to the northeast, also saw something peculiar in the sky. They reported that it had been flying faster than a jet plane, that it had trailed vari-colored flames, that it was heading toward Montgomery, and that it had behaved like a normal aircraft in the way it disappeared from the line of sight.

Here, the experts professed to hope, was something Project Saucer could get its teeth into. The whole flying-saucer mystery might be explained. The first step was to determine whether the object was an aircraft that had been partially obscured by a cloud or whose appearance had been distorted by a rainstorm. Two hundred and twenty-five civilian and military flight schedules were analyzed, and it was found that one other plane, an Air Force C-47, had been near the Eastern airliner at the time the mysterious object was sighted. Conjecture about the C-47 began to appear irrelevant, however, when the Macon ground crews agreed with Chiles and Whitted that the thing they had seen was going much faster than two hundred miles an hour, and so, unless it dawdled around somewhere, wouldn't have taken anything like an hour to get from Macon to Montgomery.

Astronomers went to work on the problem. Dr. Hynek considered the possibility that a brilliant, slow-moving meteor might be the explanation. Various bits of the apparition's description encouraged this notion—"orange-red flame," "cigar-shaped," "a tremendous burst of flame." Unfortunately, the flight schedules of meteors are not available, and Dr. Hynek had no means of testing his hypothesis. "It will have to be left to the psychologists to tell us whether the immediate trail of a bright meteor could produce the subjective impression of a ship with lighted windows," he wrote in a report on his findings. The psychologists expressed the opinion that a meteor could indeed be mistaken for a spaceship. Dr. Fitts, the Ohio State psychologist, observed that both Chiles and Whitted were human and therefore as likely to be victims of mass suggestibility as anyone else. Dr. Fitts told me during a talk I had with him that psychologists are used to the fact that even people of high mental caliber often make mistakes about what they see. "Also, I would like to make the point that pilots are trained to instruments," he said. "They grow very dependent on those instruments, and I don't know whether they are necessarily superior observers without them. I do know that during the war, when I was in the Air Force, pilots frequently gave some pretty odd reports of what they'd seen while flying their missions." Chiles and Whitted readily agreed that their report might be thought odd, but they were still certain that they saw what they saw.

At three o'clock in the afternoon of January 7, 1948, something that looked like "an ice-cream cone topped with red" was sighted over the Godman Air Force Base, at Fort Knox, Kentucky, by several military men and civilians. The Godman Base tower requested a flight of four National Guard F-51s that happened to be aloft in the vicinity to investigate the object. The flight leader, Captain Thomas F. Mantell, a veteran with a splendid combat record, reported sighting the object, saying that it was then flying at half his speed. At three-fifteen, he broke away from his formation to go in pursuit, and within minutes radioed the tower, "I'm closing in now to take a good look. It's directly ahead and above . . . and still moving at about half my speed . . . The thing looks metallic and of tremendous size . . . It's going up now, and forward as fast as I am—that's three hundred and sixty miles an hour. I'm going up to twenty thousand feet, and if I'm no closer, I'll abandon chase." Those were the last words ever heard from Mantell. His body was found later that day in the wreckage of his plane. The Air Force officially expressed the belief that he had blacked out from lack of oxygen and had suffocated before his plane hit the ground.

Five minutes after Mantell broke away from his formation, the other planes put down at Godman Field. One of them was refueled and sent up again. It flew a hundred miles south at heights up to thirty-three thousand feet. The pilot saw nothing. The Project Saucer people at first said they believed that Mantell had chased Venus. Later, they dropped this notion, and still later, influenced by Dr. Hynek, returned to it. Dr. Hynek favored the Venus theory after he learned that a peculiar object had been seen not only over Godman Field that evening but, earlier, at three other scattered points, all of them hundreds of miles away—at the Lockbourne Air Force Base, near Columbus, Ohio; at the Clinton County Air Field, in Wilmington, Ohio; and by a pilot approaching Washington, D.C. These three sightings were made at about the time Venus set, and the object was reported to have been near the point on the horizon where the planet disappeared. "In summing up the evidence presented," Dr. Hynek reported, in part, "we are forced to the conclusion that the object observed in the early evening hours of January 7th, at these widely separated localities was the planet Venus. To assume that a terrestrial object located so high as to be visible simultaneously over a wide area could be of such intrinsic brightness and would be placed essentially at the very position of Venus would be incredible. The stellar magnitude of Venus that day made it twenty-nine times brighter than the bright star Arcturus. Venus, when as bright as this, shining through interstices in a host of clouds, could very easily give the [reported] effect . . . of 'a flaming object with a tail.' " The object Mantell pursued had been sighted during the day; the other observers had seen objects in the early evening. Dr. Hynek conceded that one's eye would be less likely to be caught by the planet in daylight than in darkness, but, he wrote in his report, "Once caught, the sighter might wonder why he had never noticed it before; Venus that day was six times brighter than an equivalent area of sky." Dr. Hynek made another point: "The one piece of evidence that leads this investigator to believe that at the time of Captain Mantell's death he was actually trying to reach Venus is that the object appeared essentially stationary (or moving steadily away from him) and he could not seem to gain on it."

A year and a half later, a similar object presented itself over Godman Field. This time, investigators ascertained the co-ordinates of its position and sent them to Walter L. Moore, Professor of Mathematics at the University of Louisville, and he identified it as Venus.

On the night of October 1, 1948, a twenty-seven-minute dogfight took place between another man of unquestioned ability at finding his way around in the air and a puzzling light in the sky. The man was Lieutenant George F. Gorman, during the Second World War a pilot instructor who trained French cadets, and at the time of the dogfight the manager of a construction company in Fargo, North Dakota. He was flying an F-51, completing a routine patrol for the North Dakota National Guard, and had just asked the tower at the Fargo Municipal Airport for clearance to land when he saw what seemed to be another plane's taillight a thousand yards away. He queried the tower, and the men there reported that the only other aircraft over the field was a Piper Cub. Gorman could see the Cub plainly outlined below him. Curious, he flew toward the light. "It was about six to eight inches in diameter, clear white, and completely round, with a sort of fuzz at the edges," Gorman later told investigators, adding that he saw "no outline of anything" around the edges. "It was blinking on and off. As I approached, however, the light suddenly became steady and pulled into a sharp left bank . . . I dived after it and brought my manifold pressure up to sixty inches, but I couldn't catch up with the thing. It started gaining altitude and again made a left bank. I put my F-51 into a sharp turn and tried to cut the light off in its turn. By then, we were at about seven thousand feet. Suddenly it made a sharp right turn and we headed straight at each other. Just when we were about to collide, I guess I got scared. I went into a dive and the light passed over my canopy at about five hundred feet. Then it made a left circle about a thousand feet above, and I gave chase again." Gorman followed the light up to fourteen thousand feet, where, after another near collision, his ship went into a power stall and the light disappeared to the northwest. Gorman noticed no sounds or exhaust-trail odors. He had gunned his plane up to four hundred miles an hour without gaining on the light. It was able to maintain an extremely steep angle of ascent, far greater than that of his Air Force fighter. "When I attempted to turn with [the light], I blacked out temporarily, due to excessive speed," he said. "I am in fairly good physical condition and I do not believe there are many, if any, pilots who could withstand the turn and speed effected by that light and remain conscious."

Project Saucer suspected that Gorman was tilting with a weather balloon. For one thing, it learned that the Fargo weather station had released a lighted balloon only ten minutes before Gorman's patrol stopped being routine. The object's steady, practically vertical climb suggested the behavior of a balloon. A technician who once worked on Project Saucer told me recently that chasing a weather balloon with an airplane is comparable to diving to the bottom of a pool after a hollow rubber ball that has been submerged and then let loose. "You swim around underwater looking for it, but all the time the ball is steadily rising to the surface, and your own zigzagging maneuvers cause you to lose track of the ball and to think that it is eluding you, although it is actually going in a straight course ahead of you," the technician said. "It's very difficult for a pilot to separate target motion and his own motion, even in daylight. At night, it's just about impossible." The balloon theory was buttressed a month and a half later when another nocturnal tangle took place between an Air Force pilot and a lighted object over Andrews Field, near Washington, D.C. The pilot's account of his quarry's evasive tactics was almost identical with Gorman's. This time, it was established that the object was a balloon cluster, set loose by cosmic-ray researchers. Dr. Fitts was so sure that both pilots had been misled by deceptive relative motion that he recommended that the Project Saucer command conduct a controlled experiment with a weather balloon at Wright Field, in which the pilot would not only have the advantage of daylight but would know what he was after. The pilot who made this test duplicated the maneuvers that Gorman had made in pursuing his fuzzy phantom, proving that it was quite possible for an observer in an aircraft to think that the balloon is trying to elude him although it is actually almost stationary or slowly rising in a straight line. Gorman's target, however, despite the circumstantial evidence, was listed as "unidentified."

"Unidentified" is a designation that Project Saucer, which has often had occasion to use it, has always loathed. "As long as anything is called that," Major Boggs said to me, "people can continue to indulge their fantasies." "Unidentified" is a charitable word for some of the will-o'-the-wisps the Project was called upon to explain. In Hamel, Minnesota, two children told of seeing a strange object fall into a back yard where they were playing. It had "spun around once, made a whistling noise, and then shot straight up into the sky about twenty feet, where it stopped again and made more whistling noises." Unidentified. One evening, four residents of Logan, Utah, saw twelve flying objects that looked like birds but were moving awfully fast for birds. Unidentified. Two elderly gentlemen of San Pablo, California, gazing up at a hazy sky, spotted a large, translucent object, which they estimated to be a mile above the earth. An investigator for Project Saucer was sent to interview them. One of the men thought the object resembled an immense amoeba covered with canvas; the other said it looked to him like a vegetable crate. One said it had been going east; the other said it had been going northwest. Both usually wore glasses but hadn't happened to have them on at the time. Unidentified.

In the few instances in which bits of pieces of suspect objects were picked up and turned over to the experts of Project Saucer during the two publicized years of its existence, the fragments were quickly identified. For example, soon after Kenneth Arnold sighted those nine tailless aircraft near Mount Rainier, residents of Jackson, Ohio, excitedly reported the discovery of a fallen disk. Examination showed it was the remains of a Signal Corps weather balloon. Early in 1948, residents of Kansas, southern Nebraska, and northern Oklahoma reported a violent explosion, high in the sky, that shook buildings and broke windows. Project Saucer was, of course, immediately involved. The likeliest clue came from a farmer who lived near Stockton, Kansas. He said that he and his wife had seen a fire in the sky and then a large cloud, after which they heard the big explosion. Two months later, an astonomer, following a hunch, found embedded in the soil forty miles from Stockton the presumed explanation of the mystery—a thousand pound chunk of an achondrite, an unusual type of meteorite. Smaller pieces were found near by. Some citizens of Bellefontaine, Ohio, thought they had witnessed the disintegration of a flying saucer when a flaming "wheel" fell in their vicinity. Upon analysis at a Wright Field laboratory, what remained of it was found to contain zinc, magnesium, sodium, and lead—standard components of various types of military flares.

For a time in the spring of 1949, it looked as though a Colorado rancher had been harboring a piece of a flying saucer for three years. Back in April 1946 the rancher, riding his horse on a high, rocky mesa, had come across a bit of tattered rigging attached to a steel ring. He took it back to his house, tossed it into a closet, and forgot about it. Then, belatedly reflecting on the wave of saucer sightings, he recalled the contraption in his closet. He showed it to two friends, one of whom, an omniscient type, stated definitely that it was part of a flying saucer. "I've seen too many saucers not to know one when I'm holding one in my own hand," he said. The rancher forwarded his find to Wright Field, where it was identified as a remnant of one of the incendiary balloons the hopeful Japanese dispatched across the Pacific during the war in an effort to start forest fires.

Even pictures taken of supposed saucers failed to impress the experts. There was the case of a man in Phoenix, Arizona, who spotted a flat gray object spiraling up and down in the sky at a speed that he estimated at between four and five hundred miles an hour. He snapped two pictures of it with his Brownie. Prints were rushed to Project Saucer, and Dr. Irving Langmuir, the physicist and a Nobel Prize winner, was asked to study them. The distinguished scientist learned that a thunderstorm had occurred just before the picture-taking, and concluded that he was looking at a couple of rather poor shots of a piece of paper being buffeted by the wind.

As time went on and the skies, apparently, continued to teem with flying saucers, the generals in the Pentagon, warming to their task, decided to enlarge the scope of the investigation. Commanders of all Air Force installations in the country were ordered to assign Intelligence officers to look into sightings reported in their areas. The officers were instructed to solicit the assistance of municipal police officials, who might be familiar with the personalities of the saucer observers. The F.B.I. was also called upon for assistance, and assigned agents to help interview people who reported that they had seen disks. The agents used a standard questionnaire, drawn up by Air Force Intelligence, which called for such information as the saucer's size, speed, color, and maneuvers. The information was usually transmitted to Wright Field, but some stories were so obviously false and some "evidence" so obviously trifling that the F.B.I. men didn't even bother to fill out the questionnaire. In Seattle, for instance, an alarmed woman called the police to inform them that a flaming disk had landed on her roof. The object turned out to be a hollow, drum-shaped affair made of plywood, with "USSR" crudely daubed on it in paint. An F.B.I. man found that a turpentine-soaked cloth had caused the flame. A practical joke, he decided. A farmer near Danforth, Illinois, reported that a saucer had crash-landed in one of his fields and burned up a patch of weeds. The F.B.I. man there concluded that someone had been playing a prank when he found that the disk was an amateurish assembly of some old radio parts. When a syndicated movie columnist wrote that a Hollywood producer had taken some pictures of flying saucers in Alaska, two worldly F.B.I. agents quickly ascertained that a movie company was making a picture about flying saucers in Alaska.

It became common practice among F.B.I. agents, in their efforts to establish the reliability of someone who claimed he had seen a spaceship or a flying saucer, to talk with the person's neighbors, business associates, friends, and enemies. For instance, after Dale Stevens, a sportswriter on the Richmond, Indiana, *Palladium-Item,* reported simply, and with a restraint uncommon in such matters, that he had seen a hovering light in the eastern sky that looked five or ten times larger than a star, an agent interviewed his publisher and noted, "Employer considers Mr. S. honest and sincere. Mr. S. is a member of the local Junior Chamber of Commerce." (Stevens' credibility received another endorsement some time later, when Dr. Hynek informed Project Saucer that it was quite possible that Stevens, and not a Sydney, Australia, astronomer, was the discoverer of Comet L. 1949—a recent visitor from space.)

The investigation of one flying-saucer report, which proved to be a hoax, resulted in the death of two Air Force Intelligence officers. Two residents of Tacoma got in touch with the editor of a Chicago adventure magazine and tried to sell him a story about six flying discs they claimed to have seen while they were in a boat off Maury Island; they had been showered with fragments from one of the disks, they said, and a pet dog who was with them had been killed. The editor asked Kenneth Arnold, who, as the first to report seeing a saucer, had by this time become known as the Man Who Saw the Men from Mars, to check on the details of the story. Arnold talked to the men and then asked the Air Force to help him investigate their statements. Two Air Force officers were sent to Tacoma to question the men. The Tacoma men turned over what they said were some of the fragments of the disk. The next day, the investigators took off in a B-25 for Hamilton Field, at San Rafael, California, where they planned to have the fragments analyzed by mineralogists. The plane crashed, and the investigators were killed; the pilot and the only other man aboard parachuted to safety. Soon afterward, newspapers and wire services in Tacoma received anonymous telephone calls telling them that saboteurs had shot down the plane with a 20-mm. cannon, because of the strategic value of its cargo. Actually, flames from a burned-out exhaust had set fire to the left wing of the plane. A few days later, the Tacoma pair, under further questioning, confessed that they had taken the fragments from an unusual rock formation they found on Maury Island. They had simply made up the flying-disk story.

On one occasion, an F.B.I. agent stationed in Denver himself described a strange object in the sky. After a hard day at the office, he was driving home when he spotted an unaccountable light over the city's airport. He got out of his car and collected a group of witnesses, all of whom agreed that the light was about five miles above the earth and traveling eastward. He made a report to the Air Force, and it assigned him to investigate his own story. He started by visiting the airport the next evening. He was standing around describing his experience to some local fliers when he suddenly pointed up to the sky and shouted, "There it is!" What he saw was the night light on a weather balloon. The Weather Bureau station at the airport sent one up at the same time every evening.

The scientists attached to Project Saucer examined the results of all investigations that seemed to contain clues that belonged in their respective fields. The reports they made on them were filed in the Pentagon, and Major Boggs let me read a number of them. The first one I read was by Dr. Fitts, who pointed out that one of the first tenets of psychology is that human perception is fallible. He outlined the mechanics of optical illusion and told of the irrationalizing effects of vertigo, a kind of blacking-out to which any of us is subject. Asserting that every saucer report that had not been proved to be a hoax or a case of mistaken identity could be explained on psychological grounds, he challenged practically all the data that had been submitted by observers. How, he asked, could anyone tell how far away a saucer was if he didn't know its size? How could anyone presume to estimate an object's speed without knowing its distance from himself? He suggested that some of the sightings might be blamed on *muscae volitantes* (flitting flies), the medical term for small solid particles that float about in the fluid of the eye, casting a shadow on the retina and moving as the eye moves.

Other elements of the saucer problem were studied by such men as Dr. George Valley, a nuclear physicist at the Massachusetts Institute of Technology; staff members of the research firm of Rand

Corporation; an assortment of physicists and aerodynamicists who specialize in the study of the stratosphere and the space beyond it; and the electronics experts attached to the Cambridge Field Station. These men were all searching for physical rather than psychological explanations, and some fairly strange theories occurred to them—the possibility that extraterrestrial animals were flying into our atmosphere, for example. (No data turned up to support that arresting idea.) The theory that the saucers were hostile aircraft was carefully studied and rejected. "The performances of these saucers not only surpass the development of present science but the development of present fiction-science writers," one scientist noted. The specialists also considered and rejected the concept of disks capable of riding the air on beams or rays of some kind. They even speculated on whether the anti-gravity shield that H. G. Wells thought up for his novel *The First Men in the Moon* would work; it wouldn't, they decided. The supposition that interplanetary craft where whizzing in at us was also discredited, despite its popularity with laymen. Spaceships, the scientists thought, would have to be so large and unwieldy that they couldn't possibly zigzag as frivolously as the reported saucers did. Besides, a spaceship, regardless of its size, could not, in the opinion of these men, carry sufficient fuel to remain for any length of time in the earth's dense atmosphere. The scientists noted, too, that the supposed spacemen showed a remarkable lack of interest in the rest of the world, being, it would seem, almost unanimous in their desire to see America first. "The small area covered by the disk barrage points strongly to the belief that the flying objects are of earthly origin, be they physical or psychological," one of the scientists reported.

From the report turned in by the astronomers, I learned that they, in addition to seining out comets, meteors, bolides, and achondrites from the stream of objects people were seeing in the skies, had also thoughtfully considered our planetary neighbors. The old question of the possibility of life on Mars took on a new urgency, and a new corollary: If there *are* living creatures on Mars, would they be capable of building spaceships? The astronomers thought not. Their perhaps slightly anthropomorphic conclusion was that Mars is so desolate and inhospitable that any living beings there would be intent on merely existing; they wouldn't have time to think of spaceships, even in order to transport themselves to a better climate.

Venus, regarded as the innocent cause of several reports of flying saucers, was also considered as a launching site for them. The astronomers concluded that its atmosphere, believed to be composed largely of carbon dioxide and immense, opaque clouds of formaldehyde droplets, precluded the practice of astronomy, and hence the concept of a universe and the idea of spaceships. The speculations of the astronomers were not confined to the solar system. They took into consideration not only the planets in the solar system but the twenty-two stars in addition to the sun that are thought to have satellites revolving around them. In view of the distance between these stars and the earth, the astonomers admitted frankly that their earth-bound minds bogged down at the thought of anything traveling that far. "The nearest eligible star is one called Wolf 359," an astronomer prominent in this phase of the investigation noted. "It is eight light-years away. A spaceship pilot taking off from one of that sun's planets and traveling at one-tenth the speed of light—say, at eighteen thousand miles per second—would need eighty years to make a one-way trip to the earth. And that speed is completely beyond the reach of any predicted level of rocket propulsion."

When I had a talk with Major Boggs after reading the reports, he remarked, "You know, not one of these wonder saucers has ever malfunctioned. My God, we have our hands full with conventional planes, but these saucers never seem to get in trouble and have to make forced landings."

After two years of operation, Project Saucer had not accomplished one of its principal objectives—that of satisfying the public that the air was free of unexplainable things. Nevertheless, on December 27, 1949, the Air Force issued a public announcement that Project Saucer was about to be disbanded. Perhaps the Air Force felt that silence was the best antidote for the contagion of mass susceptibility; whatever its reasons, the fact is that Project Saucer, while it did cease to exist as an agency working hand in hand with the general public, merely underwent an organizational change and then kept right on tracking down, in a considerably more quiet manner, reports of "aerial phenomena," to use its official term. Just one man, stationed at Wright Field and bearing the title of Aerial Phenomena Officer, was assigned to it on a full-time basis, and his orders were to limit his investigations to observations reported by pilots, scientists, engineers, and others who could presumably be considered qualified observers. Whatever information of value he picked up he was to turn over to the authorities at Wright Field. "We changed the study of unidentified flying objects from a special project to a general operation," an Air Force colonel recently told me. "Analyses of the sightings went through normal staff channels, so that our experts found them in their 'in' baskets along with their regular work. Of course, if the Aerial Phenomena Officer needed a kind of expert we didn't have on the payroll at Dayton, we'd put him in touch with the right fellow. In the fall of 1951, I remember, the officer suspected that a formation of lights seen over a southern state might be ducks, so we arranged for him to consult an ornithologist who was an authority on the migratory habits of waterfowl. Well, all we know is they weren't ducks."

The immediate effect of the Air Force's announcement that Project Saucer was about to fold was a decrease in the number of crackpot sightings, but seemingly reliable reports of objects seen in the sky continued to come in. "Not a month has gone by without our receiving reports that seem worth investigating," Captain Edward J. Ruppelt, the Aerial Phenomena Officer, informed me. "I've flown all over the country interviewing people who are as intelligent as any I've ever met. They've been entirely co-operative in talking with me. Some of them say they regret having seen what they saw, because up till then they'd always thought that all this talk of flying saucers was just so much foolishness. They don't want their names publicized, for fear of being ridiculed by their friends and professional colleagues. I always promise them there's no danger of that—that while the information they give me may be made public, their names never will be." In most cases, Captain Ruppelt said, investigation has shown that the people he has interviewed had been deceived by things that have been deceiving others all along—balloons, planes, meteors, and so on—but a nettling residue of around twenty per cent of the cases have wound up in that exasperating old pigeonhole labeled "Unidentified." Nothing, for example, could be found to account for the "something silvery directly overhead" reported by a mystified Civil Aeronautics Administration inspector at Terre Haute. A commercial pilot who, flying near Battle Creek, Michigan, spotted "an oval-shaped silver object" ahead of his ship, posed a similarly unsolved problem, as did a highly respected naval officer, stationed at the dirigible base at Lakehurst, New Jersey, who reported that he had stared through his binoculars at a brilliant image making turns that were far too tight for any known aircraft.

Twenty-five per cent of the observers interrogated by the Aerial Phenomena Officer since early in 1950 have been military pilots. Eight per cent have been commercial pilots, some with as much as twenty years' experience in the air, and at one stage in the current phase of the investigation, even a few physicists at Los Alamos, New Mexico, men who make a fetish of objectivity, were interviewed after they reported having seen puzzling lights hovering above their atomic-energy laboratories. "If you took any one of these incidents by itself, it might not mean much," Captain Ruppelt said. "But in view of the number and caliber of the informants, you couldn't help taking their claims seriously."

In February 1951, Dr. Urner Liddel, a nuclear physicist attached to the Office of Naval Research, at Washington, D.C., declared that at last, thanks to the lifting of certain security restrictions, he could provide the solution to the mystery of the flying saucers: They were "skyhooks," he said—balloons a hundred feet in diameter, which the Navy had secretly been sending up for the past four years in order to study cosmic rays. Dr. Liddel's assertion was immediately disputed by Dr. Anthony O. Mirarchi, who, as former head of the Air Force's Atmospheric Composition Bureau, had assisted in the diagnosis of Project Saucer reports. Dr. Mirarchi said he thought the saucers might be missiles from some foreign country carrying out reconnaissance missions over our atomic-energy plants. Dr. Liddel's explanation also made little impression on two Wright Field pilots, Captains E. W. Spradley and J. E. Cocker, who had seen a baffling something in the sky at a time when they were extremely balloon-conscious. They reported that they were tracking a large weather balloon over Alamogordo, New Mexico, not far from where the first atomic bomb was detonated, when they saw a flat "milky" object near the balloon. They estimated its altitude at between fifty and sixty thousand feet. Suddenly, they said, it gave off "three brilliant flashes, like photo flashes," and disappeared. Nor did Dr. Liddel's statement put a stop to the steady flow of reports of sightings—a "propelled bluish-white star" seen by an American Airlines pilot near Phoenix; "three circles of light spinning counterclockwise" that a Pennsylvania control-tower operator saw above his airport; "globe-shaped orange objects" that airmen over Korea said they saw. "In recent months, our informants have stressed light and color to us," Captain Ruppelt told me. "They rarely talk about disks any more, or anything else that might indicate solidity. That's pretty near the only generalization we've been able to draw from our data. We've tried every possible way to establish patterns for these—well, things. We've plotted them out on maps in an effort to find out if they're concentrated in any particular part of the country. They do seem to be more or less grouped around certain atomic installations, but that point isn't really worth much if you take into account the fact that people in such vital areas are liable to be more watchful of the sky than, say, a taxi driver in New York. We've plotted frequency of sightings by the hour of the day, the day of the week, and the month of the year. We've tried to determine if there isn't at least some common denominator to their shapes and colors. We've done our best to find out if they've been moving in any general direction. We've got nowhere."

In March 1952, Captain Ruppelt's records show, seventeen sightings were reported. In April, the figure rose sharply to ninety, a development that some Air Force people attribute to the publication in *Life* that month of an article entitled "Have We Visitors from Space?" In May, the reports of sightings dropped to seventy, but in June, when *Life* ran a sequel to its April article, they went up to a hundred and eleven. By July, the daily press, which had been fairly restrained about the matter for the past two years, stepped up its number of saucer stories, for the most part of the one-paragraph variety. On July 21st, however, saucers again became front-page news. That was the day a Senior Air Traffic Controller for the Civil

Aeronautics Administration at the National Airport's Air Route Traffic Control Center, in Washington, informed the Air Force, and the public, that early that morning his radarscope had picked up ten unidentifiable objects flying over various parts of the capital, including the prohibited area around the White House.

Shortly after midnight, the controller, Harry G. Barnes, related in a newspaper article that appeared under his signature, one of his crew of eight had asked him to look at the radarscope, jocularly remarking, "Here's a fleet of flying saucers for you." Barnes looked and saw seven "pips"—pale-violet spots that are supposed to represent aircraft but in this case were behaving like no plane pips Barnes had ever observed. They followed no set course, kept no formation, and could be tracked for only about three miles at a time, instead of the orthodox twenty-five or thirty, before disappearing from the screen. They seemed to be moving at a speed of between a hundred and a hundred and thirty miles an hour. At times, they moved together in a cluster, at other times wandered about singly. Barnes had two radar controllers look at the screen and they saw what he did. He had technicians check his radar equipment and they found it in perfect order. He called the airport control tower and the radar operator there said that the same curious pips were showing up on his screen.

One of Barnes' men then radioed Captain S. C. Pierman, who had been a Capital Airlines pilot for seventeen years and who had just taken off from the Washington airport, asking him to look for the objects. In a short while, Pierman radioed back, "There's one, and there it goes." During the next fourteen minutes, Pierman saw six bright lights that resembled tailless shooting stars, but three of them were moving horizontally, unlike any shooting star he had ever seen. Another commercial pilot who was reached in flight near by said that he saw a light off his left wing; Barnes found a corresponding pip on his radarscope. Other pilots in the vicinity reported, however, that they could see nothing unusual. Toward daybreak, ten peculiar pips were counted simultaneously on Barnes' screen. "There is no other conclusion I can reach but that for six hours on the morning of the twentieth of July there were at least ten unidentifiable objects moving above Washington," Barnes wrote. "They were not ordinary aircraft . . . Nor in my opinion could any natural phenomena account for these spots on our radar. Neither shooting stars, electrical disturbances, nor clouds could, either. Exactly what they are, I don't know. Now you know as much about them as I do. And your guess is as good as mine."

A week later, at 9:08 p.m. on July 26th, the Air Route Traffic Control Center's radarscope again showed unidentifiable objects over Washington. So did the screen at the Andrews Air Force Base, just outside the capital. Two jet interceptors, capable of doing six hundred miles an hour, were dispatched from a base near New Castle, Delaware, to investigate. When the interceptors appeared on the radarscopes, they were guided toward the objects. One of the pilots sighted four lights approximately ten miles in front of his plane and slightly above it, but they vanished while he was trying to overtake them. Twenty minutes later, he saw "a steady white light," but within a minute it, too, disappeared. "We have no evidence they were flying saucers," an Air Force representative said later. "Conversely, we have no evidence they were not flying saucers. We don't know what they were."

As a result of these two incidents, particularly the one involving the interceptors, public agitation reached a new height. The Air Force was bombarded with hundreds of letters, telephone calls, and telegrams demanding information and offering advice. One of the smaller airlines supplied its crews with cameras and ordered them to photograph any saucers they encountered. A civilian wrote to the Air Force that he would let it in on "the secret" in return for a colonelcy. A Los Angeles pastor wrote to Einstein, beseeching him to clear up the mystery, and Einstein wrote back, "Dear Sir: Those people have seen something. What it is I do not know and I am not curious to know." The Civil Defense director of Nassau County, Long Island tried to recruit members for his Ground Observer Corps by announcing, "Here is a chance for everyone to get first-hand knowledge of the flying-saucer hokum. All observers will be able to discern the difference between or among the sun, moon, stars, meteorites, searchlight beams, weather balloons, propeller and jet aircraft." Two Wisconsin disc jockeys, who apparently had never heard of Orson Welles, told their audience that they had found a flying saucer with a two-foot man inside; the management of the station spent the next day or so broadcasting assurances that it had all been just a gag.

Many communications received by the Air Force have dealt with the question of whether or not the saucers should be shot down. Some letter writers urged the Air Force to knock the lights out of the sky—assuming, of course, that the lights weren't United States property. The majority, however, were for making friends with the visitors. "Why should we be the first to kill?" one correspondent inquired plaintively. A twelve-year-old girl implored the Air Force to spare "the Saucerians," and a Unitarian minister in Massachusetts asked, "Why not entice them to land? The attitude of our people (and the Air Force) seems to me to be outwardly very immature with reference to these visitors to our planet. It seems to me that a very little publicity with a friendly slant to it would entirely change the picture . . . Isn't it worth a try?" The possibility that the visitors might not consider it an unmitigated blessing to be invited to land here was suggested by a distinguished theologian. In an article written for the National Catholic Welfare Conference News Service, the Very Reverend Francis J. Connell, Dean of the School of Sacred Theology at Catholic University, in Washington, D.C., declared that if rational beings do exist on other worlds, and if they have supernatural and preternatural gifts and have never sinned, they may be living in a state of paradise. "With their preternatural gifts, it would be reasonable to suppose they would be far ahead of us technically," Father Connell wrote. "With their superior intellect they might well have mastered interplanetary travel. If these supposed rational beings should possess the immortality of body once enjoyed by Adam and Eve, it would be foolish for our super-jet or rocket pilots to attempt to shoot them. They would be unkillable."

In an effort to quiet the gathering tumult, Major General John A. Samford, the present head of Air Force Intelligence, submitted to a press conference a few days after the jet chase over Washington. Major General Roger M. Ramey, the Air Force's Operations Director, was present, as were several Intelligence officers, including Captain Ruppelt. General Samford was by turn grave, skeptical, defensive, and informative. He didn't consider the radar incidents unusual. He said that over the past few years Air Force interceptors had made hundreds of fruitless responses to radar pips. Birds, balloons, ionized clouds, and light civilian planes had been their usual harvest. Radar had been designed for dealing primarily with aircraft, he said, but as more and more is learned about the device, perhaps it may offer possibilities for scientific observation of a nature for which it was never intended.

General Samford suggested that "temperature inversion" might have been responsible for the radar pips, especially since for quite a while there had been hot, humid air over Washington. As a result of temperature inversion, the General explained, with the help of an aide who was an electronics expert, radar sometimes makes objects that are actually on the ground look as if they were in the air; inversion takes place when a warm layer of air comes in over a cool one, increasing the density of the cool one so that it will bend light rays. In the region where the two layers meet, an atmospheric reflector, or "overhead mirror," is formed, creating some curious mirages. The General recalled the experience of the pilot of a night fighter who, while using his radar to follow an object apparently in flight, suddenly found himself heading straight for the ground. The pilot had pulled out barely in time.

The "highest probability" concerning the saucers, General Samford stated, is that they are phenomena associated with "intellectual and scientific interests that we are on the road to learn more about." The real difficulty in disposing of the reports about them has been that none of the reports to date have contained measurements made by standard devices that could "convert the thing or the idea of the phenomenon into something that becomes manageable as material for any kind of analysis that we know." Incidentally, the General pointed out, astronomers, whom he called "our best advisers . . . in this business of visitors from elsewhere," photograph the sky continuously, but they had reported no saucers. The General was reminded that many of the people who had told of seeing the most spectacular things were considered the most reliable. He replied that he had no intention of discrediting them, but the fact remained that none of them had offered data of the kind a scientist would find useful. An Air Force officer whom General Samford personally knew to be a competent witness had told him of seeing a saucer in the Middle East. This man, too, had been unable to obtain accurate measurements. "We have many reports from credible observers of incredible things," the General remarked.

Like General Moore, his predecessor in Project Saucer days, General Samford denied that the Air Force was attempting to cover up secret experiments. When he was asked if the saucers might be the guided missiles of a foreign country, he replied that he didn't see how, on the basis of their weird performances, they could be unless "someone" had achieved a means of developing unlimited power—"power of such fantastic higher limits that it is a theoretical unlimited; it's not anything that we can understand"—and utilizing it under conditions in which no mass is involved. As for the latter, the General told the press, drawing a laugh, "You know, what 'no mass' means is that there's nothing there."

While General Samford's interview probably reassured the public as evidence that the Air Force was still on the job, it did nothing to lessen the nation's saucer-consciousness. The reporters had hardly thanked the General for his comments when, on August 1, 1952, a Coast Guard photographer produced a picture showing four bizarre lights burning brilliantly in a daylight sky. He said he had taken it over Salem, Massachusetts. The next day, a Harvard astrophysicist called the photograph worthless because it was accompanied by no scientific data, such as temperature distribution and altitude. On August 6th, an Army physicist at Fort Belvoir, Virginia, created the equivalent of flying saucers in his laboratory by introducing molecules of ionized air into a partial vacuum in a bell jar, and three days later an internationally known authority on atmospheric conditions said of the physicist's experiment, "I know of no conditions of the earth's atmosphere, high or low, which would duplicate those needed to make the laboratory models." That same summer, a number of newspapers printed rumors that an Air Force plane had shot down a flying saucer, and the United Press, quoting a Cleveland paper, said that the plane had been "repeatedly attacked" by the saucer. An Omaha man wrote the Air Force that the saucers were God's way of tormenting us for having deified science; a man in Kansas City,

Kansas, saw their visitation as an occasion for rejoicing. He cited Ezekiel 10:4: "Then the glory of the Lord went up from the cherub, and stood over the threshold of the house; and the house was filled with the cloud, and the court was full of the brightness of the Lord's glory."

In mid-1954, more competent observers than ever before were reporting saucers, Captain Ruppelt's successor, a Captain Charles Hardin, told me. The Air Force was buying a hundred special cameras, which it hoped would help determine what the provocative objects were made of, and it was considering buying several photographic telescopes of a new type, costing as much as five thousand dollars apiece, with which a continuous photographic record could be made nightly of the sky over the whole hemisphere. After the better part of a decade and close to three thousand reported sightings of a serious nature, there was no discussion in Air Force circles of abandoning the pursuit of the elusive saucers. Too many people were waiting for the answer.

CHAPTER 22 | MARCH, 1958

EVOLUTION OF A MESA

EVERY TOWN HAS some favorite myth about itself, and Los Alamos, the home of the Los Alamos Scientific Laboratory, where the world's first atomic and hydrogen bombs were assembled and where new bombs are now being designed, is no exception. Situated atop a New Mexican mesa seventy-three hundred feet high, Los Alamos fancies itself a remote outpost of civilization, gallantly going it alone. Practically everyone I met there paid almost ritualistic homage to this myth. "Why, even our telegraph office shuts down at six in the evening," a physicist informed me the day I arrived there, neglecting to mention that telegrams can be phoned at any hour at all to Western Union in Santa Fe, thirty-five miles away. "We're as isolated as a Himalayan hill station," a chemist added, and went on gravely, "It's our altitude, of course." I refrained from pointing out that Santa Fe, which, as the capital of the state, considers itself something of a hub, is on just about the same elevation as Los Alamos. With a wide sweep of his hand, the chemist indicated the peaks of the Jemez Mountains, to the west of the mesa, and the Sangre de Cristo range, to the east, their slopes covered with aspen, western yellow pine, and patches of fresh white snow. "We're lost in the wilderness," he said, and so earnest was his tone that I momentarily forgot the highways winding down from the Hill, as this strategic mesa is known in these parts, to the Pojuaque Valley and the rest of the United States.

Los Alamos's sense of being marooned goes back to the war years, when it was *supposed* to be cut off from the outside world, and has survived what should perhaps have been its death blow—

the opening of the Hill to the public, early in 1957. About ten years ago, when I was last there, I felt on arriving at the Los Alamos gates that I had reached the frontier of a mysterious and probably hostile enclave. Back in that dim time, when the United States had a monopoly of nuclear weapons, the entrance to Los Alamos crawled with uniformed guards, their holsters bulging and their manner forbiddingly suspicious as they interrogated visitors and checked identification papers. The guards' posts, which used to be strung across the road like toll stations, have now been torn down, and what was once their field office, off to one side of the road, has become the Gate Drive-In, a hamburger joint with a jukebox and a sizable teen-age clientele. In the old days, once past the guards, one entered a sprawling, half-finished settlement that, with its unsightly green laboratory buildings right in the middle of things and its scattering of prefabs and trailers and barracks, indeed gave the appearance of being at the edge of the civilized world. Now one drives freely into Los Alamos, and finds oneself in a neatly ordered town that might, except for the distinctive landscape, be a young suburban community anywhere in the United States.

The letting down of the barriers was greeted with anything but joy by the residents of Los Alamos, who had grown to like their aerielike inaccessibility. In 1956, the Atomic Energy Commission, democratically feeling its way, took a straw vote of the local population on the question of opening the gates, and the response was overwhelmingly negative. "Certainly we wanted our gates," one woman told me the other day. "We felt safe, and we had privacy. Relatives couldn't just drop in on us any time they felt like it." The A.E.C., however, was eager to cut loose its guards—there were twenty of them, and their salaries amounted to a hundred thousand dollars a year—and on Friday, February 15, 1957, it summarily announced that, except for certain areas surrounding the Laboratory buildings, Los Alamos would become an open city the following Monday. Jitters swept the town that weekend. The mesa, people said, was going to be overrun by tourists, door-to-door salesmen, and unsavory characters from Santa Fe and the Valley, who would instantly precipitate a crime wave. On Saturday, there was a run on pistols and rifles at the sports shop. One father declared that as of

Monday his teen-age daughter would cease to be available for baby-sitting; she was going to stay home after dark. "A spinster secretary asked us to protect her against saboteurs," Paul A. Wilson, the A.E.C.'s area manager for Los Alamos, told me. This xenophobic binge was of short duration. Monday came and went—as have many Mondays since—with little change in the life of the community. To be sure, there was a crime wave not long afterward, but it was a minuscule one, brought on by some Hill youngsters who stole a car or two and performed sundry other acts of mischief. Salesmen did come, but not in swarms, and tourists stopped off only occasionally, usually making a side trip to Los Alamos on their way home from Bandelier National Monument, the site of some Pueblo Indian ruins, fifteen miles to the south. The town, in short, has been pretty much left to its residents—though this is not to say that outsiders have evinced no curiosity about Los Alamos since the disappearance of the gates. I learned of one example of such curiosity from Dr. Jane H. Hall, a pleasant-faced physicist who is assistant director of the Laboratory. Last winter, Dr. Hall said, when she and her husband—he is Dr. David B. Hall, the head of the Laboratory's reactor-development division—were vacationing in the Virgin Islands, they became acquainted with another couple, and the wife raised a question that had been on her mind since she visited some pueblos near Los Alamos a few years back. She hoped she wasn't asking the Halls to violate security, or anything like that, she said, but, looking up from a distance at the secret city of Los Alamos, she had observed a tall plume of smoke; she wondered, now that the gates were down, if it was all right to ask what that was. "She was so tentative, so expectant," Dr. Hall recalled, "I hated to have to tell her that the plume of smoke came from the town garbage dump."

While the opening of the gates is probably the surest indication that the Hill is getting to be like ordinary places, other such indications have appeared since my last visit. The community was then a government reservation, and its people could not vote in state or national elections; they were governed by an A.E.C. official who had practically autocratic powers, though, as one might suppose in a community having such a high collective I.Q., he exercised them with discretion. Today Los Alamos is the county seat of Los Alamos County—

New Mexico's newest (and smallest)—with a senator and a representative in the state legislature. Along with the vote, the citizens received the privilege of paying local taxes, levied by a county council of three commissioners, who serve for a dollar a year. The commissioners also exercise such powers as maintaining a county court and issuing traffic regulations, and a few summers ago they took the radical step of putting Los Alamos County on daylight-saving time—confusing things sadly for those Laboratory workers who live down in the Valley, where Mountain Standard Time is in effect the year round. It might be said that in many respects Los Alamos is now leading a reasonably normal civilian life, even if some of its older residents are not quite adjusted to the fact. In the graduating class of Los Alamos High School last year, there were a number of students who had received their entire education, from kindergarten up, on the Hill, but some parents here, who still think of themselves as temporarily transplanted from New York or Madison, Wisconsin, are astonished to get letters from their children in college referring to the Hill as "back home."

Despite all these recent developments, the federal government's influence in Los Alamos remains strong. For one thing, the Atomic Energy Commission still owns something like ninety-nine per cent of the town's real estate—a state of affairs that dates back to the war, when the government bought the mesa from a boys' school. The A.E.C., having plenty of things to worry about besides real-estate management, would be delighted to bow out as landlord, but, as is generally the case, it takes a lot of legislation and negotiation to dispose of federal property. All things considered, it was quite an event when, a few weeks ago, a twenty-acre parcel of land, divided into seventy-one lots, was placed on sale for home construction—the first bit of real estate to go on the block. And there may be greater things to come, according to Wilson, the A.E.C. man, who told me that, if everything goes right, a good many A.E.C.-owned homes will begin passing into private ownership before long. Most residents look forward to the change, since under the present setup they naturally feel a lack of roots. There are some, however, who will miss having a landlord as paternalistic as the A.E.C., which has done its best to make life easy for the tenants. "The government really coddles us, and I, for one, am glad it does," a researcher remarked to me. "I must confess that I find it comforting to know that I can call on the government to fix my plumbing." He smiled, and went on more seriously, "Make no mistake, though, the coddling has its practical side. Many of us could earn twice as much with private industry as we do here on the Hill, but our rent and other expenses out in the cruel world would be twice as high. My house costs me a hundred and seven dollars a month, and it has four bedrooms, two bathrooms, a garden, and a fifty-mile view. Besides, we have no mosquitoes on this mesa. That alone is worth three thousand dollars of whatever salary an aircraft company in southern California might offer me."

The strongest sentiments in favor of the A.E.C.'s decision to pull out are being expressed by some of the local merchants. Under the present arrangement, such businessmen lease their establishments from the A.E.C., and any improvements that they make automatically become the property of the government. Since I was in Los Alamos last, the A.E.C. has done a great deal to expand the town's commercial facilities—there are now almost fifty shops, or four times as many as there were then—but the merchants are impatient to do some expanding they can call their own. In other ways, though, the Hill is practically made to order for small businessmen, according to Elmo deBaca, the president of the Los Alamos Merchants' Association, who runs a garage and an automobile sales agency. "Up here on the mesa," he told me contentedly, "we have a captive trade, the per-capita income is high, and there's no unemployment. It just isn't allowed. No job, no home. It's a one-industry town, of course, but that industry ought to be good for a long, long time."

Los Alamos officials believe that it may be ten years before the A.E.C. has completely disposed of its non-scientific property on the Hill, but they feel that whenever it does, the chances are that it will be handing over a clean, good-looking town. The town is clean and good-looking right now, for that matter, and its appearance seems to be improving daily. The original labs have come down, and the new ones—concrete and metal buildings from one to ten stories high —are grouped in a pleasant forested area just south of the town proper. Gone is the sloppy patchwork of prefabs and trailers, and in their place are new houses of frame, stucco, or adobe and cinder block, in a sort of modified Western architectural style, that stand on quiet, winding streets with names like Spruce and Quince and Peach. The improvement in living quarters is all to the good, since most of the Hill's entertaining takes place in homes. There are few restaurants and no cabarets on the Hill, and the dining room at the Lodge, the town's one hotel, is a gloomy place with a limited cuisine. The height of local epicureanism is reached when a hostess is lucky enough to enlist the services of a certain experimental physicist here, who is well versed in Chinese cookery, and his wife, who is an excellent pastry chef; every now and then, when they are in the mood, this accomplished pair will volunteer to serve as caterers for some party-giving friend.

The original complement at Los Alamos consisted of about two hundred people, including a few dozen wives—just about enough for a big cocktail party. The place now has thirteen thousand inhabitants, and almost half of them are children. "Pediatrics and obstetrics are big business here," one Los Alamos mother told me. Despite the high percentage of youngsters, though, the average age of Los Alamos citizens today is thirty-five, as compared to twenty-five during the war, when the director of the Laboratory, Dr. J. Robert Oppenheimer, was a doddering thirty-nine. Their age notwithstanding, the present inhabitants get about spryly enough. Los Alamos has one of the most ardent parachute-jumping clubs in the country, and not a single physicist has blown away yet. Some of the Laboratory people display a youthful prankishness even at work, to judge by the vermouth atomizer that was launched a few years ago at Yucca Flat, the proving ground in Nevada where bombs designed on the Hill are tested. On that occasion, a scientist told me, "a couple of the boys" tied a bottle of dry vermouth to an atomic bomb just before it went off, as a personal favor to a colleague who likes his Martinis extra dry. The fallout, it was reasoned, would supply their friend with all the vermouth he required for years to come. "All he has to do now is stick the shaker out the window and get vermouth from the atmosphere," the scientist explained to me.

For all the physical improvements in Los Alamos, perhaps the most striking change—or so it seems to a returning visitor—is not in the look of the place but in its mood. Back in 1947, one couldn't spend even a few hours in Los Alamos without hearing discussions of whether bombs should be made at all in a time of presumed peace, and the tone was uniformly sombre and soul-searching. One researcher, whom I talked with at some length, weighed the pros and cons of what a worldwide scientists' strike might accomplish in the way of straightening out the policies of governments, and another asked me, as I was leaving, to give his regards to Broadway—"the country's best target." A year or two earlier, just after the Japanese surrender, many scientists, appalled by the climax of their labors, had left the Hill—forever, they said. Nowadays, the consciences on the Hill are apparently much clearer; almost all the scientists I have talked with calmly accept the necessity for making weapons. "Things don't seem to make as much difference as they once did," one scientist told me vaguely, and I had lunch one day at the home of a veteran researcher, who had taken part in the world's first atomic explosion—the Trinity test, on July 16, 1945, in the Alamogordo desert, about two hundred and fifty miles south of the Hill—and who seemed to have forgotten he had ever been plagued by moral qualms. As far as he was concerned, he remarked, he took weapons assignments in his stride, and always had. "Really, dear?" his wife asked quietly. The scientist stared at his plate for a moment, and then, shaking his head, said, "No, I guess not. I guess there wasn't one of us who came back from Alamogordo without asking himself, 'My God, what have I done?' "

The general attitude toward munitions that one finds in Los Alamos today might be described as cerebral rather than emotional, and political rather than moral. The scientists look upon their work as a reasonable Cold War operation that gives American diplomats time to work out an effective peace. Unless the United States can inflict casualties as efficiently as the next nation, these scientists say, in effect, its bargaining position will be seriously compromised. "We think we are contributing to the only kind of stability available—namely, this uneasy peace," Dr. John H. Manley, a distinguished physicist, told me. "We can merely help the State Department in its efforts to improve this peace. Scientists cannot improve it alone. They are not diplomats." Dr. Alvin C. Graves, a forty-eight-year-old physicist who is the head of the Los Alamos weapons-testing division and also an elder of the United Church, the largest Protestant church on the Hill, said, "I pray that nuclear weapons are never fired in anger, and my feeling is that our stockpile and the Russian stockpile are promoting peace right now—unsatisfactory though this sort of peace may be." Dr. Graves, who suffered a heart attack last year and a radiation injury to one of his eyes in 1946, maintains that many of the scientists remain at their posts in Los Alamos, rather than go elsewhere for more money, precisely because they think their work is promoting peace, and he recently advanced this belief in a lecture at his church, called "Nuclear Research and My Christian Conscience."

Dr. Graves' pastor, the Reverend Archer Anderson, isn't quite so sure that the Hill's residents are as serene about their work as they may sound. Several scientists, he told me, have come to him for counsel, troubled by the thought that they may be subverting their profession to "evil." Only recently, one of the most learned members of his congregation had been much upset upon reading a condemnation of scientists on just this ground in a religious publication. "I consoled him by quoting from Luke—'When a strong man armed keepeth his palace, his goods are in peace,' " Dr. Anderson told me. "Believe me, the hunger for spiritual reality is stronger here than in any other community I've served in." But, rewarding as his pastorate was, he added, it presented special problems. "How do you manage to stay ahead of those Ph.D.s?" a fellow-minister had once asked him. "I never speak of science," Dr. Anderson had answered. "I just stick to preaching."

Whatever the moral aspects of bomb-making may be, the average Hill dweller finds one kind of justification for his presence in Los Alamos whenever he gazes at the countryside. Almost anyone would be tempted to settle on the Hill for the sake of its beauty alone. In the spring, the aspens are green on the Sangre de Cristo range, thirty miles away; in the autumn they turn yellow, amid the green pines; and in the winter there are vistas of distant snow squalls. All year round, tumbled mountain rock, iridescent in the shifting twilight, suggests an endless past and—the possessors of nuclear weapons willing—an endless future. It came as no surprise to me to learn that Sunday painting outranks even parachute jumping as a local diversion. Just breathing the Hill's clear air is a delight for anyone who has known the dust and smoke of a big city—and nearly every adult in Los Alamos has, for it is possibly the most cosmopolitan small town in the United States. On winter and spring weekends, whole families crowd into station wagons and drive over to ski runs at Sawyer's Hill or Pajarito Mountain, twenty minutes away. When the weather gets warmer, there is picnicking among the ruins at Bandelier. Even in the summer, though, it is cool on the Hill—cool enough to induce physics and chemistry professors from all over the country to come to Los Alamos and take summer jobs with the A.E.C. They carry on research—availing themselves of the Laboratory's superb equipment, and, in return, affording staff people the stimulation of outside minds—while their families use the place as a summer resort.

Among the summer guests have been several of the scientists who vowed, when the war was over, never to set foot on the cursed Hill again, and the climate alone does not account for their return. Nostalgia, too, plays a part, for, as the years have passed, many scientists have come to look back upon the time they spent on the Hill during the war as days of glory. It was a period when many of the greatest scientific minds outside the Axis countries were gathered in Los Alamos (Einstein was perhaps the notable exception), and the quality of the discussions that were then held on the mesa, it is said, may be unique in scientific history. "This was Athens," I was told by one experimental physicist who left the Hill in 1945 and has returned permanently. "It was wonderful. The best scientific intellects in the world were here, and the talk ranged all over the cosmos. Luckily, Oppenheimer was strong enough to knock all those minds together." Dr. Oppenheimer is still revered in Los Alamos, and one discovers this in the fairly general feeing about Dr. Edward Teller, a former member of the Los Alamos Scientific Laboratory and now the director of the A.E.C. laboratory in Livermore, California, who testified before a special investigative committee of the A.E.C., in 1954, that it would be "wiser" not to grant security clearance to Dr. Oppenheimer. One would think that Dr. Teller had given his testimony only yesterday, so ready are many Los Alamos scientists to condemn him for it. A while ago, when Dr. Teller came to the Hill on a visit, a colleague publicly and pointedly refused to shake his hand.

The Cold War being the ambiguous phenomenon that it is, one of the Los Alamos Scientific Laboratory's major concerns is to stay limber. It must design weapons, but if it doesn't also push ahead with pure research, it runs the risk of becoming, in the event of the millennium, a defunct monument to a dead armaments race. "We want to be a national resource, not just an arsenal," one scientist told me. So, while the emphasis is on munitions, the Laboratory is also conducting basic investigations in several fields of science. From the point of view of the scientists, I gathered, this is fortunate. Just designing bombs, no matter how sanitary, can grow tedious for a mettlesome scientist, and it was pointed out to me that though there may be excellent reasons for dreaming up new models, the essential truth about nuclear weapons is already in—they can kill us all at least once. As Dr. Manley put it, "Can you improve a toothbrush indefinitely?" Of course, he went on quickly, the Laboratory's concern with pure research stems from something more than a desire to assuage scientific boredom. "There are several reasons for our current program," he said. "One, needless to say, is A.E.C. policy. Another is the need to use our manpower properly—to deploy our forces. We're now about three thousand strong, and if we all concentrated on weapons, we would soon reach a point of diminishing returns. Suppose—and this is strictly hypothetical—a ten-per-cent improvement in weapons were possible. Would it be intelligent to go all out for that—to use personnel who might otherwise be working on, say, the improvement of reactors? Would it be fair to the taxpayer, after the vast investment that he has made in the Laboratory?"

The A.E.C., I gathered from Dr. Manley and some of his colleagues, allows the scientists a good deal of leeway when it comes to the deployment of their own brains. The Laboratory receives broad directives from Washington, establishing projects and priorities, but the day-to-day decisions are left to the men at Los Alamos, and, scientific work being what it is, this means that they can have considerable autonomy. Different men, of course, react differently to Washington directives. Some are quite literal about carrying them out. Middle-of-the-roaders try to strike a balance between pleasing Washington and following their own line of thought and research. Then, there are those who consider themselves authoritatively in touch with the situation at hand and who instinctively look upon the directives as just a bureaucratic shuffling of papers. No one I have talked with in Los Alamos, though—and I have talked with a couple of real mavericks—has been so infatuated with his own ideas as to pass over political and economic realities. Like Dr. Manley, they frequently refer to "the taxpayer"—and with what might strike those who know little of government service as an odd reverence. "Yes, we take the taxpayer pretty seriously," Dr. Graves told me. "I doubt if you'll find a single thing on the Hill that could be described as plush."

Specifically, the bulk of the Laboratory's work involves four principal "programs." One of these is straight weapons design, plus supervision of tests in Nevada and the Pacific. Another is research on nuclear reactors. A third, Project Rover, is an attempt to exploit the atom as a propellant for space vehicles—a highly practical field of research, I was told by Dr. Raemer Schreiber, the head of the project, since a pound of U-235 has ten million times as much energy as a pound of chemical fuel. Finally, there is Project Sherwood, aimed at controlling the stupendous energy released by thermonuclear fusion. (Laboratories at Livermore, Princeton, Oak Ridge, and N.Y.U. are also taking part in this one.) Project Sherwood could ultimately result in man's independence of coal, oil, and all the other fuels that have been at the bottom of more than one war in the past, and, moreover, since the only raw material needed for fusion is deuterium, a substance that is extracted from water and so is found almost everywhere in unlimited quantities, it could bring about the blooming of deserts and all the other glorious visions ever associated with the peaceful uses of atomic energy. The United States is supposedly in a race with Britain to see who can bring off the taming of fusion first, and, as it happens, it might not be quite as far along as it is were it not for the British-educated brain of a Los Alamos man named Dr. James L. Tuck, who, I was informed, has directed the research that has solved a number of vexing problems posed by fusion. A tall, mustached physicist of forty-eight, who was a member of the British scientific mission to Los Alamos during the war, Dr. Tuck became an American citizen three years ago. Soon afterward, he began to take part in the hydrogen-bomb work that had started on the Hill in 1954—something he couldn't have done without becoming a citizen. During this research, certain data dealing with temperatures stimulated thinking along lines leading to the control of fusion, and when the H-bomb effort was licked, Tuck and various colleagues of his found themselves well embarked on Project Sherwood. Not too much is being said about the project these days, and Tuck himself displays a commendable British reserve on the subject. "Sherwood is going very well—very—but there are no thermonuclear reactors around the corner," he told me, and that was that.

Besides the four big programs, other work is going on in Los Alamos. For one thing, the effects of fallout on health are being extensively studied, as they are in other parts of the A.E.C.'s empire. As might be expected, the men in charge—members of the Laboratory's Health Division, and mostly doctors of medicine—subscribe to the general position of the A.E.C. that up to now the effects of fallout from bomb tests have been negligible. Perhaps these men have lately been chafing atop their mesa at the widespread condemnation of the tests; in any case, I was not prepared for the defensive way in which some of them have brought up the subject. "As a physician, may I say to you that I have no desire to hurt people, including my own children," one of them told me. "Some amazing claims have been advanced by the enemies of fallout," another physician said. "Are you a *friend* of fallout?" I asked him, and he smiled and told me that he wasn't, of course, and that he freely conceded we might all be in danger if the present rate of testing, which he characterized as "reasonable," should be unduly accelerated. The men spoke as experts in their field, and they insisted that all the available data—"the numbers," as they put it—support their position. They were puzzled that the numbers had failed to budge their opponents, particularly since these included old friends for whose integrity and gifts they vouched unreservedly. "Suppose you had no responsibility for weapons development," I said to one scientist. "Can you imagine yourself calling for an end to the tests?" He frowned thoughtfully for a moment, and then said, "I can't imagine myself ever not going by the numbers."

Los Alamos has always had a peculiar interest in radiation, Dr. Thomas L. Shipman, head of the Health Division, told me. The Trinity shot, he pointed out, disseminated the first fallout of fission products known to man, and the only two deaths in this country from radioactive burns occurred on the Hill, in laboratory accidents "back in the early days" of 1945 and 1946. If only people knew what a roentgen or a millicurie was, the way they do a pint or a bushel, Dr. Shipman said, they wouldn't be so alarmed. While crops and grazing cattle were admittedly taking up substances like cesium 137 and strontium 90, he went on, it was the amounts that had to be considered, and here the public's lack of familiarity with roentgens and millicuries, the units in which radiation is measured, had produced a great deal of uncalled-for panic. He wasn't one to maintain that the test program constituted a zero risk, he said, but if it was complete safety we were after, we might as well abolish General Motors, too; after all, automobiles kill. He couldn't think of a single industry that was as carefully regulated as the atomic-energy industry. "Why, it had safeguards before it ever started," he told me.

Dr. Shipman said that Los Alamos itself proved his point about roentgens and millicuries. Those weren't strange terms in that town, and, as a result, when a small amount of polonium, a radioactive material, got loose in 1954 and spread all over the Hill, the community remained calm. The polonium had been encased in a small nickel container in one of the Laboratory buildings; the container, it seemed, had cracked, and the stuff had spilled out on the floor, where it lay in the form of dust. When particles of it were discovered there, in the course of a periodic checkup of laboratories, Dr. Shipman immediately organized an exhaustive hunt for the rest, which by then had been scattered all through the community by the people who had walked on the contaminated floor. Only a few days elapsed between the mishap and the checkup, Dr. Shipman said, but fully fifty residences were thought to be likely repositories of polonium. "The Hill is a very sociable place," Dr. Shipman remarked. "There had been an awful lot of visiting back and forth." His trackers, with their detection instruments, took weeks to run down all the radioactive dust. Some women lost the use of their kitchens for a day or two. Bassinets and cars had to be cleaned. The monitors even found some polonium in Valley homes, a couple of polonium bearers from the Hill having visited friends there. Two visitors from Oak Ridge went back to Tennessee in borrowed overcoats, since theirs had set the needles on the instruments dancing. "We knew that altogether a few thousand millicuries of radiation were involved," Dr. Shipman concluded, "but we knew, too, that the polonium had been spread thin. Our men simply went out and washed the polonium away with soap and water. No one pushed the panic button."

Whatever the outcome of the present controversy over fallout, the Laboratory is amassing a good deal of information on the subject. By examining food samples collected at a network of stations, it keeps a close check on the amount of radioactive material descending on every part of the United States. Forty thousand pounds of dried milk, in fifty-pound cardboard drums, has been sent to Los Alamos this past year by the American Dry Milk Institute, which is commercially concerned with the fact that some people have stopped ordering milk for fear of getting bone cancer. Vegetables have also been tested in Los Alamos, and so have beef, pork, and venison—the last brought in by local hunters. The machines used for testing food specimens are so sensitive, I was told, that they can detect and measure radioactivity a hundred times weaker than the radioactivity normally found in nature.

The Laboratory has devised what it calls a "human counter"—a kind of giant Geiger counter that can measure the radiation emitted by a whole human body, rather than just a hand or foot. The counter is a horizontal cylinder, which will accommodate a person weighing as much as two hundred and fifty pounds; it has an inner wall of stainless steel and an outer wall of lead, four inches thick, that weighs twenty tons. Last year, eight hundred and twenty people, from thirty-two states—each person, in effect, a geographical point, I was told by Dr. Wright H. Langham, of the Health Division—were measured by the machine, and the radiation given off by the cesium 137 they had absorbed from fallout came to no more than one-twentieth the radiation given off by the potassium of their own bodies. All sorts of volunteers submit themselves to the machine, it seems. The day I inspected it—in the company of Dr. Langham and a colleague of his, Dr. Payne Harris—a group of Los Alamos Cub Scouts, complete with den mother, had just had a go at the counter and were being gratefully dismissed by a technician, Mrs. Billie Clinton. "Congratulations," she was saying to them. "Each of you is now a statistic."

"How would you like to try it?" Dr. Harris asked me. "You're a geographical point."

When I agreed, he showed me to a booth, where I took off my clothes and put on white pajamas. Then I lay down in a cradle of stainless steel, which would lug me, mechanically, into the interior of the counter. Mrs. Clinton handed me a switch, and said that if I pressed it, I would be released automatically from the machine. "We've rigged up this switch—we call it the chicken switch, or the scram button—because some people get claustrophobia in there," she explained. "You'll be inside for four minutes." Dr. Harris, meanwhile, had seated himself at a small console at one side of the counter, where my gamma-ray activity would be recorded. Then, switch in hand, I was drawn jerkily into the lead tunnel, and within a few seconds was entombed. It was close in there, in terms of both atmosphere and space. An electric bulb was burning weakly above my head, and I shut my eyes for the rest of the four minutes, which seemed forever. The mechanism that had trundled me in finally returned me to the brightly illuminated room, where Mrs. Clinton handed me a graph of my gamma-ray activity as a souvenir. Dr. Harris suggested that I call him the next morning, when he would have my numbers worked up. I did, and he said, "Typical New York. Cesium activity three and a half per cent of natural potassium activity. You're at the low end of the average scale." It was a nice thing to know.

Two Fragments on Fallout:

"Without radioactivity, we'd have less to think about today. Without radioactivity, as a matter of fact, we'd have nothing to think about—we'd all still be slime in the primeval swamp."

"Of course, it's too bad about those Japanese fishermen, but look at it this way—the particles that fell on the LUCKY DRAGON *may be the biggest break the cause of peace ever received."*

An A.E.C. official, April 1955

FALLOUT

FALLOUT, the radioactive debris that accumulates in the upper atmosphere following the detonation of a nuclear bomb and sooner or later comes to earth, often many hundreds, and even thousands, of miles from the scene of the explosion, is usually less visible than the soot that settles on New York every day at the rate of a ton to every square mile. The particles of dust that constitute most fallout look like any other dust, cannot be smelled, felt, or tasted, and descend and land soundlessly. As a general rule, fallout can be detected only by instruments—notably, of course, by the Geiger counter but also by such less celebrated devices as the scintillation counter and the ion chamber. Scientists checking on the density of fallout frequently differ in their interpretations of their findings, but there is clearly no room for disagreement about one thing: This dry rain of tainted matter increases the degree of radiation in any locality it visits. The point of conflict among the experts, as I have come to realize while looking into the problems presented by fallout, is over the danger, if any, of the increase, and this at present seems to be more a matter of opinion than of scientific determination. It appears indisputable, however, that no community need be apprehensive over a slight rise in the level of radiation (as commonly used, the word is synonymous with radioactivity), for in normally rainy weather certain radioactive natural gases that almost everywhere are constantly emanating from the ground do not diffuse as readily as they do at other times, and so increase the amount of radiation in the immediate vicinity, occasionally as much as four hundred per cent—a phenomenon that has been commonplace all over the world since long before anyone ever heard of fallout and has been definitely proved to be harmless.

Fallout varies greatly in intensity, depending, in part, upon the amount of energy released—or, to use the technical term, "yielded" —by the bombs that create it. America's high-yielding bombs are tried over remote islands in the Pacific and its low-yielding models over the Atomic Energy Commission's Nevada proving ground. Early in 1951, the A.E.C. became sufficiently impressed by the fallout that its low-yielding bombs were precipitating on widespread portions of the United States to set up a nationwide system of observation stations for monitoring fluctuations in the density of radiation. The system now has eighty-nine stations, and not one of them, whether near the test area or thousands of miles away from it, has ever failed to report a rise in radiation following a "shot," which is the A.E.C. people's term for the setting off of a bomb. Seemingly satisfied by the reports from these stations, Lewis L. Strauss, the chairman of the A.E.C., issued a statement last February declaring that as far as the Nevada experiments were concerned, "the hazard [of dangerously radioactive fallout] has been successfully confined to the controlled area of the Test Site." A month later, however, two scientists at the University of Colorado were reported by the newspapers as having asserted that fallout over their state had reached a point where it could no longer be ignored by those concerned with public safety. The Governor of Colorado, a former United States senator who served on the Joint Committee on Atomic Energy while he was in Washington, responded to this by calling the scientists' warning "phony" and saying that they ought to be arrested. The clamor quieted down when the president of the university issued a statement to the effect that the two scientists had qualified their warning by saying that the fallout would be dangerous if its radioactivity was maintained at the peaks it occasionally reached.

The Colorado furor was only one, and by no means the first, of a number of public warnings and bickerings over the issue of fallout. In 1953, the chairman of the Physics Department of the University of Utah, in Salt Lake City, in a state bordering on Nevada, expressed the belief that Americans' capacity for tolerating radiation was being sapped by fallout, and that same year five sheep ranchers in Cedar City, Utah, some two hundred miles from the Proving Ground, sued the government for damages, claiming that fallout had been fatal to approximately a thousand of their animals. The A.E.C. investigated and found no evidence to support the contention that the death of the sheep had been caused by fallout. The case of the sheep ranchers, which is still pending, brought back memories of the explosion of the first atomic bomb, on July 16, 1945, in New Mexico, which, among many other things, inflicted burns on a nearby herd of cattle and caused the animals' hair to turn gray. (The cattle were presently sent to Oak Ridge, Tennessee, where they and, more recently, their progeny have been studied ever since by members of the faculty of the University of Tennessee School of Agriculture, who are endeavoring to determine the long-range effects of overexposure to radiation.) Fallout from that first explosion in New Mexico also contaminated cornstalks in Indiana that were later converted into strawboard to make packing cartons; some of these found their way to Rochester, New York, where the Eastman Kodak people innocently used them to ship out a supply of film, which is exceptionally sensitive to radiation. The film was ruinously fogged. It is now standard practice for the A.E.C. to forewarn photographic-supply companies of impending test blasts, so that they can take certain well-established protective measures against possible fallout, but so far nobody has come up with any similar measures to alert the owners of cornstalks.

Others who appreciate advance notice of forthcoming shots include archeologists, who, if they failed to allow for fallout, might be off by several centuries in calculating the age of ancient relics on the basis of how much carbon 14—a radioactive isotope that is present in a constant amount in all living things and disintegrates at a known rate after death—they still contain. Uranium prospectors, too, like to be warned ahead of time; back in the days before the far-reaching effects of the tests were understood, more than one prospector was momentarily led to believe that he had at last come upon a bonanza when his Geiger counter set up a wild clicking in response to fallout.

The manner in which a bomb is detonated also strongly affects the intensity of its fallout. If the bomb is exploded at a high altitude—high enough, that is, so that the mass of luminescent gas known as the fireball, from which rises the now all too familiar mushroom, does not touch the earth's surface—its radioactivity has nothing to condense with except whatever dust it encounters in the air and the vaporized bomb casing. In such instances—and all shots of any consequence within the continental limits of the United States are of this kind—the dust and vapors, swept upward by the blast to an altitude of possibly forty thousand feet, are carried away on the strong winds of that altitude, which, owing to the earth's rotation, are generally westerly, and may remain aloft for months. By the time the dust particles finally settle, they may well have travelled clear around the globe, becoming so thoroughly scattered and having so thoroughly dissipated their radioactivity in the atmosphere that they are presumed to be harmless. The higher the explosion the better, from the point of view of the eventual effects of its fallout, for the descent of the dust particles is apt to be hastened if they happen into a formation of rain clouds, which they are not likely to encounter until they have drifted down to within twenty thousand feet of the earth.

A surface or near-surface shot—the sort the United States restricts to the Pacific area—is something else again; indeed, radiologically speaking, it is an extremely dangerous proposition. Immediately after such a shot, the bomb's fireball (the biggest one yet reported measured from three to four miles in diameter) sucks up millions of tons of material from the surface of the earth—rocks, sand, vegetation, water—as it rises, almost with the speed of sound. Moving up through the stem of the mushroom to its head, this hideously contaminated, or "hot," material also soars up into the stratosphere, where it too is eventually blown away by the wind. But, unlike the radioactive dust of a high-altitude shot, much of this debris is far too heavy to be blown around the world. The winds that beneficently carry the dust of high-altitude shots such great distances blow the fallout from a ground-level shot only far enough away from the testing area to make it a menace. The debris falls rapidly while still intensely radioactive, polluting to a probably lethal degree what the A.E.C. has described as a "comparatively localized" area. Just outside the comparatively localized area, however, lies a much larger one that is definitely jeopardized by the fallout from a ground shot, for during the first few hours after the explosion some of the lighter fragments of debris spread out over thousands of square miles. Given reliable meteorological information, scientists can predict the size and general course of this fallout with a fair amount of accuracy, but, owing to the different weights of the bits and pieces that constitute the mass, and the erratic nature of the winds in the upper regions, they can't do much more than that. For whatever comfort it might afford people who fear the fallout from surface shots, Dr. Willard F. Libby, a commissioner of the A.E.C., a while ago ventured a guess that in the event of a thermonuclear attack on the United States the enemy would set off "a large fraction" of its bombs high above the earth, since the blast and heat damage of aerial explosions is tactically superior to that of ground blasts. "In other words, the fallout problem might be minimized by the enemy's attempt to maximize the blast and thermal effects," Dr. Libby said.

The fireball of a very large thermonuclear bomb that was set off on March 1st, 1954 on a coral island in a lagoon at Bikini Atoll touched the surface of the earth. This was the shot that made the world fallout-conscious, and it earned its sorry distinction not only by dangerously contaminating seven thousand square miles of land and sea—an area somewhat larger than Connecticut and Rhode Island together—but by injuring people who were nearly a hundred miles away from the site. The Commission naturally felt deep chagrin at this outcome of the blast, especially since it had gone to great pains to make sure no lives would be endangered. Weeks before the bomb was detonated, the Commission saw to it that marine and aviation navigational publications printed announcements of the forthcoming test and gave their readers explicit information about the boundaries of a thirty-thousand-square-mile danger zone that had been decided upon. For days prior to the blast, aircraft crisscrossed the zone and the waters adjacent to it to warn away shipping. A meteorological study of the whole region was made, in which special attention was paid to the behavior of winds at all relevant altitudes. "The area for which meteorological data had to be compiled and analyzed was far greater than just that thirty-thousand-square-mile danger zone," an official of the A.E.C. said later. "In fact, it was greater than that of the United States, and we had only eight or ten observation stations to cover it." In its report of the shot and of what went wrong with it, the A.E.C. made the mildly consolatory point that without the knowledge derived from the test "we would have been in ignorance of the extent of the effects of radioactive fallout and, therefore . . . much more vulnerable to the dangers from fallout in the event an enemy should resort to radiological warfare against us." In addition to the unanticipated lessons it learned about the vagaries of fallout during the March 1st test, the Commission collected some grim testimony as to its potency, expressed in terms of roentgens—one of the units in which radiation is measured. Having previously established that a person exposed to a total accumulation of four hundred and fifty roentgens in the arbitrarily set period of thirty-six hours stands only a fifty-per-cent chance of surviving, the Commission found that during the first thirty-six hours after the March 1st blast, anyone on Bikini, ten miles downwind from the explosion, would have been exposed to five thousand roentgens, and even if he had had sufficient warning to get to Rongelap Atoll, a hundred miles to the east, the roentgen count against him in at least one section of that tiny island would still have been twenty-three hundred.

The March 1st bomb went off shortly before four in the morning, announcing itself with a blinding flash over a broad expanse of the Pacific. The islet that had served as its platform abruptly disintegrated into pulverized coral, which was swept up into the stratosphere, and it was there that things began to go wrong. As the particles of coral gathered like a pendulous cloud in the sky—this was one time when fallout was all too plainly visible—the wind, which had been counted on to blow them to the northeast, unexpectedly veered a few degrees and began to drive them due east. Natives of the Marshall Islands, Americans participating in the test, and Japanese fishermen—all of them outside the official danger zone, which extended some fifty miles east of Bikini—were now directly in the path of the fallout, which, as it billowed toward them, assumed the shape of a monstrous cigar, two hundred and twenty miles long and up to forty miles wide.

A total of two hundred and thirty-six Marshall Islanders, all residents of the atolls of Rongelap and Utirik, were evacuated as hastily as possible by destroyer to Kwajalein. There only those from Rongelap—seventy-four of them, constituting the island's total population—were found to have been seriously exposed. (Happily, none had been in the twenty-three-hundred-roentgen section of the atoll.) All the Rongelapians were suffering from radiation burns of the scalp or neck—the most sensitive parts of the body that are usually exposed—and all had ingested, as the nuclear people put it, small amounts of fallout-blighted foods or beverages; the hair of thirty-nine of them had dropped out in patches. Five Navy doctors reported to the convention of the American Medical Association in Atlantic City the following year that the children of Rongelap had lost more hair than their elders and that the counts of the children's white blood cells, which fight infection and which are always affected by serious exposure to radiation, had dropped to lower levels. According to the A.E.C., the islanders' burns are now healed, hair has grown back on their bald patches, and they all appear to be in good physical shape. They have not yet been taken back to their island, because it is still contaminated, but have been moved to Majuro Atoll, where, the Commission says, they are temporarily occupying "buildings built for them . . . of a new and improved type, better adapted to the comfort and the needs of the people than the usual type of island houses." There they have been shown their first Wild West motion pictures, which they think are terrific. There, too, they are being studied by American physicians. Now and then, one of the doctors makes a stab at trying to explain radiation to the Rongelapians, but without much success. As a rule, the attempt quickly turns into a party of some sort. "You start talking to a couple of the islanders, and pretty soon the whole population has gathered around you, smiling and beaming and ready for some kind of fun," an A.E.C. physician who was assigned to Majuro for a while told me. "They're an extremely friendly people, which I suppose, considering the circumstances, is just as well."

The Americans who were threatened by the fallout—thirty-one

members of the Army, Navy, and Air Force—were on Rongerik Atoll when the wind shifted. They, too, were evacuated to Kwajalein, where they were examined by American physicians, and from there they were sent on to Tripler General Hospital, in Hawaii, for further examination. None of them was found to have been seriously affected and none has shown any aftereffects.

The Japanese in the path of the fallout were, as the whole world presently came to know, the twenty-three members of the crew of the *Lucky Dragon,* a hundred-ton trawler engaged in fishing for tuna. On the morning of the big blast, the vessel, which the warning aircraft had somehow missed, was about ninety miles east of Bikini, some forty miles outside the official danger zone, when several members of the crew who happened to be on deck saw a white flash tinged with red far away on the pre-dawn horizon. Seven or eight minutes later, they heard a loud explosion. In about three hours, a fine white dust of radioactive coral particles began to fall on the superstructure of the *Lucky Dragon;* it was so dense, one of the crew later reported, that it was faintly audible as it landed on the deck. The strange downpour continued until about noon, and by the time it let up, the dust had covered the boat, the men, and their catch like a white sheet; it lay so thick on the deck that the men left footprints when they walked on it. The fishermen had no idea what all this meant, but it was something that they had never experienced before, and plainly something weird, and it made them so uneasy that they hauled in their lines that same day and headed for their home port of Yaizu. As a matter of good seamanship, they washed down their vessel, and this probably saved the lives of a good many of them. The voyage home took thirteen days, during which a number of the men filled bottles with the odd dust to keep as souvenirs, and the whole crew, it was subsequently estimated by Japanese scientists, was exposed to the baleful assault of between two hundred and five hundred roentgens. By the time the *Lucky Dragon* reached Yaizu, on March 14th, practically every one of the fishermen was ridden with nausea, blisters, fever, conjunctivitis, abdominal pains, and other symptoms of overexposure to radiation.

Americans who were in Japan in the days that followed the cruise of the *Lucky Dragon* had some difficult moments in their relations with people there, but, in retrospect, most of them agree that the Japanese, tragically aware as they already were of the effects of a nuclear explosion, reacted to the incident pretty much the way the citizens of any other country might have. The Japanese were angry, anxious, and voluble. As soon as word of the peculiar condition of the *Lucky Dragon*'s mariners reached knowledgeable authorities, the fishermen—or at least those who could be rounded up at once—were hustled off to Tokyo and hospitalized. A few days elapsed before the last of the twenty-three was accounted for, in the course of which a couple of them were picked up as they were bicycling through the streets of Yaizu, each with a grossly radioactive dried shark fin from the boat lashed to his back mudguard. Japanese scientists, wearing protective gauze masks and rubber gloves, trooped aboard the *Lucky Dragon,* where they found some samples of radioactive coral ash still on the bridge and carried off the tuna that had not yet been sold. When they debarked, their masks were radioactive, which gave them good reason to believe that the crew had suffered serious internal injuries.

Back in the laboratory, analysis of various items taken from the trawler, including some tuna that were still waiting for a buyer, revealed the presence of two telltale radioactive elements common to all fallout—radioiodine and radiostrontium, both of which the body can ingest or inhale. Radioiodine tends to single out and damage the cells of the thyroid gland; radiostrontium has a special affinity for the bones and, if enough of it works its way into them, may produce cancer. Word went out to the public-health authorities to confiscate the tuna that had got to the market, but it was discovered that fishmongers in the Osaka Prefecture had already sold parts of them to about a hundred customers. (Fortunately for the customers, the fish were dead at the time of the blast, so only their skin, according to the Japanese scientists, was affected and this had been removed before eating.)

American radiation specialists in Japan offered their fullest cooperation, but their Japanese counterparts, while always personally cordial, indicated that they would prefer to handle the situation themselves. American physicians were not allowed near the fishermen, although they might have been able to make some helpful therapeutic suggestions. But even if there had not been this atmosphere of professional coolness, it is unlikely that the widespread resentment that boiled up in Japan over what had befallen the crew of the *Lucky Dragon* could have been avoided. And, as time passed, more or less extraneous events seemed to conspire to add heat to the resentment. On March 19th, the A.E.C., in preparing for two more shots on Bikini, announced that the danger zone would be expanded—a step that some Japanese appeared to feel was rather belated. Nor did the shots themselves, which came less than a month after the return of the *Lucky Dragon,* act as a precisely soothing influence upon the population. At about the same time, a rainstorm over the Atsumi Peninsula blurred the glass panes of several greenhouses with a peculiar substance that a researcher at the Nagoya Technical Research Institute said was dust infused with artificially induced radioactivity, and presently a professor at Kagoshima University asserted that he had found some local vegetables, milk, and drinking water to have been mildly affected by another "radioactive rain." On April 1st, a Japanese newspaper reported that a second fishing vessel had returned to Japan with a cargo of radioactive fish, which had had to be dumped; this ship had been eight hundred miles southeast of Bikini on March 1st and had got almost back to Japan by the time the second shot was fired. In the days that followed, more reports of a similar nature and of varying degrees of accuracy appeared in the press. According to Japanese sources, out of 905 boatloads of fish, weighing 33,000 tons, that were brought in between March 16th and June 20th, seventy-seven loads, totalling 135 tons, were condemned as radioactive and discarded.

In late summer, a thirty-nine-year-old member of the *Lucky Dragon*'s crew, Aikichi Kuboyama, who was suffering from hepatitis, took a turn for the worse, and his case became a primary national concern. Buddhist priests prayed for his life. Hospital bulletins reporting his condition were more prominently displayed in the press than most news of international importance, and they were broadcast hourly over the radio. Kuboyama died on September 23rd (all his fellow-crewmen have survived and seem to be recovering) and his death took on political implications of the first magnitude. The Japanese Foreign Minister and other dignitaries crowded into the hospital to pay their last respects to the fisherman, and the American

Ambassador in Tokyo sent a letter of condolence to the Japanese Foreign Ministry and a check for a million yen (about $2,800) to Kuboyama's widow "as a token of the deep sympathy felt by the Government and people of the United States." A Japanese Minister of State called publicly on the United States to show "more sincerity" by increasing the amount of money—a million dollars—that had already been offered to his government as compensation for the injuries to the crew and for the loss to the nation's fishing industry. (The United States eventually paid two million dollars in reparations.) Japanese labor organizations, newspapers, leading citizens, and public opinion in general, impressed by the indiscriminating nature of fall-out, called for an end to thermonuclear bomb tests anywhere, by any country. As the national temper rose, only one incident occurred that somewhat mitigated the wave of anti-American feeling, and this, ironically, was a disaster of greater proportions, even if not of greater significance, than that of the *Lucky Dragon*—the drowning of more than twelve hundred persons, including about eighty Americans, when a ferryboat capsized in northern Japan just a few days after Kuboyama died. "The Japanese were quite sympathetic," an A.E.C. man who was in Japan at the time told me. "The accident seemed to clear the atmosphere a little by reminding them that Americans can also die."

The Japanese are not the only ones who have demanded that no more thermonuclear bombs be tested. Their views have been echoed by some highly articulate authorities in the United States as well as by various qualified critics in other countries. One of the latter—Dr. Frederick Soddy, a British winner of a Nobel Prize for studies in the chemistry of radioactive substances and the origin and nature of isotopes—has warned of the dangers of "fouling the air with radio-activity." In particular, much concern has been expressed over the hereditary effects of increased radioactivity on the genes of the human race. Estimating that seventy-five hydrogren bombs exploded at inter-vals over a period of thirty years will double the natural amount of radiation in the world, Joseph Rotblat, Professor of Physics at the Medical College of St. Bartholomew's Hospital, in London, has written, "Rough as this estimate may be, it certainly shows that we are sailing much closer to the wind than many of us thought. . . . It is no longer a question of two nations, or groups of nations, devastating each other, but of all the future generations of *all* nations, who will forever pay, through disease, malformation, and mental disability, for our folly."

In the United States, the Federation of American Scientists has urged that the United Nations "obtain and evaluate scientific opinion on the biological and genetic effects of radiation on human beings," and Senator Frederick G. Payne, of Maine, has introduced a resolution calling on the President to instruct the chief American delegate to the United Nations to propose such a study. Apparently, the President did so, for at the tenth-anniversary meeting of the U.N. in San Francisco three weeks ago, Henry Cabot Lodge suggested that all member nations pool their research on fallout to allay "unjustified fears." The National Academy of Sciences, the most distinguished scientific body in the United States has, with the help of the Rockefeller Foundation, embarked on an exhaustive survey of the problem. Dr. Linus Pauling, a Nobel Prize-winning chemist at the California Institute of Technology, noting that radioactive rains have fallen in Japan and Germany as a result of the tests, has suggested that these may have started "a new cycle" of leukemia. And Dr. James R. Arnold, an associate professor at the Institute for Nuclear Studies of the University of Chicago, has come forward with the proposal that in the future the A.E.C. conduct all its thermonuclear tests within the continental limits of the United States. "It may be objected that the number of casualties would very likely be increased," he wrote in the *Bulletin of the Atomic Scientist* last November. "This is true, but they would be American citizens. A nation which feels itself in danger has some right to ask certain of its citizens to run special risks on behalf of all. This is the principle behind compulsory military service. Even though the Japanese are our allies and the Marshallese our wards, we have no such right with them, in a world which holds to the idea of national sovereignty. Americans who were hurt would doubtless be properly indemnified. All the same, the taxpayer would benefit greatly, since the lowering of costs of the test operation would pay for any probable casualty list many times over."

In the face of all this outcry, the A.E.C., which possesses more information about fallout than any other agency—or individual—

steadfastly maintains that the tests have not got out of hand. The Commission contends that in the ten years since the United States started testing nuclear weapons—to be followed presently, of course, by the Soviet Union and Great Britain—not more than one-tenth of a roentgen has been added to the amount of radiation normally absorbed by each individual in the United States. This is the equivalent of what a patient is subjected to in a single chest X-ray, and as for its genetic effects, it is only one one-hundredth of the normal radiation to which most men and women have always been exposed up to and through their reproductive lifetimes. "Most of the categorical predictions of adverse genetic effects are about as reasonable as claiming that meteors from outer space are a major threat to highway safety," Dr. John C. Bugher, Director of the A.E.C.'s Division of Biology and Medicine, assured me.

The A.E.C. considers the amounts of radioiodine and radiostrontium that have fallen in the United States insignificant insofar as their immediate effect upon the population is concerned. In view of the fact that these elements, absorbed in the soil, may become part of plant tissues that are either eaten by human beings or eaten by grazing animals that, in turn, provide food for man, the Commission, by means of roving teams and experimental farms, carries on a series of year-round checkups on the radioactivity in many localities all over the nation. Radioiodine has been found in the thyroids of cattle and sheep grazing near the Nevada Proving Ground; the thyroids of living human beings cannot be tested for small amounts of radioiodine, but urine analyses of persons living in the same area have indicated that they have been less severely affected than the livestock, showing only a minute fraction of the amount of radioiodine that would cause damage. As for radiostrontium, Dr. Bugher estimates that the amount now present in the United States would have to be multiplied by a million before an increase in the frequency of bone cancer would be perceptible. On the other hand, Dr. Bugher revealed some months ago in an address before the seventh annual Industrial Health Conference, held in Houston, Texas, that laboratory experiments conducted on animals have demonstrated that one of the possible effects of overexposure to radiation is a shortening of life expectancy. "This phenomenon does not result from any specific cause of death but apparently from a general acceleration of the aging process," he said, adding wryly that human beings have yet to experience the distinction between a condition that does not cause death but shortens life.

However sound the A.E.C.'s position may be, the commissioners are finding it hard to win quite a number of worried citizens over to it. "One of our big difficulties is a popular tendency to confuse close-in fallout with distant fallout," an A.E.C. radiation expert told me. "When people in this country read about the hundreds of roentgens that hit those Japanese fishermen, they think it's sheer luck the same thing hasn't happened to them, and figure maybe the next shot will be their turn." Distant fallout, he explained, is the only kind of fallout that people in the United States need expect as a result of any and all nuclear tests. This is fallout and does not descend to the earth until it is two hundred miles or more from the scene of a shot, and its intensity is measured in milliroentgens, or thousandths of a roentgen. It is simply not in the same class with close-in fallout, which comes to earth within two hundred miles of the test site. "The total distant fallout from all tests to date would have to be increased a million times to produce visible deleterious effects," Dr. Bugher told me. So far, the greatest increase in radioactivity caused by distant fallout in this country was recorded at Rensselaer Polytechnic Institute, near Troy, New York, on April 27, 1953, forty-eight hours after an explosion had taken place twenty-three hundred miles away, in Nevada. Rain had fallen in Troy the evening before, and when some researchers arrived at R.P.I.'s radiochemistry laboratory in the morning, they found their Geiger counters chattering, especially those nearest the outside walls of the room. Tests made during the next ten weeks showed that the amount of radiation on the R.P.I. campus, though steadily decreasing, added up to eighty milliroentgens instead of the usual twenty-five. The National Committee for Radiation Protection has declared, and the A.E.C. agrees, that a constant lifetime exposure to three-tenths of a roentgen a week—or of three roentgens over a period corresponding to that covered by the R.P.I. tests—is safe for the community in general, and that ten times that much is safe for atomic-energy workers, whose ranks do not include children, invalids, or pregnant women.

Another thing that handicaps the A.E.C. in its efforts to present its case is the fact that the very word "radiation" evokes dread in the public mind. "On wet days, we get anxious phone calls from men and women who want to know if the rain is bringing fallout down on them," a man in the A.E.C.'s New York office told me. "That's a perfectly rational question, but then they suddenly break down completely—crying and carrying on about what's going to become of the world." It may be, he suggested, that radiation's bad name goes all the way back to the famous case of the girls who, working in a New Jersey factory during the First World War, painted watch dials with radium, tipping their brushes with their tongues, and years later began dying, one by one, from overexposure.

The big point the A.E.C. is trying to put across is that the cumulative exposure is what counts, and not the mere presence of radiation. Air, water, and soil emit radiation under normal conditions; so do the cosmic rays that are constantly assaulting the earth from outer space. For that matter, man himself is radioactive, since his body contains potassium 40, carbon 14, and radium 226—all radioactive isotopes. "The world is radioactive," Commissioner Libby stated in an address he delivered in December, 1954 at the Conference of Mayors, in Washington. "It always has been and always will be." And Merril Eisenbud, Director of the A.E.C.'s Health and Safety Laboratory, points out that since the very beginning of life, radioactivity has been one of the principal factors in the furtherance of evolution, causing changes, or mutations, in the genes of living organisms and so bringing man to his present stage of development, whatever one's opinion of that stage may be.

But in these times, as the A.E.C. knows all too well, the subject of mutations is a touchy one. Many people find it much easier to contemplate—in theory, at least—the possible destruction of the world while they themselves are still inhabiting it than to reflect that their descendants, centuries hence, may inherit genes that were impaired by the current tests. There are sound scientific reasons for apprehension over radiation's effect on genes. Radiation, the A.E.C. believes, causes from ten to twenty per cent of all mutations, and about ninety-nine per cent of all mutations result either in prenatal death or in sterility or some other functional disability; what the public knows as "monsters" and scientists call "lethal mutants" are nearly always stillborn. In those rare instances where mutations are beneficial to an organism, the law of natural selection dictates that the new form survive at the expense of weaklings or the parent form. In any society, the frequency of mutations depends largely on the total amount of radiation that its members' reproductive organs are subjected to before parenthood, and not on the intensity of exposure on any particular occasion. Dr. E. L. Green, the A.E.C.'s geneticist, starting with the premise that for every billion genes (about one hundred thousand people) five thousand mutations turn up, estimates that exposure to the extra tenth of a roentgen introduced by the nuclear tests will mean an additional ten to twenty mutations among each hundred thousand of the population. The field of genetics is still a mass of unsolved riddles, but the authorities are generally agreed that if and when the tenth-of-a-roentgen mutations start showing up, it will be difficult to single them out as the direct results of nuclear explosions.

According to Professor H. J. Muller, a Nobel Prize-winning geneticist, "each detrimental mutation, even though small in effect and lost to view in the jumble of a heterogeneous population, tends to continue from generation to generation and to hamper successive descendants, until at last it happens to tip the scales against one of its possessors, and that line of descent then dies out in consequence of the inherited disability." In a speech before the National Academy of Sciences in early 1955, Muller condemned prominent publicists of the government, including physicians, who have claimed that the bombing of Hiroshima and Nagasaki will have no harmful effect on the future populations of those cities and, indeed, may even improve them. He also cited the A.E.C.'s favorite analogy of the chest X-ray, but he gave it a somewhat different twist; in genetics, he implied, the reproductive organs are really rather more important than the chest. Muller pointed out that the additional radiation to which Americans are being exposed because of the bomb tests must be considered in terms not of the individual but of the whole population; that is, one-tenth of a roentgen multiplied by 160,000,000, or 16,000,000 roentgens. Muller noted that this means that the United States may expect about as many mutations to result from the current nuclear tests, wherever held, as he anticipates will turn up in Hiroshima, since the 160,000 survivors in that city were exposed to an average of one hundred roentgens. In both instances, he said, the number of mutations caused by the artificial increase of radiation to date will probably someday amount to around eighty thousand—or from two and a half to five times as many as Dr. Green predicts—and in the end, several times that many lives will be adversely affected. Still, Muller went on, in view of the total number of people involved during the scores of generations in which the mutations will be occurring, it is unlikely that the population as a whole will be undermined, and he recommended that before calling for a ban on all future tests, thought be given to what the alternative damage might be if the tests were discontinued. In a way, he said, the case was similar to that of people who visit their doctors regularly for X-ray examinations as a precautionary measure against serious illness even though a Public Health Service survey has shown that every year the average person receives much more radiation from this source than from the nuclear tests. "Have we no right to expect individual sacrifices when the stakes are democracy and intellectual freedom themselves?" Muller asked rhetorically. To this, any person now alive would appear to be obliged to give a stoutly affirmative answer, but the question also, of course, raises the nagging dilemma of the propriety of attempting to speak for those who are yet to be born into a world the nature of which no one can predict.

There are those who believe that some of the A.E.C. scientists might, if they were not restrained by loyalty to that agency, be just as vocal as their present adversaries in expressing anxiety over the dangers of fallout. However that may be, it is unlikely that the scientists on either side of the fence are enjoying their wrangling. "It's no fun, this constantly being cast in the role of villain," an A.E.C. man told me. "Some people apparently think that from our point of view it's all a great big game, and that we're just blowing up bombs for the hell of it. They seem to forget entirely that their country is mixed up in an international situation that makes these tests necessary. Is it a crime to try to hold our lead in this miserable race for superior weapons, in view of what might happen to all of us if we should lag behind?"

To many laymen who have come to expect scientists to be starkly objective in their approach to technical problems and whose schooling pretty much encouraged the belief that there is always only one right answer to any question concerning science, the current disagreement among the authorities is both exasperating and baffling, if not actually frightening. Part of the trouble is, of course, that in this instance the question is not purely scientific but is also a matter of ethics, statesmanship, and clairvoyance—three notoriously treacherous quagmires for theorists. Moreover, so much about the workings of genetics remains obscure that, as the A.E.C. has gently observed, "there is still a wide range for admissible opinion" on the subject, and many scientists feel that there is an equally wide range when it comes to the more immediate effects of radiation. In other words, even if there *is* only one right answer to any question concerning science, those who are critical of the A.E.C.'s seeming complacency feel that until more is known about the awesome mysteries involved there should be no attempt to give any answer at all. Such critics might be said to belong to the play-it-safe school of thought. And to them the A.E.C. may justifiably reply, "Yes, but which is the safe way to play it?"

THE USUAL CLOUD

LEWIS L. STRAUSS, Chairman of the Atomic Energy Commission, announced this evening that the Soviets today conducted another nuclear weapons test at the usual Siberian test site.—*From an A.E.C. news release.*

From the usual testing site in old Siberia
(Or new Nevada),
Let us bid bon voyage to the usual particles
For whom, for where?
Oh, Tovarischi, gathered in the purposeful dawn,
Our black glasses scanning the young sun's night,
Is this new cloud, no bigger than the hand of man,
Bound for the hardy bracken of an Arctic inlet?
Or for the nostrils of the Lama of Tibet?
Giants of Patagonia, beware!
Flee the spring rain
Lest gentle showers shrink you to dwarfs, millennia hence.
Sailors of Australia, your guns, unlimbered and blazing,
Cannot stay the Pacific's attacking air.
Grazing cows of all the Santiagos,
Choose your blades well,
And oats, peas, beans, and barley, grow, grow,
But grow clean of root
In Akron's and Bizerte's soil, and, alas,
Odessa's, too,
For true democracy reigns everywhere at last,
Set free by our usual blast.

CHAPTER 24 | MAY, 1959

A MOST VALUABLE ACCIDENT

OVER THE YEARS, many people have served as guinea pigs in potentially lethal scientific experiments—some of them voluntarily and others, as in the days of Nazi medical research, involuntarily. In either case, it is safe to assume, most of them realized that their bodies were being experimented with. Today, however, there are hundreds, and perhaps thousands, of Americans who are just learning that more than a quarter of a century ago they underwent a hazardous experiment that has since turned out to be immensely useful. This singular group of guinea pigs is made up of people who, for one reason or another, swallowed radium in varying amounts at the time of the First World War and on into the thirties, when the possible effects of that highly radioactive element—twenty times as damaging as the strontium 90 that nowadays is falling on crops, pastures, and reservoirs—were widely and sometimes disastrously miscalculated. A good many of them are middle-aged and elderly women who, as girls, had the job of applying radium paint to the figures on watch dials and found that their work went faster and more accurately if they licked their paintbrushes to a point, and most of the rest are old-time sufferers from arthritis, gout, and similar ailments who received radium injections, inhaled emanations from radium solutions, or swallowed medicines containing radium—a sovereign remedy in the eyes of many doctors of the period.

At the time, something was known about the effects of external radium radiation on the human body—the bad effects and the beneficial ones, such as in the treatment of cancer. But very little was known about the behavior of radioactive substances that had been taken internally. Such substances, it was supposed, were rapidly and entirely eliminated. Nobody had any idea that radium could be retained in the body for years, still radioactive and lodging in the bone, which it gradually deformed or destroyed. ("Boneseekers," experts today call substances like radium and strontium 90 that are absorbed by the bones; certain other radioactive substances are absorbed by the body tissue.) Nor was anybody aware of the fact that radioactive matter could affect the formation of blood in the bone marrow, causing leukemia, anemia, and other disorders. In the early nineteen-twenties, when a number of the dial painters fell ill and died, one after another, their deaths were attributed to any of several common diseases or to mysterious causes. These girls were probably the world's first victims of internal emissions of a radioactive substance, but only gradually was the evidence pieced together that what had killed them was radium. As the years went on, more and more people, notable and obscure, succumbed to the effects of radium, for while these may show up swiftly, they may also show up slowly. In 1928, at the age of forty-five, Sabin A. von Sochocky, an M.D. and a Ph.D. who originated one widely used radium-paint formula, died of radiation injuries—external and internal. (Writing of the wonders of radium in the January, 1921, issue of the *American Magazine,* Dr. von Sochocky, who was an amateur artist, had extolled radium-treated oil paints. "Pictures painted with radium look like any other pictures in the daytime, but at night they illuminate themselves and create an interesting and weirdly artistic effect," he declared. "This paint would be particularly adaptable for pictures of moonlight or winter scenes, and I have no doubt that some day a fine artist will make a name for himself . . . by painting pictures which will be unique, and particularly beautiful at night in a dark or semidarkened room.") In 1934, Mme. Marie Curie, who, with her husband, Pierre Curie, had won a Nobel Prize thirty-one years earlier for discovering the metallic element, died as a result of an assortment of radium injuries. And just within the last twelve months two dial painters who put aside their brushes thirty-five years ago have died because of the radium they swallowed.

Many of the people—dial painters and others—who ingested radium back in those days are alive, however, and a little over a year ago the Atomic Energy Commission embarked on a systematic search for them, as part of its program of amassing all available information about the effects of radioactivity on human beings. One phase of the Commission's program deals with the ingestion of radioactive substances, and here the survivors of the reckless days of radium consumption are known to make enlightening, if sometimes unfortunate, exhibits. A number of these survivors have been under observation for years—principally at the Massachusetts Institute of Technology and at the Argonne National Laboratory, in Lemont, Illinois, which is administered by the University of Chicago. In 1931, for instance, thirty-one schizophrenic inmates of the Elgin State Hospital, in Elgin, Illinois, received injections of radium salts, which the doctors hoped would restore their sanity, and scientists of the Argonne Laboratory have been studying sixteen of them since the forties. But it was with the purpose of collecting a statistically significant sample that the Commission hit upon its idea of a large-scale hunt. The job of tracking down and conducting studies of the survivors has been farmed out to three research contractors—M.I.T., the Argonne National Laboratory, and the State Department of Health of New Jersey, where most of the dial painters lived and had their jobs—and they have been proceeding steadily, if quietly, picking up clues where they can. Around 1930, to take one example, many Americans were drinking a radioactive patent tonic called Radithor, which its manufacturer described as "perpetual sunshine" and a therapeutic agent for gout, high blood pressure, neuritis, and declining sexual powers. Last October, M.I.T. placed the following ad in the New York Sunday papers: "University research center looking for persons who received radium injections or drank radium solutions such as 'Radithor' before 1935." The response included not only a gratifying number of letters but a case of Radithor that a woman in Pennsylvania had kept in her cellar for more than two decades.

Exactly how many people ingested radium is unknown, but each of them now has an abnormally high "body burden," as scientists call the amount of radioactive material in an individual's system. To date, the three contractors have located about four hundred survivors, and they expect to find several hundred more, though the job isn't an easy one. Some survivors are unaware of the fact that they are being sought, and others would just as soon ignore it. More than a few of these, it is suspected, will not divulge their condition for fear of social ostracism, and there are those who see no earthly use in coming forward, since little could be done for them if their body burdens were found to be dangerously high. The one thing that can stop a radioactive substance from emitting its rays is the passage of time, and it takes sixteen hundred and twenty-two years for any given bit of radium to lose half of its original intensity. (Strontium 90 loses half of its intensity every thirty years.) The sole purpose, then, that the survivors can serve by making themselves known to the A.E.C. is to provide the data that has been contained in their irradiated bodies for decades (much longer than the data provided by the victims of Hiroshima and Nagasaki, who, in any case, offer a different sort of evidence, since their radiation injuries came primarily from external sources), and an exceedingly worth-while purpose this is proving to be. The like of these individuals, indeed, may never be encountered again unless the rate of fallout keeps increasing indefinitely, for it has been estimated that, on the average, they took in several hundred times as much radioactive material as anybody has thus far ingested because of fallout. "All in all, this is a strange project," one researcher told me. "Something that happened far in the past is going to give us a look far into the future. Why, when these people took in their radium, there was no such thing as strontium 90, and yet they may help us determine today how much of it children can safely consume. The way I see it, we're trying to follow up a wholly unintentional experiment that has taken on incalculable value."

The followup is still in its early stages, and the scientists do not expect to come up with statistically reliable results for two or three years. One thing that they are willing to say now is that by no means all of the people who swallowed radium appear to have suffered ill effects; it is assumed, though the reasons are still unknown, that these people retained much less of the stuff than the rest did, or else had a peculiar resistance to it. Among other things, the investigators are seeking to ascertain at what level and in what ways internal radiation affects illness rates and life expectancy; whether it can induce still-births; whether, contrary to current thinking, it passes through the placental barrier to offspring; and to what extent it produces changes in the genes. If these questions are answered, it will not be the first time that the New Jersey factory girls have furnished the government with important information. Their misfortunes may indeed have influenced the outcome of the last war. It was Merril Eisenbud, manager of the A.E.C.'s New York Operations Office, which is headquarters of the Commission's National Monitoring (Fallout) System, who told me about this. "Historically speaking, the New Jersey cases and the others, coming when they did, were a most valuable accident," he said. "If they had occurred twenty years later, we might have gone into our wartime atomic-bomb project without knowing how boneseekers do their work. Our Manhattan District might have proved to be a tremendous booby trap. We might not have foreseen the internal-emitter problem in all its seriousness, and even if we had, we might have been five years arguing it. With the evidence before us, however, there was no room for debate. If it hadn't been for those dial painters, the project's management could have reasonably rejected the extreme precautions that were urged on it—the remote-control gadgetry, the dust-dispersal systems, the filtering of exhaust air—and thousands of Manhattan District workers might well have been, and might still be, in great danger."

This time, when the A.E.C. study is completed, the dial painters' experience will have implications for hundreds of millions of people all over the world, and the results of the study will be international property. They will go not only to the United States Public Health Service, the Department of Defense, and other federal agencies that, along with the Commission, are concerned with fallout but to the United Nations Scientific Committee on the Effects of Atomic Radiation, to the World Health Organization, and to all member governments of the United Nations. Then this study of a relative handful of people who had so curious a medical adventure will be pondered by physicists, hematologists, radiologists, pathologists, toxicologists, and other experts in every corner of the globe.

It was in 1915 that Dr. von Sochocky devised his formula for luminous paint—a yellowish zinc sulphide compound, containing radium. Later on, it was discovered that mesothorium—a radioactive isotope of radium, and considerably less expensive—could do the job adequately, and sometimes it was used, either by itself or in combination with radium. As it turned out, whether a dial painter used radium or mesothorium was to make a great difference, for while the latter is the more immediately damaging of the two, it loses half of its intensity every six and seven-tenths years. At any rate, in 1915 Dr. von Sochocky and some associates founded the Radium Luminous Materials Company and soon thereafter established it in a two-story factory at the corner of Alden Street and High Street in Orange, New Jersey. Early in 1916, the company, which presently was to change its name to the United States Radium Corporation, contracted with watch manufacturers to paint their dials. It was a novel but fairly simple kind of job, requiring not much more than deftness in handling a paintbrush, and teen-age girls, for the most part, were employed to do it, on a piecework basis. As time went on, the company attracted new business—painting light pulls and crucifixes, for instance—and after the United States went to war, the girls painted instrument faces for submarines and aircraft. Other companies—in Connecticut, Illinois, and New York City—were doing the same sort of work, but the United States Radium Corporation was the leader in the field; at times it employed as many as two hundred and fifty girls, and over the years it employed a total of more than eight hundred. The girls went about their work on the second floor of the Orange plant, in a large room they called the Studio, because it had huge windows that let in the north light. Seated at long, heavy benches that served them as worktables, the girls dipped camel's-hair brushes into crucibles of the yellowish paint, licked them into shape, swallowed a little radium, and added to their body burdens forever.

Early in the nineteen-twenties, the first few mysterious cases of illness and bone injury began to occur among the Orange dial painters. Some doctors in the neighborhood ascribed them to conventional causes—bacterial infections, venereal disease, and so on—but several physicians were more alert than that. One of them was the late Dr. Harrison S. Martland, the Medical Examiner of Essex County, in which Orange is situated—a now celebrated practitioner and researcher, for whom the Martland Medical Center, in Newark, has been named. In September, 1924, Dr. Martland got a clue to what might be wrong when, while reading the current issue of the *Journal of the American Dental Association,* his eye fell on a footnote to an article on osteomyelitis of the jaw. The footnote said that one patient, a dial painter, was suffering from "radium jaw," and went on to suggest that her complaint might be of occupational origin. To the best of Dr. Martland's knowledge, this was the first time such a suggestion had been made, and he was impressed by it, particularly since the author was a noted oral surgeon—Dr. Theodor Blum, of New York, who was an M.D. as well as a D.D.S. Dr. Blum's diagnosis of "radium jaw" had followed an examination of a twenty-four-year-old girl who was referred to him by a puzzled New Jersey dentist. "A good look at her mouth and I knew I had never seen what she had before," Dr. Blum, who is now seventy-five, and still practicing, told me recently. "Clinically, I couldn't diagnose a thing, but she told me where she worked, and I surmised that her jaw had been invaded—yes, and pervaded—by radioactivity. And so I made my suggestion in that paper Dr. Martland read. He went on from there."

Spurred on by Dr. Blum's hunch, Dr. Martland inspected the plant in Orange, examined stricken dial painters, and sought the advice of colleagues—among them Dr. von Sochocky, who had left the company and who now teamed up with Martland. Martland gave years of study to the new occupational disease, but before the end of 1924 he and his associates were certain that the key to it was the paint. By this time, nine girls had died. Their family doctors had attributed the deaths to syphilis, Vincent's angina, and anemia, among other diseases, and none of them had conducted autopsies. When further deaths occurred, Martland conducted autopsies himself. Among his first, in 1925, was that of the company's chemist, a man who had handled unsealed radium and mesothorium and had inhaled radioactive emanations, as well as contaminated dust particles; his body was found to contain fourteen micrograms (or fourteen-millionths of a gram) of radioactive materials, including two and one-tenth micrograms of radium—twenty-one times the maximum amount now considered safe. Martland found that by using this man's bones as the source of radiation he could take pictures similar to X-rays.

Martland and his co-workers learned a great deal about how radioactive matter works inside the human body. They discovered that the microscopic bits of radioactive matter, entrenching themselves in the bone and giving off radiations that travelled at between one-twelfth and one-twentieth the speed of light, could cause an attrition of physical resources that sooner or later was beyond repair, and they observed the various diseases that could arise in the bone and blood. And, presently, Martland found that the initial effect of the particles was to stimulate the body into defending itself by manufacturing an extraordinary number of red blood cells. These gave the victim the illusion of being in excellent health, but the body could not keep up with such defensive demands year after year, and in the end disease usually took over. It was probably this transient stimulation that gave rise to the legend of the healing powers of radium.

Martland was not without scientific opposition, some of it directed at him by Frederick B. Flinn, an assistant professor of physiology specializing in industrial hygiene at Columbia. Flinn made three studies of the dial-painting situation for the United States Radium Corporation. His first report, published in the *Journal of the American Medical Association* for December, 1926, stated flatly that "an industrial hazard does not exist in the painting of luminous dials." In reaching this judgment, the industrial-hygiene expert stressed that the Orange cases were the only ones that had come to light in any dial-painting factory, and speculated on whether that particular plant might have been plagued by a bacterial infection. But in May, 1927, when his second report appeared, he was not so sure. Having examined two stricken dial painters employed in a Waterbury, Connecticut, plant, he had modified his position. "In view of the evidence in front of me, I feel that radium is partially if not the primary cause of the pathological condition described," he wrote. In his final report, made public in January, 1928, Flinn declared that he had been led "to suspect that radioactive material is at the bottom of the trouble even if the mechanism by which it is caused is not altogether clear and not previously suspected." Martland took care of that "not previously suspected" shortly thereafter, in quite untechnical language, in an article in the February, 1929, issue of the *Journal of the American Medical Association.* "Not only were these cases suspected . . . in 1925, two and one half years before these statements by Flinn," he wrote, "but the disease was accurately described in all its features by me and my associates."

By then, the dial-painting affair had become public property and the United States Radium Corporation was being maligned on every hand. Indeed, it had become the defendant in a highly publicized suit brought against it by five injured girls who sought a quarter of a million dollars each. The litigation, which took place mainly in the New Jersey Court of Chancery, began in the spring of 1927, and it turned out to be a marathon affair, in which the opposing lawyers sparred shrewdly over fugitive details without ever quite acknowledging the original ignorance that had entrapped both plaintiffs and defendant. The defense attorney argued that since the New Jersey statute of limitations put an end to liability in damage suits after two years, the girls, who had incurred their injuries at least five years previously, had no case. On the contrary, the girls' lawyer said, the statute applied not to the original contracting of the disease but to the recent onset of its symptoms. Moreover, he went on, unless the defense counsel quit stalling, the girls, all of whom were heavily in debt and were probably dying, might never benefit from the restitution rightfully due them. The company was not going to forfeit its day in court, the defense counsel retorted—not when its good name had been impugned up and down the land.

As the case dragged on, the company's chances of winning it diminished steadily. The very presence of the girls in the courtroom was enough to account for that. They were young and destroyed—disfigured by radium jaw, crippled by rotted spines or shrunken legs—and all of them had to be either assisted or actually carried to the witness stand; one of them could not raise her right arm to take the oath. As the case progressed, more dial painters were hit by disease, joining what one newspaper called "the Legion of the Doomed." The Legion, Martland indicated, might be larger than anyone thought. "Many [dial painters] may have gone to other towns and died without physicians' being aware of what caused death," he testified. "A physician not acquainted with radium poisoning might treat such patients for rheumatism or God knows what." His words were corroborated when the body of a dial painter who had died five years before—she was the sister of two of the plaintiffs —was exhumed from an Orange cemetery and was found to contain forty-eight and four-tenths micrograms of radium; syphilis had been recorded as a contributory cause of her death.

The proceedings in the Court of Chancery were a grim topic of conversation everywhere. In France, Mme. Curie publicly extended her sympathy to the girls. "I would be only too happy to give any aid that I could," she said, and advised them to eat raw calf's liver to counteract anemia. A Russian doctor suggested a lead solution. Scores of nostrums were mailed to the girls from all over the world, and one of the doctors treating them deplored these gestures of good will. "They [the girls] are swamped with all kinds of literature from quacks and faith-cure specialists who do more harm than good," he complained to a newspaperman. Welfare groups throughout the country took up the cause. In a speech at the Workmen's Circle Lyceum, in Newark, during the Presidential campaign of 1928, Norman Thomas, the Socialist candidate, said that the dial painters were getting nowhere with their case because "every legal device is employed by the corporation and insurance company's lawyers to cheat them of this compensation." The press was strongly on the side of the plaintiffs. *Time,* then a fledgling enterprise, said, "Newspapers took the five dying women to their ample bosoms. Heartbreaking were the tales of their torture." The Orange *Courier* declared, "Edgar Allan Poe in all his weird stories never utilized a theme more harrowing than that of death by radium." Probably the single most influential editorial appeared in the New York *World* on May 10, 1928. Assailing the company for having "barricaded" itself behind the statute of limitations, the editorial reviewed the case to date, and then concluded, "We have set down the facts as soberly and as coolly as we know how to do it. Having done that, we confidently assert that this is one of the most damnable travesties on justice that has ever come to our attention."

On June 4, 1928, after thirteen months, the case was settled out of court. A public-spirited federal judge, William Clark, who had no official connection with the litigation, had volunteered his services as mediator and had quickly worked out an agreement. The company agreed to pay legal costs of twenty thousand dollars, and to pay each of the dial painters a lump sum of ten thousand dollars, an annual pension of six hundred dollars, all past medical expenses connected with her injury, and all future expenses provided that she consented to periodic examinations by a board of three physicians, who were to certify whether or not she was rid of her radioactivity. The terms were no sooner announced than the company lawyers sent a public thank-you note to Judge Clark, saying, "You, as a private citizen, have intervened and asked the United States Radium Corporation to consider the matter solely in its humanitarian aspect, irrespective of whether or not it is liable. . . . The Company, in accepting your suggestions, is actuated solely by the humanitarian considerations which you have urged." The plaintiffs' lawyer commented, "I am glad to find that . . . members of the Radium Corporation have been actuated by humanitarian motives."

The girls' own reactions were mixed. One considered the award far too small. "I signed the agreement because the others seemed to think the terms were all right," she said. Another welcomed the money because it would enable her to visit a religious shrine in Quebec. "God will cure me there, but even if He doesn't, I want to go," she said. Two days after the settlement, the Newark *Star Ledger* reported that "the girls have been advised to invest the money in some reliable securities that will pay 6% interest." Whether or not they acted on this advice is unknown; they are all dead. In 1932, the American Medical Association removed radium for internal administration from its listing of new remedies. Radium continued to be, and still is, applied to watch dials—but only with virtually foolproof precautions. As for Martland, he was pleased but hardly smug about his accomplishment. In a paper he wrote for a professional publication about his long campaign in Orange, he said, "The great trouble with most investigations is that they always start after the harm has been done."

A few months ago, having followed the A.E.C.'s study of the long-range effects of exposure to radium, I began spending some time with the research team provided by the New Jersey State Department of Health. The team has set up its headquarters in a small building at 11 Washington Street, in West Orange, and the search in that area is on in full force, I was told by the head of the team, a young radiation physicist named Lester A. Barrer, who has been working for the Department since 1956. Fortunately, he said, a number of the surviving New Jersey dial painters—women now in their fifties and sixties, and most of them in modest circumstances—have remained in the area, and some of them live within sight of the old plant at Alden and High, which has been converted into a plastics factory. Barrer has prevailed on the New Jersey State Police to lend him one of its special investigators, and this operative has picked up the thread of more than one apparently broken trail. The detective is Stanley Prusek, a strapping fellow with an earnest manner. "Missing persons, that's the deal here," Prusek told me. "These dial painters are a tough proposition, because so many years have rolled by since anyone cared where they were. Right now, for instance, I've got a lot of clues to one case, but according to one clue she's dead, and according to another she's living in the Jersey shore area and she's single, and somebody else says she married twenty years ago and moved to California."

The search has run up against even more serious obstacles than that particular one. In 1929, for example, the federal Department of Labor conducted an investigation of radium-poisoning cases; the names and data it gathered might be extremely useful now, but the files were destroyed in 1944 as a routine space-saving measure. Barrer has been trying to locate former executives of the Jersey factory who might conceivably know where a payroll list is lurking, but he has had no luck; he is somewhat consoled by the fact that in those days, when a pay envelope contained cash, not a check, many employees didn't care whether the paymaster had their name and address straight as long as they received their wages. "If Social Security had existed then, we'd have access to a pile of accurate records today," Barrer told me. In the absence of such records, he and his associates are using whatever is available. They are poring over old newspaper files for the names of dial painters mentioned in the spate of articles that were printed when the first strange deaths of dial painters were reported. Thousands of marriage records are being gone over by clerks of the New Jersey Vital Statistics Registration Program in an effort to learn the present names of some of the girls, and voters' registration lists, realty records, and files of the Bureau of Motor Vehicles are also being combed. Death certificates are being checked not only to preclude vain hunts but to learn presumed causes of death. One certificate describes the death last autumn of a fifty-eight-year-old former dial painter, whose autopsy Barrer attended, as an "accident," giving as its cause "generalized radium intoxication."

Public appeals by the Department of Health have brought in more names. Their number might be higher, Barrer is inclined to think, if some former dial painters didn't take it for granted that their employment was too brief to make them of any value to the study. "That factor isn't necessarily important," he told me. "A good deal of radium can be ingested in a short time, and anyway it isn't just injurious amounts we want to learn about. We're equally interested in seeing how much people have absorbed safely." Several of the women he has interviewed have given him paintbrushes and crucibles of paint they took from the plant, sometimes in order to paint the numerals of a boy friend's watch—a real treat in the days when artificial phosphorescence was a novelty. He is delighted to receive the brushes and crucibles; he has them analyzed to see whether they contain radium or mesothorium or both, and this is a great help in determining the subject's type of body burden. One sixty-year-old woman presented Barrer with a tooth of hers, extracted years ago as a result of radiation injuries; he has turned it over for analysis to the project's dental adviser. Barrer has also come into a small collection of old photographs of the factory and some of its employees, and these, he says, are useful in jogging hazy memories. He showed me a faded snapshot of six girls, all dial painters, who had ranged themselves in a mock chorus line on the sands of a Jersey beach. They made a pretty group, their hair bobbed in the style of the times and their figures lithe despite their encumbering bathing suits.

When Barrer telephones a former dial painter out of the blue, his approach is to say, "My name is Lester Barrer. I am with the Department of Health, and we know from records that you were formerly employed in one of the radium-watch companies. We are conducting a research project in which you can help us, and I would like to send you information on how you can do this, and then, if I may, come to see you at your convenience." Often the woman at the other end of the line says, "But I'm perfectly well. What has this to do with me?" He courteously explains that even the perfectly well can be helpful, and generally the woman agrees, a bit uncertainly, to an appointment—often for an evening or a Sunday. Barrer than mails her a mimeographed description of the study, in which the state's Commissioner of Health, Dr. Daniel Bergsma, declares that without the coöperation of the large contingent of dial painters in New Jersey there will "be lost a significant amount of information about the latent effects of radiation which is not available elsewhere in the world at this time to our knowledge."

When Barrer visits a dial painter, he takes an assistant along. The dial painter is rarely alone; members of her family are usually with her. Barrer is conscious of being regarded warily at first, and even though he is a veteran of scores of interviews, he told me, he always feels like an intruder. Once in a while, he said, a subject may take on an air of self-importance, but in general there is an attitude of respectful suspense, which is partly, if not entirely, relieved as the interview goes on; sometimes the subject will end up by offering him and his aide coffee and cake. To start matters off, Barrer asks the subject and the others present to bring up any questions they may have. Members of the family often ask whether they could have inherited or "caught" radiation, and he answers that internal radiation cannot be caught and, as far as has been determined, is not passed through the placental barrier; if asked about the possibility of genetic mutation, he says that it is one of the factors under study. He is very seldom asked about fallout, and he doesn't bring that subject up, either, though, like all the other people involved in the A.E.C. study, he has it very much in mind. "The dial painter, at least while I'm talking with her, is thinking strictly in terms of her own health and her family's," Barrer told me. He himself contributes to the conversation by mentioning the names of dial painters he has recently visited. On recognizing one of the names, the subject may exclaim, "Oh, yes, I remember her! I hope she's well," and then inquire, guardedly, after other old co-workers. Once these preliminaries are over, Barrer gets down to the main business of the interview—a fifteen-page questionnaire. He asks the questions, his assistant takes down the answers, and the process usually lasts a good two hours. Most of the questions deal with the subject's medical history and that of her immediate family, but the concluding section, a flurry of apparently ludicrous questions, is designed to stimulate her memory for names: "Most obnoxious person [in the factory]?," "Did anyone ever play practical jokes?," "Did you ever have a crush on anybody in the company?" The final question, "Is there anything I haven't asked?," coming after so long an interrogation, is often good for a laugh, and then Barrer and his assistant, taking their leave, tell the subject that they would like to return soon to take a breath sample—a test that is used to determine the amount of radium an individual's body contains.

When Barrer makes this second trip, a week or two later, he is likely to find that the dial painter has been reflecting on his initial call, frequently to the advantage of the study. "Psychologically speaking, the biggest single problem I run into on the first visit is the attitude of let sleeping dogs lie—why rake up the past?" Barrer told me. "Well, the wait helps them get over this feeling and face up to the fact of the study. It's as though those sleeping dogs were allowed to wake up." At all events, he continued, subjects may greet him with new information on his return. In the interval, they are apt to rummage through attics and cellars, where crucibles of paint, photographs, and other forgotten souvenirs have been stowed for years, and this immersion in the past sometimes helps them remember additional names. On one jackpot occasion—Barrer doubts whether it will ever be repeated—a woman came up with forty-six new names. She and another former dial painter, it seemed, had got together on their own initiative and, goading each other's memory, had compiled their long list.

On the second visit, Barrer is always accompanied by the same assistant as on the first, largely because the taking of the breath sample may fluster the subject, and it is preferable not to bring in a stranger. The test is short and painless, Barrer told me, but it does involve bringing a steel cylinder of purified air and some other apparatus into the subject's home, and this may remind her vividly of her distant experience with radium. For further reassurance, Barrer has his assistant take the test first, while he points out how easy it is. All the subject has to do is to hold a plastic mask over her nose and mouth, inhale air from the cylinder, and then exhale it, through an aluminum valve, into a glass flask. The whole process takes seven minutes.

The analysis of the breath sample is performed by technicians in the A.E.C.'s Health and Safety Laboratory, in New York. It is an extremely precise and delicate business; the exhalations contain radon, a gas given off by radium, and the amount of it present indicates down to millionths of a microgram the quantity of radium in the body. According to current calculations, the presence of more than one-tenth of a microgram of radium in a subject indicates that sooner or later the subject's body burden may prove injurious, or even fatal. As a matter of fact, I was told, some experts suspect that even this tenth-of-a-microgram limit, which was established in 1940, is too high, for radiation injury has been observed in a few people with lower quantities. On the other hand, Barrer pointed out, one of the New Jersey women who died last year lived a normal and, indeed, a vigorous life for twenty-five years with thirteen micrograms. "How did she withstand it that long?" he asked me, but the question was rhetorical, for he went on, "That, of course, is what the study's all about—limits, safe and dangerous. It's not really surprising that we don't know them yet. Even if there weren't such relatively new puzzles as the effects of strontium 90 and other nuclear products to consider, radiation would have to be considered a pretty young field. After all, its existence was not even suspected a century ago. There's plenty to learn, but still we've come a long way since the day those first Jersey dial painters reported for work."

Barrer arranged for me to be on hand at several of his interviews with the former dial painters. In each case, the subject had agreed in advance to have me present, and in no case am I using her real name here. The first of the women I saw was Mrs. Mabel Chilton, and the place was Barrer's living room—a fair-sized, cheerful room, dominated by an orange wall and a large aquarium, in which catfish and angelfish darted through illuminated water. Barrer and his wife, Myra, who is a member of his staff, live in a housing development outside New Brunswick, and, at his suggestion, I had stopped in on a Sunday afternoon to hear about the study and, afterward, to meet Mrs. Chilton, who works as an invalid's companion in Newark and is unavailable the rest of the week. Barrer explained that he was about to see her for the first time, and that she spent Sundays at her daughter's home, in New Brunswick, but had told him on the phone that she would rather not be interviewed there. In midafternoon, Mrs. Barrer drove off to fetch Mrs. Chilton, and before she arrived Barrer told me what he knew about her. She was fifty-eight, and had worked at the United States Radium Corporataion plant from 1916 to 1918. She might be called the "sixth girl," he said, since she had fallen ill in 1922, and had been invited by the five to join them in their suit against the company. She had not done so, but when the case was over the company had settled with her for four thousand dollars. She had done a good deal of hiring for the firm in its early days, which meant that she might know quite a few new names. Barrer was just adding that he couldn't be sure of that when the two women walked in.

Mrs. Chilton's manner seemed detached as, smiling politely, she permitted Barrer to help her off with her coat and then sat down on a sofa near a low coffee table that held bowls of candy and figs. To me, she looked like a healthy woman. Her blue eyes were slightly magnified by the thick lenses of tortoise-shell glasses, and her hair was gray-black; her dress was a green print, and she was wearing a cameo ring. Barrer began by asking her if she had any questions, and she said no. She was all business, waiting for him to get on with things. Taking out the questionnaire, Barrer fired away, and Mrs. Barrer took notes. Mrs. Chilton's answers were as businesslike as her approach, and after little more than an hour, half the time of an average interview, it was over, and Mrs. Barrer served tea. The break seemed to induce a conversational mood in Mrs. Chilton, and as the four of us drank our tea she said, "I feel as though I'd been through this interview before. The doctors and the questions and all the curiosity about my radium jaw and those other things—that's what it reminds me of. But I must say I thought the whole business was over and done with."

"Of course, our study has a different aim," Barrer said soothingly.

"Yes, I know, now it's bombs," Mrs. Chilton said. "Well, anyway, you had to find me. I didn't get in touch with you, even though I read in the papers that you were looking for people like me. I had my fill of the papers long ago, when my name and my picture were all over them. All my life, regardless of how I've felt, I've told people 'I'm fine,' but how could I go on saying that with headlines about me like I might not live till Christmas? Finally, I made my family move to a different neighborhood, where no one knew me and I didn't have to tell strangers about 1922, when I couldn't open my jaw for six weeks, or 1925, when my legs had no feeling, or 1929, when the doctors decided there was nothing to do but take all my teeth out." Mrs. Chilton laughed, and added, "I remember, that last time in the hospital, lying in my bed and asking the doctor if the stuff would ever wear away, and his saying to me, as nice as he knew how, 'No, it won't, my dear, not if you live to be a thousand.' I'd like to tell him I'm fine now, but the poor man's been gone for years."

Barrer asked Mrs. Chilton to identify some watches and crucibles of paint that he took out of a desk drawer; he wanted to know if she had handled similar articles. Adjusting her spectacles, she peered at the watches, and said, "Oh, sure, Midgets and Yankees." Then came the radium paint, which looked like canary-yellow sand, and Mrs. Chilton, nodding vigorously, asked if she might look at it in the dark. Barrer opened the door of a clothes closet, and Mrs. Chilton, carrying one of Barrer's crucibles, stepped inside. Holding it at eye level, like a hand mirror, she gazed at its mild, steady glow for a moment and then came out.

"Those things bring back a lot—especially the watches," Mrs. Chilton said. "They were shipped overseas to the doughboys, and we girls would scratch our names and addresses inside the casing. They were cheap watches, and when they broke, we girls figured, the A.E.F. men would look inside them. Sure enough, eight or nine months later one of us would get a letter from some fellow over there saying how lonely he was. But don't get me wrong. We were a fine upstanding bunch of girls, even though not many of us had been to high school. We were always neatly dressed—in our shirtwaists and skirts—and we worked hard in the Studio. But things might loosen up when our forelady wasn't around and some of the fellows at the plant would try to date us. One of them, I remember—a fellow by the name of Ralph—gave me a box of candy one afternoon and carried on about how pearly my teeth were, until I had to get back to the painting. By the way, our forelady wouldn't have cared for the numerals on those watches you showed me. Too lumpy. Mine used to come out as smooth as cream, and I was very fast. Maybe that was why the plant supervisor asked me to help him when the company expanded. We took on about a hundred new girls and instructed them."

"Do you remember the names of any of the girls you employed?" Barrer inquired.

"Only two, but they wouldn't do you any good," Mrs. Chilton replied. "They were among the five who sued the company."

"I see," Barrer said.

"Those two and all the others—naturally I instructed them to lick their brushes. That was all I'd ever seen done at the plant. It was what I'd been doing myself. That brush tip—it had no taste, but it was sandy and gritty."

After a pause, Barrer asked if he might read off the names of a dozen former co-workers of Mrs. Chilton's whose whereabouts she might conceivably know. He read the names slowly and clearly, but Mrs. Chilton kept shaking her head.

"No, names aren't the things I remember," she said finally. "I can remember some of the headlines about myself, for instance, or a message I got from a stranger who must have thought I was a heathen—'Don't ever give up. God is with you.' And, of course, I remember the doctors' questions and their bills and my pearly teeth."

On the following Saturday afternoon, I met one of the former dial painters before Barrer did—Mrs. Ruth Gorska, a plump, brown-haired woman of fifty-six, with open features and a benign expression. He and I had planned to meet at her house, in a Jersey town near Montclair, and I got there first. Mrs. Gorska and her husband and a grown daughter live in a high-stooped frame building on a quiet street. The parlor was a musty but comfortable room full of old-fashioned pieces that had seen better days. A grandfather clock, its tarnished pendulum swinging creakily, stood in one corner. Two overstuffed chairs, upholstered in ancient velvet, were draped with antimacassars. Between the chairs, on newspapers spread over the thin carpet, were a portable phonograph of black leather, a small can of gold paint, and an artist's brush; these had been left there, I presently learned, by Mrs. Gorska's daughter, Rachel, a hospital technician of thirty or so, who was spending the afternoon puttering about the house. Mr. Gorska was out of town. After coming to the door to let me in, Mrs. Gorska sat down alone in the middle of a wide sofa, directly underneath an ornate lighting fixture that lacked bulbs.

I had scarcely settled myself in one of the overstuffed chairs when Mrs. Gorska told me that the fact that Mr. Barrer was coming to see her had relieved her in some ways but left her anxious in others. Frankly, Mrs. Gorska said, she was surprised that she had any feelings about it at all, because it was thirty-nine years now since she had painted dials in Orange and she hadn't been sick once. "I come of good Bohemian stock," she informed me earnestly. "I've seen a doctor only once in my life, and that was for childbirth." Nevertheless, she continued, when she read about the Commission's study in a local newspaper, she had immediately phoned a cancer specialist she knew of and had asked him to let Barrer know about her. The doctor had said it was right for her to get in touch with Barrer and had told her about what lay ahead—the interview and the breath sample. "Now that I think of it, I could have written Mr. Barrer directly, just like it said in the paper to do," she added. At any rate, she told me, a flood of questions had occurred to her since she had phoned the doctor—among them the number of girls who had died, how long the study would last, and, especially, when her breath sample would be taken. "I want to know if I'm all right—not sick like some of the strong girls I used to sit with at the plant," Mrs. Gorska said. "I realize I've had a secret worry for a long time."

Since she had known that Barrer was coming to see her, Mrs. Gorska went on, her mind had often drifted back to her career as a dial painter—clear back, in fact, to her two-week training period for the job, when, she told me, she swallowed the paint at a far greater rate than she did later on. However, she thought that the paint given to apprentices may have contained no radium, since it was used solely for practice purposes, and company officials were constantly stressing the costliness of the metal. "I remember a man telling us one day about how many miles the donkeys out West had to carry radium on their backs to get it to us," Mrs. Gorska told me. "And I can remember, too, a lively Italian girl at the plant who painted her teeth with the stuff whenever she had a date, so that they'd shine in the dark."

Mrs. Gorska's daughter, who was dressed in blue jeans and a cotton shirt, looked into the room, saw that her mother and I were talking, and, excusing herself, proceeded to gather up her phonograph, brush, and can of paint. "Guess I'd better gild my record-player in another room if I'm not going to disturb you," she said pleasantly.

"Good," Mrs. Gorska said. "I've been waiting for you to get that brush out of my sight. It's the exact same kind I used."

"How could anything be wrong after so many years?" the girl said. "This whole thing is over my head."

When she had left, Mrs. Gorska said that she had never told her family about her dial-painting days until after she had spoken to the cancer specialist. She added that she did not want me to think she felt only uneasiness about her impending interview and breath-sample test; as a matter of fact, she was looking forward to them with a certain calm. The prospect of a visit from a scientist had gone a long way toward dispelling her secret worry, she said. Everything would be out in the open now, and it was a relief that it should be so. She liked the idea of her family's being in on her old secret, and had even told a few friends about it. Perhaps, she added, she had never really had so much a desire to keep the secret as a fear of being upset by any mention of the gamble she had once taken. Anyway, right or wrong, that was what she had decided. "It couldn't have been much of a secret—not if a total stranger like Mr. Barrer could walk into my home and start asking me all sorts of questions about it," Mrs. Gorska said. "The whole world probably knows about it."

Barrer and an assistant, a pleasant and efficient girl named Charlotte Long, arrived about half an hour late, and he said they had just had an interview that had taken a little longer than usual. After answering two or three of Mrs. Gorska's questions, he went through his questionnaire. Mrs. Gorska seemed relieved when the interview was over, and immediately asked Barrer when he would be back for her breath sample. In about a week, he said; he would phone her. It was nearly dinnertime before we left, but Mrs. Gorska insisted on serving us a cup of coffee.

The next woman I saw had already had her breath-sample test, and the results had been excellent, though that did not surprise her. She was a Westchester matron, Mrs. Adele Bonner, who had painted her dials here in New York, at a small factory near City Hall. Barrer, who was in New York on a variety of missions, had arranged to meet her at an office in the A.E.C. building, on Columbus Avenue at Sixty-second Street. He had not seen her before—two of his assistants had conducted the interview and taken the breath sample—but the plant she had worked in was an obscure one, and he wanted to hear about it and her experience there. As he and I sat waiting for her, he told me that Mrs. Bonner, too, had business in town apart from their meeting. "She told me she's having a dental checkup," he said. "I hope it turns out as well as her breath sample." Soon she was shown in—a slender, pretty woman of fifty, with green eyes and reddish-blond hair, not a strand of which was out of place. She was extremely well dressed, and more poised than the other dial painters I had met. Mrs. Bonner is an artist—a water colorist, who has had several exhibitions in New York galleries. She has a Master's degree, too, and is the wife of a highly successful architect. Scarcely had she seated herself when she volunteered the information that her dentist had found her teeth in excellent shape. "Just a tiny cavity," she said, almost airily.

Mrs. Bonner told us that she had worked as a dial painter for six or seven months over a period of two summers, in 1923 and 1924. It had been her first job—a vacation one, for she was then still in high school. She was fourteen and in pigtails that first summer, she said, when she and a friend, Alice Marcy, had come over the bridge from Brooklyn, where they lived, to answer a newspaper want ad for "artists." Both of the girls wanted to be artists when they grew up, but neither imagined that they could fill the bill. "It was a long shot," Mrs. Bonner recalled. "We arrived with portfolios of our drawings that we thought the employer—I can't remember his name—would want to look over. Well, he didn't. He just wanted youngsters who could handle brushes skillfully enough to paint dials. Alice and I were the last of six girls he took. Alice was very fast. We were told to lick the brush, and she took to it like a machine, dipping it into her mouth and dabbing at the numerals. Dip and dab, dip and dab. I was the slowest of all. I didn't want to put that brush in my mouth. I was fastidious, *very* fastidious." Mrs. Bonner looked at Barrer and then at me to make sure we had understood her.

"I was my grandparents' only grandchild and the only niece of many aunts and uncles," she went on. "They all adored me, and when my father died and my mother had to go to work, they became even more doting. Naturally, they weren't going to let a pretty little girl have anything to do with dirt. And foreign objects were definitely to be kept out of the mouth. Everybody was really quite strict about that—perhaps too strict. I never used lipstick. I never chewed gum. And as a dial painter, I certainly was never going to put a brush that had been swished around in turpentine into my mouth. I don't even like the *smell* of turpentine, which is why I won't paint in oils to this day. Well, Alice was fast and I was slow. It was piecework, and she earned twice as much as I did, and she'd come home to Brooklyn each summer afternoon with her hair and dress speckled with yellow. Sometimes we'd ask the neighborhood kids in to watch Alice glow in a dark closet. They'd get a good laugh out of that. The last I heard of Alice, she'd become an artist, but that was long ago."

Mrs. Bonner paused. Then she turned to Barrer and said earnestly, "I wish I could give you her address, but it's been years since I was last in touch with her. I know you'll look for her hard enough. You people certainly got in touch with me quickly when I wrote to you. Naturally, I consulted with my husband before I did that, and he agreed with me that I might as well help out if I could. He hadn't known I'd ever been a dial painter, and, to tell the truth, I barely knew it myself, it all happened so long ago. It hadn't crossed my mind in years, and, really, why should it have? It was just one of the things one does as a kid."

Several days later, I was present at a breath-sample test, administered not to a dial painter but to a dial painter's daughter. An unmarried blonde of thirty-seven named Maria Benevento, she lives with her parents on the two upper floors of a wooden house in East Orange. Her mother, Carla, was present, and so was her aunt, Mrs. Amelia Giorno, and the occasion, I thought, seemed an unexpectedly cheerful one. The mother had had her test two months earlier, and it had turned out well. There was no question but that the daughter, who is a secretary in a state agency, would have an even better report, but she wanted the test very much and importuned Barrer to let her have it. Miss Benevento explained to me that her determination to have the test derived from her recent discovery that her mother had been pregnant with her while working as a dial painter. She had learned about this from her aunt, Mrs. Giorno—a nurse's aide at the hospital in which one of the two New Jersey dial painters who died last year had been a patient. Mrs. Giorno had helped take care of the woman, and although she didn't mention it to anyone in the family at the time, the daily sight of the unfortunate patient reminded her of the possibility that the same fate would overtake her own sister. After nearly a year of silence, she felt constrained to tell Miss Benevento about it. "Aunt Amelia wanted me to let our doctor know that Mother had worked in that factory, and to see if anything could be done for her while there was still time," Miss Benevento explained. "I told Aunt Amelia I'd need to know when Mother had painted dials, and she said that she couldn't remember exactly but that Mother was carrying me at the time."

"I guess I started the whole thing," Mrs. Giorno, an amiable, heavyset woman, interjected shyly.

Miss Benevento had immediately informed the family physician, and inquired if a blood-pressure condition of her mother's might be related to her ingestion of radium. The doctor had doubted this but had suggested, in the interests of science, that Barrer be notified of Mrs. Benevento's existence. Miss Benevento agreed, and Barrer's two visits followed within a month or so. "It was just when Mr. Barrer took Mother's breath sample that everything seemed to crowd in at once," Miss Benevento told me. "The woman that Aunt Amelia had taken care of had died, and it was in all the papers. It was in all the papers at that time, too, about Mr. Barrer's search for dial painters of long ago, and, to top everything, Mother's blood pressure was none too good. I stayed pretty close to home that week, waiting for Mr. Barrer's report. The day we got it, Mother's condition took a turn for the better, so I could have told myself that things were uncrowding themselves at last, except for one little matter—I'd taken it into my head that I might have been born a radium baby. And now that I don't have to worry about Mother, I want to know something about *my* future."

Turning to Barrer, she thanked him for coming. His aide, Margaret Doyon, in the meantime, was unpacking the equipment.

"Just by living on this earth, all of us have some radioactivity," Barrer told Miss Benevento reassuringly.

"I can't even watch those explosions on television any more, let alone *think* of them," Mrs. Benevento put in.

The glass flask, the air tank, and the plastic mask were soon set up, and Barrer told Miss Benevento that he would have Miss Doyon take the test first.

"That won't be necessary," Miss Benevento said. "I watched Mother's."

Barrer nodded to his assistant, who thereupon fitted the mask snugly over Miss Benevento's nose and mouth; two hoses trailed from the mask, one to the flask, the other to the silvery tank.

"Just breathe naturally now," Barrer said.

For a moment, Miss Benevento looked rather flustered; then, as her steady inhaling and exhaling became the only sound in the room, her eyes took on a pleased light. Mrs. Giorno smiled. Mrs. Benevento nodded approvingly.

One afternoon a week or so later, I was sitting with Barrer in his office in West Orange, and he brought me up to date on some of the people I had seen and heard about. There was still no trace of Alice Marcy. Miss Benevento's test had turned out fine. So had Mrs. Gorska's. I asked him what he did if a sample was not so good, and he said, "Well, we tell them anyway—as gently as we can. We let their doctors know, and we keep in touch with them. But, basically, there's just not much anybody can do."

As if his last sentence had reminded him of it, Barrer told me there was one woman he wanted particularly to see—a dial painter he had heard about who had been under medical observation for almost twenty years. She was a Mrs. Lawrence, who had worked in the Orange plant for a year and a half, starting in 1916, and had been ill since 1940; in 1956 she had lost a leg as a result of her illness. Barrer proposed that we try to see her that very afternoon. When I agreed, he dialled Mrs. Lawrence's home in East Orange, to arrange a meeting. After speaking just a few words, he hung up quickly. Mrs. Lawrence, he told me glumly, had died of her body burden. "I told her husband we'd come out anyway," he said, and we got into his car. Our destination proved to be a modest frame house, and there Mr. Lawrence, a vigorous, white-haired man who is a truck driver, made us welcome in the small living room, which was hung with reproductions of modern French paintings. Barrer said he hoped we weren't intruding, and Mr. Lawrence replied that we were not—that the idea of his wife's passing had been with him for years. Barrer had two or three questions to ask, and when they were out of the way, Mr. Lawrence politely prolonged our visit by talking briefly of his wife's last years. She had avoided neighbors since her amputation, he said, and though she had been confined to a wheelchair, she had managed to pursue her hobby of refinishing furniture. Neither he nor his wife had ever referred specifically to dial painting as the cause of her condition, Mr. Lawrence went on, but he was reasonably certain she knew that it was, because many years ago, one afternoon when she was feeling relatively well, she had remarked to him, "It's not good to know things too far ahead. It makes life more waiting than living."

A STROLL IN THE GARDEN

AMONG THE HUNDREDS of scientists working at the Brookhaven National Laboratory, in Upton, Long Island, where atomic energy is being studied in its many phases, there are about a dozen botanists, and not one of them, to judge from my experience on a recent visit out there, has anything but kind words to say for nuclear radiation—at least insofar as it affects his chosen field of research. Working away in their small corner of this vast installation—and it is a small corner, representing only some five per cent of Brookhaven's operations—the botanists are in a position to realize more concretely than most of their colleagues just how radiation maims and destroys living organisms, but this in no way dims their singularly cheerful professional view of it. For radiation, with its power to raise havoc among genes and chromosomes, and thereby spawn mutations that alter all forms of life, is the clue to countless genetic mysteries, and at Brookhaven the scientists are able not only to observe its workings closely but to perform unprecedented experiments with it, often in a laboratory unique in the history of science—a carefully sealed-off ten-acre garden, where, from February to November, for all but a few hours of every day, a collection of trees, vines, shrubs, vegetables, grasses, and flowers is deliberately exposed to gamma rays emanating from a captive specimen of cobalt 60, a substance that is a powerful source of nuclear radiation.

Rising to a height of nine feet near the center of this garden is a stainless-steel tube, four inches in diameter, which also extends four feet below the ground to a cinder-block pit. The cobalt 60, generally referred to as the "source," is encased in a cylindrical stainless-steel jacket—eighteen inches long and two inches in diameter, and with a four-inch-thick lead plug on top—that fits inside the tube and can be moved up and down inside it, like a piston, by a pulley system. Waiting to envelop the source when it is lowered to rest in the pit, and to absorb its rays as long as it remains there, is a cylindrical lead shield, eight inches thick. At four-thirty every afternoon during the spring, summer, and fall, after elaborate precautions have been taken to make certain that all visitors to the garden have departed, the source slowly emerges from its shield in the pit and rises to a point about four feet above the ground. There it remains during the night and the next morning, while its rays permeate every living thing within a radius of perhaps a hundred yards. Then, at one o'clock in the afternoon, it slips back down into its cinder-block chamber, relaxing its grip on the garden long enough to let the botanists move in and study the effects of its presence.

If the botanists, unlike the other scientists at Brookhaven, can experiment freely with the malignant, as well as benign, powers of radiation, the reason, of course, is that their victims are plants. As they roam about in their garden, their consciences need not be troubled at the sight of, say, a maple that, instead of serving as an erect and gracefully proportioned ornament to the landscape, stands stunted and malformed, with strangely convoluted, leathery leaves. While showing me some of Brookhaven's eerie botanical exhibits, Dr. Seymour Shapiro, coördinator of the laboratory's Radiation Mutations Program, remarked, "As far as I know, only one man—an Indian named Sir Jagadis Chunder Bose, who wrote a book called *The Irritability of Plants*—has ever maintained that plants can feel pain. And the evidence on which he based his claim has not inspired widespread support." The botanists do not hesitate to admit that their program involves large-scale destruction of life, since harmful mutations far outnumber helpful ones (for every mutation that may lead to an improvement of the strain, there are hundreds that render it weak or sterile or monstrous), and, as Shapiro, a reflective, pipe-smoking man of thirty-three who is rather given to understatement, put it, "Of course, a program of this sort would be out of the question for human beings, however beneficial it might be in the long run. With plants, though, we can go ahead just as we like. So far nobody has complained about the casualties."

The victims of the ritual in the garden are being sacrificed in a worthwhile and what many of the botanists believe to be an urgent cause—a campaign to produce and manipulate plant mutations in a way that will improve the various species for the benefit of mankind. A cereal grass that will stand up well against disease and frost, a flower of some rare hue, an uncommonly nutritious fruit from an uncommonly robust tree—it is this sort of thing that the botanists are searching for. Radiation, many experts believe, is the chief, if not the only, cause of mutations, and when it is concentrated and intensified, as in the garden, it drastically speeds up the process of evolution—essentially a process in which the relatively few beneficial mutations thrive and spread while the great mass of useless or retrogressive ones wither and die out. In the past, this process, stimulated only by the small and widely diffused amounts of natural radiation that are present in soil, air, and water, has moved at a pace so leisurely as to be almost imperceptible to man. Now the botanists at Brookhaven, with their ready access to the laboratory's sources of radiation, possess the means of forcing nature to hustle along, prematurely revealing her plans for the future. Compared to plants growing in accord with nature's dawdling timetable, the plants in the Brookhaven garden produce mutations in fantastic profusion. In one study made of corn, to cite a not unusual example, an examination of thirty-five thousand kernels taken from ears that had been exposed only to a natural dosage of radiation turned up eleven mutations, or not quite one in three thousand, while the corn grown in the Brookhaven garden showed one mutation for every ten kernels.

Brookhaven, where the study of plant mutations has been under way since 1949, is so far the only institution in the United States to have undertaken a large-scale program of this sort. (The University of Tennessee's School of Agriculture recently embarked on a similar project at Oak Ridge, but at present the scope of the work being done there is comparatively modest.) Word of the novel botanical doings in the heart of Long Island has spread, and in consequence horticultural-minded agencies and researchers in many part of the world have been sending in seeds and plants, or cuttings of plants, with the request that these be given a strategic place in the Brookhaven garden. The botanists in charge of the garden—or "gamma field," as they call it—are delighted to hear from these correspondents, whom they refer to as coöperators. Owing largely to climatic differences, it is sometimes impractical to install a coöperator's contribution in the garden, and in that case the botanists insert it in Brookhaven's giant reactor, or nuclear furnace, and leave it there for as long as five hours, after which it is set out in one of a number of greenhouses that form a less spectacular portion of the botanists' domain. Among the foreign coöperators whose entries have received the reactor treatment are a botanist in Thailand, who submitted some seeds of the native rubber plant and expressed the hope that radiation would help bring forth a strain more resistant to disease; another botanist, in Pakistan, who mailed in some jute seeds, along with a note to the effect that taller-growing jute would be much appreciated; and a third, in Italy, who wrote that growers of almonds in his part of the country were eager to get hold of a species that would ripen earlier, and sent along some cuttings from their trees to find out what might be done about it.

Up against problems like these, the botanists at Brookhaven are reluctant to make unqualified predictions about the results of their work. They prefer to wait until the returns are in, and most of these will not be in for some time, since the artificial development of mutations, though breathtakingly swift by nature's standards, still depends on the speed at which plants grow. The fact is that while a few hours in the reactor or a few weeks in the garden may result in striking changes in the appearance of a plant, this is only the first step in what is bound to be an extended period of experimentation. The changes that the botanists are most deeply interested in are the invisible and still largely inexplicable changes in the plant's chromosomes and genes, which affect heredity—the plants of the future. So the botanists are methodically taking cuttings from the trees, shrubs, and grasses in the gamma field, planting them in non-irradiated fields, and giving mutations a chance to emerge. "Visitors sometimes seem impatient when we explain that we haven't been in business long enough to report much in the way of achievement,"

Shapiro told me. "They expect something sensational overnight. Outsize fruit—that's what many of them want to see, and see right away, as if we could raise a whole new generation of trees in a few weeks! Everyone seems to be hankering for an apple as big as a basketball. What's wrong with the lunch-pail size we've got?"

While the botanists are cautious about forecasts, it is evident that many of them feel the discovery of a way to accelerate evolution hasn't come along a moment too soon, and this feeling sometimes leads them to provide a glimpse, at least, of what they hope to accomplish. One of the Brookhaven men I met, for instance—a young geneticist named Calvin Konzak—appeared to be convinced that the prospects for agriculture in general are far from bright, and that its salvation depends on the speed with which radiation is able to come to the rescue. In Dr. Konzak's opinion, a serious consequence of today's large-scale farming techniques, which devote immense areas of land to a single variety of a single crop, in contrast to nature's way of intermingling a wide variety of plants, is that the world is rapidly running out of plant strains strong enough to resist disease. "There's an imbalance between predator and prey," he told me. "Those great belts of wheat or corn are easy marks for the attack of certain fungi. The resiliency of nature—or of nature as it is now constituted—is being steadily sapped, and agronomists have all they can do to fend off the constantly increasing hordes of pests, without looking ahead to the development of improved varieties of plants. They're like the Dutch boy who had to keep his finger in the dike." In this country alone, he added, crops valued at over three billion dollars are being lost to fungi each year. But now, I gathered, it is beginning to look as if man might be granted more than a mere reprieve, for artificial radiation has begun to produce mutations that are either immune to some of the most virulent scourges or sturdy enough to hold their own against them. Specifically, Konzak told me, a number of cereal seeds—cereals are his specialty—have in recent months yielded strains that show every indication of being able to withstand such killers as Victoria blight, a root-rotting parasite, and stem rust, which weakens plants to the point where they topple over. "And radiation may help us do something else, too," Konzak went on. "It may help us remodel crops. Radiation breaks up chromosomes, and that could permit some pretty improbable unions. Wild grass and common wheat, for instance. Who knows what kind of offspring they might generate? Perhaps a food we have no conception of today." He paused for a moment, and then said reflectively, "With radiation, you see, we can help nature along—guide her to do the things that need doing but that we can't do ourselves. No matter how much remodelling we attempt, we'll always need nature herself. She's our source—our raw material. We can't create something out of nothing."

To a certain extent, Konzak's work is being complemented by that of one of his colleagues—Dr. Erwin Schwinghamer, a tall, spare man of thirty-six whose field is plant pathology. As he sees it, in the long run—the very long run—it won't help much to bring forth strains of crop plants that are impervious to existing forms of fungi if nothing is done to anticipate the new strains of fungi that may be hatching. Dr. Schwinghamer, therefore, is currently spending his time applying radiation techniques to fungi, in an effort to determine those species in which mutations occur most frequently, since they are the ones best equipped to catch healthy crops off guard. "We've stopped waiting helplessly for enemy organisms to make the next move in their own sweet time," he told me. "With the aid of radiation, we hope to reach the point where they will do it when we want them to."

While most of the Brookhaven botanists, like Konzak and Schwinghamer, clearly still have a considerable distance to go before they can announce any great triumphs, a few of them—mainly those who are concerned with the immediate results of radiation, rather than with the potential workings of mutation—are in the satisfying position of having completed at least one of the many studies involved in the program. Among these fortunate individuals is Lloyd Schairer, a twenty-nine-year-old radiation technician, and on a table in his office in the Brookhaven Biology Building—the headquarters of the program—he laid out for me a demonstration of his success, in the form of three potatoes. In 1953, Schairer became a member of a team of Brookhaven scientists who set out to confirm a theory that a limited dose of radiation would substantially increase the length of time that potatoes could be stored without deteriorating. His three potatoes reveal, as dramatically as potatoes can reveal anything, that this is a scientific fact. One of the three is little more than a tangle of whitish sprouts massed on the shrunken remnant of a potato. Another is obviously no longer edible, either, for while it is not quite so shrunken, it is similarly matted with sprouts, and its body is flaccid. The third potato—the pride and joy of Schairer and his teammates—might easily get by on the vegetable stall of a busy market. It is a trifle shrivelled, but it has no sprouts and is still far from squashy. This potato, Schairer explained, owes its relatively dapper condition to a sojourn of forty-eight hours in the botanists' garden, close enough to the cobalt 60 to receive ten thousand roentgens; this treatment stopped the growth of sprouts, which, essential though they are to the underground germination of the plant, are ruinous to a potato in storage, feeding on its starches and reducing it to pulp. The so-so specimen, Schairer went on, had spent the same amount of time in the garden but farther away from the cobalt 60; its dosage had been five thousand roentgens. The third potato hadn't been anywhere near the garden. All three had been kept for the last two years in the same dark cellar, at a temperature of forty-two degrees.

In one sense, however, Schairer and his colleagues, hopeful though they appear to be that they have spared potato wholesalers of the future the high cost of refrigerated storage, aren't entirely out of the woods, for the Food and Drug Administration requires that irradiated foods be tested on animals for a minimum of three years before it will consider approving them for human consumption. So far, no irradiated foods have been through the complete round of tests, but the Army Quartermaster Corps, faced with the problem of supplying potatoes to overseas military outposts, has shown a lively interest in the Brookhaven discovery, and is now feeding irradiated potatoes to dogs and rats. The animals seem to be doing fine, and Schairer believes that in the end his team's technique will be given a clean bill of health. "They're not bad—the tubers in this group," he said, lightly tapping the ten-thousand-roentgen potato with a forefinger. "I've tasted a couple of them. No ill effects whatever, and their flavor stands up very well."

Ornamental flowers are being studied intensively at Brookhaven, and lay visitors to the laboratory tend to show more interest in what is being done with them than in the scientists' work with prosaic plants like corn and potatoes. From time to time, visiting congressmen are taken around on an inspection tour, and it is not until their guide reaches into a refrigerator and presents each of them with a boutonnière from an irradiated plant that they seem to feel they are really getting the jump on history. Carnations, in particular, have received a great deal of attention at Brookhaven, which may be attributable to the fascination these flowers have long held for Professor Gustav Mehlquist, a horticulturist on the faculty of the University of Connecticut, who has, over the last thirty years, been conducting experiments with the cross-breeding of plants—a few years ago, after prolonged trial and error, he produced a sturdy pure-yellow carnation—and who has been taking an active interest in many of the Brookhaven projects.

I heard about Mehlquist from a former student of his who is now a Brookhaven staff botanist—Dr. Yoneo Sagawa, a Hawaiian-born Japanese-American. Every week or ten days, Sagawa told me, as he was showing me through some of the laboratory's greenhouses, he loads the back seat of one of the laboratory's cars with irradiated carnations or larkspur and drives over to the Connecticut campus, at Storrs, to show them to his friend and talk over further experiments. Their most striking achievement in the Brookhaven garden, Sagawa said, has been to make two different carnations—a red blossom called the William Sim, after its originator, and a white one called the White Sim—appear on the same plant. Left to their own devices, Sagawa explained, red and white carnations rarely share a single plant—so rarely, indeed, that only once in approximately a decade does someone spot a mutation of this kind, even though about two hundred million of the plants are raised every year in the United States alone, mostly by professional horticulturists, who are naturally on the lookout for just such phenomena. But it's an altogether different story at Brookhaven, where in the past three years six of these two-colored specimens have turned up among not quite a thousand carnation plants set out in the radiation garden.

Offhand, Sagawa said, he supposed that developing a plant bearing blossoms of different colors might strike a layman as a rather aimless stunt, but, as a matter of fact, the achievement was part of a large project that has very broad implications. Not only has it led to a better understanding of the transmission of color among plants but it has added to the fund of knowledge about genetic changes in general. Three years of thinking and experimenting went into the Sim project, Sagawa told me. It all began when he and Mehlquist noticed that if White Sims that had not yet blossomed were exposed to radiation, eighty per cent of them eventually produced red flowers—William Sims. Very odd, the two friends agreed. Mutation could not be the answer, since even among irradiated carnation plants color mutations occur no oftener than once in a hundred cases. So Mehlquist and Sagawa had to start pretty much from scratch. The color of a flower, they knew, is determined by the genes in the outermost layer of the plant's tissue. Since White Sims that had not been exposed to radiation almost never produced anything but white blossoms, the genes in the outer tissue of the undoctored plants were obviously of the white variety. But since so many irradiated White Sims produced William Sims, they concluded that there must be red genes somewhere in the plants' tissue and that somehow these genes had taken over the role of color determination. How had this happened? That was the problem. As a first step toward solving it, the two collaborators established by experiment that radiation could destroy the outer layer of tissue without damaging the layer immediately beneath it. Then they turned their attention to the behavior of the cells in the second layer. "Weeks and weeks of research," Sagawa recalled, gazing absently at some African violets. "Sitting in front of a microscope day after day and staring at section after section of stem, sliced transparently thin, and watching the healthy inner cells gradually replace the dying outer tissue. And at last, one fine morning, we saw red petals peeking out of the calyx of one of the White Sims we'd been studying." Turning away from the violets, Sagawa said, "The experiment showed us a number of things. It showed us just how those red genes took over. It showed us that some of the White Sims were highly sensitive to radiation; their outer tissue died, and they produced red flowers. Other, stronger plants, relatively insensitive to radiation, kept producing white flowers. And still others—sensitive here, insensitive there—produced both. We've got one of those strange plants here now. Let me show it to you."

I followed Sagawa into an adjoining greenhouse, and there, in a clay flowerpot set between pots containing dandelions and Easter lilies, was the plant. Sure enough, a scarlet William Sim carnation had blossomed near the top of its tall, slender stem, and about halfway down was a White Sim. As my companion considerately stepped aside to give me an unimpeded view of his masterwork, a feeling of self-consciousness came over me. His attitude toward the plant, I knew, was essentially scientific, and I was sure he did not think me qualified to appreciate it on that basis; at the same time, I felt that some polite display of admiration, however perfunctory, was expected of me, and, to my embarrassment, I found myself incapable of making it. To me, the plant seemed freakish to the point of absurdity. (I have never cared much for carnations anyway; I've always considered them puffy, excessively petalled flowers, and associated them with the lapels of floorwalkers.) Gradually, though, this perverse reaction subsided—dispelled in large measure, I suspect, by the atmosphere of the greenhouse itself, with its soft, uneven earth floor, the rich smell of damp soil issuing from its flowerpots, and the drowsy warmth of the sun pouring through its glass roof. It occurred to me that I might well be standing in the presence of a symbol of the most peaceful use of atomic energy yet dreamed of, and I found a certain pleasure in the realization that I had involuntarily applied aesthetic standards to a product of nuclear radiation. I don't know what Sagawa was thinking while I stood there, silent and unmoving, but when at last I nodded approvingly, he said, in a patient tone that enhanced the serenity of the moment, "It isn't something that the average gardener can grow in his back yard. But from experimental work of this kind we have already acquired knowledge that should enable us to achieve new shades of color in flowers. And it is only a matter of time, I believe, before amateur gardeners will begin to enjoy some of the benefits of our work."

Brookhaven's botanical program may still be in its infancy from the scientists' point of view, but to an outsider who visits its garden it would appear that a great deal has already been achieved. That, at any rate, was my impression when, soon after my walk through the greenhouses with Sagawa, Shapiro drove me out to have a look at it and we spent an hour or so wandering about among its ten acres of plant life. He proposed that, as a prelude to our visit, we have lunch in the Brookhaven cafeteria, a plan to which I readily agreed. While we were eating, I chanced to mention Sagawa's account of the long struggle to find out the reason for the William Sim blossoms on White Sim plants, and Shapiro asked, "Did he tell you how his two-colored carnation plants once played a part—a very minor one, I grant you—in relations between this country and Russia?" When I shook my head, Shapiro said that the incident had taken place during the First International Conference on the Peaceful Uses of Atomic Energy, at Geneva, in August, 1955. There was to be a series of national exhibits in the Palais des Nations—the old League of Nations headquarters—and the Atomic Energy Commission had called upon the botanists at Brookhaven to provide a display devoted to plant genetics, as part of the American exhibit. "We thought first of putting up a set of photomurals," Shapiro continued, "but then we decided that that would be lifeless. Life is what we deal in, so we finally settled on displaying the four William-and-White Sims we had on hand at the time. At once, we began to run into difficulties, consisting mostly of red tape. For example, I asked the A.E.C. to find out whether the Swiss had any regulation against bringing carnations into their country. I gathered that the A.E.C. would pass the question along to the State Department, which would communicate it to the Swiss Embassy, which would pass it along to the Swiss Department of Agriculture back home. Well, I'm still waiting for an answer from the A.E.C. After weeks had gone by without any word, I called up the Swiss Consulate in New York and was put through to an agricultural attaché, who gave me the answer right off. He said sure, carnations were all right; the only thing the Swiss were worried about in the plant line was a grape disease that was prevalent in California. Then it occurred to me that maybe *our* plant-quarantine people would object to our bringing the carnations back into this country. Yes, it appeared that they would. They were leery of plants that had had an opportunity to pick up diseases in foreign soil. Well, that took some thinking, but we came up with what we hoped was a solution. We offered to ship some of our Brookhaven soil to the American Consulate in Geneva and to repot them in that whenever necessary. The plants, we claimed, would then technically never leave American soil. The plant-quarantine people had to agree that our plan was foolproof."

Shapiro went on to say that he had flown over ahead of time to arrange for the billeting of the carnations at night, and had succeeded in finding them splendid quarters in a Geneva cold-storage vault, which they shared with cheeses, eggs, and meats. The show at the Palais des Nations lasted fourteen days, and for most of that time the Sims gave an excellent account of themselves. Shapiro had brought along a scale model of the Brookhaven garden, with a miniature reproduction of the source, which he or an assistant kept cranking up and down, and while it aroused considerable interest, he thinks the carnations drew a larger and more sympathetic crowd. "Everybody knows what a flower and a leaf and stem are," he told me. "Maybe people couldn't see any connection between our flowers and the atom, but they certainly seemed to like our show." Among those who seemed to like the show were a number of Russian botanists who kept coming back for another look but invariably voiced the suspicion that the William Sims had merely been grafted onto the White Sim plants, and that radiation had played no part in the process.

"Four days before the end of the conference, a truckman who was returning the plants to their vault for the night dropped one of the pots and broke the William Sim off the stalk," Shapiro recalled. "Then, two days later, by coincidence, all the remaining Sims' blossoms died. With the flowers gone, there wasn't any point in keeping the plants in cold storage any more, so we moved them over to a greenhouse in the Geneva Botanical Garden. A couple of days before we were due to go home, I had an idea. I cabled Brookhaven for permission to give those doubting Russians two of the plants. The O.K. came through just as the Russian botanists were packing up to leave, and I looked up one of them—a pleasant, baggy-trousered young fellow named Chirchov—and asked him if he'd like a couple of our carnation plants. He said he certainly would, so I drove him to the greenhouse and handed him the two pots. I didn't want Chirchov and his colleagues returning to Russia with nothing but notes on what we'd accomplished. The plants themselves would give the Russians a much clearer and more lasting impression of our work. Maybe by now they've subjected those plants to anatomical, physiological, and biochemical tests, or maybe, as I hope, they believed us, and instead of destroying the plants in order to perform autopsies on them, they just left them alone for a year, until they blossomed again, producing their Williams and their Whites. I've been meaning to write Chirchov and find out exactly what they did do with them. I have the address of his lab around somewhere. It's not too far from Moscow, as I recall. I remember thinking it must be about the same distance from Moscow as Brookhaven is from New York."

After lunch, Shapiro and I got in his car and headed for the garden, which lies about two miles from the Biology Building, in a remote stretch of the laboratory grounds, and presents anything but a hospitable exterior to the world. People who drive along the road leading to the site are brought up short while they are still a good five city blocks from it by a yellow sign, lettered in black: "RADIATION—DANGER—STAY AWAY!" The garden itself is surrounded by an eight-foot chain-link fence, with barbed wire on top, which is broken only by a shack that serves as the entrance and as a shelter for the mechanism that raises and lowers the source in its tube, some five hundred and fifty feet away. This is a hand winch, and from it a cable runs underground nearly to the base of the stainless-steel tube, then up alongside the tube and through a pulley, and finally down to the cylinder holding the cobalt 60.

In compliance with a Brookhaven regulation applicable to all who enter the garden, Shapiro and I, upon reaching the shack, each attached to one of our lapels a small badge containing a strip of film, which would be developed after we left the garden and would show how much radiation, if any, we had been exposed to. When I remarked that this didn't seem to be much of a precaution, he told me not to worry—there was a whole system of safeguards aimed at minimizing the chances of accident. Only one man—Frank German, the Biology Department's field and greenhouse supervisor—is authorized to raise and lower the source, he said. The winch has spokes, and to prevent anybody else from monkeying with the crank, German simply inserts a bar through the spokes and snaps a padlock through a hole in the bar, thereby immobilizing the whole mechanism. Shapiro showed me the winch, with the bar held firmly in place by German's padlock. There were other holes in the bar, and he explained that each botanist has a padlock of his own, which, as a self-protective measure, he is required to fasten to the bar before going out into the garden; this arrangement makes it certain that if he should be overcome by heatstroke or if German's watch should run fast—to suggest only two of many possibilities—the source cannot be raised until he is safely back. Shapiro pointed out the scientists' padlocks to me—a couple of dozen of them hanging on a wall, each with its owner's initials painted on it and each with a key in it. In addition to serving its primary purpose, he said, the multiple-padlock system takes a big load off German's mind, for when four-thirty rolls around, he can be sure that if his is the only padlock remaining on the bar, it is safe to go ahead and crank the winch, bringing the source aboveground.

Shapiro said he liked to think the padlock system was foolproof, although he realized that, human fallibility being what it is, nobody could conceivably anticipate every contingency. As a matter of fact, he went on, human fallibility is responsible for one of the few disadvantages of the system that have come to light thus far. "On afternoons when Frank comes in to raise the source and finds one of our men's padlocks still on the bar, he immediately goes out in the garden to look for him," he said. "But sometimes there's no one there. That's when a man has forgotten to take his lock off the bar and put it back on the wall before leaving. Frank really has a time of it then, trying to track the fellow down, so that he can raise the source. He has a set of duplicate keys in a jar in his office over in the Biology Building, but, like everybody else around here, he dreads the outside chance of error—maybe the missing man was out in the garden after all, behind a tree or bending down to examine a shrub—and he doesn't go near the jar until he knows definitely where the man is. What's more, the jar is sealed, because we don't want to make it too easy for Frank, or for anybody else, to get at those duplicates. You know how it is—people are likely to grow careless about such things after a while. Well, if Frank finally finds out that the man who forgot about his padlock has gone off for the weekend, or something of the sort, then and only then does he smash the jar."

On the floor of the shack were two boxes—an old insulated icebox, and a smaller box, made of heavy concrete. Lifting the lid of the icebox, Shapiro brought out a Geiger counter. "Optional equipment," he said. "Some people think I'm finicky, but I always take it along." Then, raising the lid of the second box, he produced a tiny fragment of cobalt 60 embedded in a thick shield of transparent pink Lucite. The cobalt, a bit of silvery metal, reminded me of a fishline sinker. "We have to keep checking on our checks," Shapiro told me. "This sample of cobalt gives off ten milliroentgens an hour through its shield, and that's what the counter should read if it's working properly." He held the two objects near each other, staring intently at the needle on the counter's dial. "O.K.," he said after a moment. "Ten it is." He put the sample back in its box, and, taking his padlock down from its place on the wall, snapped it on the bar and turned toward the door leading to the garden. Then he paused to point out to me that the door had no knob on the inside. It could be pushed open from the shack, he explained, but only when the source was resting underground; as soon as the source was raised, a bolt rigged to the winch automatically slid into a locked position, where it remained until the source was lowered again. "Well, I guess we're all set for our stroll," he said, leaning his weight against the door and ushering me out into the garden.

"Blueberries from Rutgers, redbud trees from the Brooklyn Botanic Garden, sour cherries from Penn State," Shapiro announced, with an expansive sweep of his arm, as we stood just outside the shack, looking at the growing things around us. It was a hot early-summer day, with a cloudless sky, and the garden was approaching full bloom. The steady chirping of crickets sounded shrilly through the shimmering heat, and perched on a branch near the top of one of Penn State's sour-cherry trees was a thrush, pecking unconcernedly at the irradiated unripe fruit. Insects and birds, Shapiro said, are more vulnerable than plants to radiation, but not nearly as vulnerable as man. Embryonic tissue, though, is something else again; no matter what the form of life, it is highly sensitive to radiation. Indicating a patch of grass some distance away, he told me that a pair of killdeer had nested there the previous spring and produced a clutch of eggs. The botanists had wondered whether they would hatch. They did, but ten days late. The young birds seemed lively and healthy, and eventually the whole family—parents and young—flew away, apparently in the pink. "I don't know about those fledglings," Shapiro remarked amiably. "Maybe when they're full grown, it will turn out that we've added to the whooping-crane population."

The stainless-steel tube gleamed dully in the sunlight, and we began walking toward it slowly, stopping here and there to examine instances of floral aberration. Underfoot, daisies and clover were growing wild—mere weeds, as far as the official program is concerned, although if some unexpected mutation should be found among them, it would not be neglected. Near the perimeter of the garden, the plants looked normal, but closer to the tube there were indications—increasingly grotesque—that radiation had been at work. Trees squatted near the ground, like bushes, their gnarled branches tipped with bulbous growths. Stooping over a strawberry plant—a University of New Hampshire entry—Shapiro fingered some of its leaves, which were of a leathery texture, yet extremely brittle, and then picked one of its berries and, straightening up, thrust it into my hand. It was like no strawberry I had ever seen before—a lopsided, many-lobed blob of matter that had nothing but color in common with the familiar heart-shaped berry—and it felt curiously repulsive. We passed some tobacco plants whose leaves, half an inch wide instead of the normal six inches, might well cause a cigar maker to start learning another trade in a hurry. A number of fairly common plants had been so warped that they had become totally unrecognizable. "Look at that bush over there," Shapiro said. "It's a lilac, but even an expert wouldn't recognize it. A lilac's leaves are usually triangular. See how rounded these are? And how mottled?"

Leaving the shrub that had once been a lilac, we passed a clump of forsythia, from Harvard's Arnold Arboretum. On its leaves radiation had had a different effect; instead of the characteristic toothed edges, there were occasional deep forkings. Near the forsythia stood a stunted Norway maple that had been planted for the Brooklyn Botanic Garden. Autumn was already at hand for this tree; its leaves had turned reddish. "A little early in the baseball season for that color, don't you think?" Shapiro observed, with a smile. "Those are sugar maples over there. They come from the University of Vermont, and their leaves are about to turn, too. We ought to have some really vivid October foliage here in a week or two." Next, we came upon the Rutgers blueberries—a patch of bushes bearing unripe fruit whose grayish-green skin was taut with youth. Both the bushes and their berries looked healthy enough to me, but Shapiro said there was something very peculiar about them, for growing on the same stems with the berries were many of the small white flowers of the blueberry plant. "That's most unusual," he told me. "Blueberry plants develop a stage at a time, but here we have two stages occurring simultaneously—berries starting to ripen while the bushes are still producing flowers. Radiation has upset their cycle. And notice how low the bushes are—about a third the height of normal blueberry bushes in this general area. It's remarkable that a plant whose growth has been so drastically impaired can go on producing fruit, isn't it? Well, that's just an illustration of nature's inflexible will to survive."

Some sixty feet from the tube, we encountered an even more stubborn illustration of nature's will to survive. This was an apple tree, from the State Agricultural Experiment Station, at Geneva, New York, that was completely bare of foliage, its leaf buds having been killed by radiation. I had never seen a deader-looking tree, but Shapiro assured me that it was by no means dead. Food that it had stored up in its roots, he said, was keeping it alive, and it would continue to grow—its branches thickening just as if nothing untoward had happened to it—until the food was gone. "If that tree should survive long enough to sprout new leaves and buds, it would probably yield a bonanza of mutations," he said, staring hopefully at the bleak object. Then he pointed out a few apple trees a couple of yards farther away from the source. They were a much less sorry lot; their branches were marred by wartlike swellings, to be sure, but they had leaves and fruit. "An odd thing happened here a couple of years ago," Shapiro said as we continued toward the center of the garden. "Somebody walked off with some apples that were growing on one of those trees. It was a plain case of thievery. We notified the police, but they got nowhere. I doubt whether those apples had been sufficiently exposed to hurt anyone, but the mystery still puzzles me. Who could it have been? Small boys? There aren't any within miles. Visiting scientists? Maybe it was just someone who felt he had to taste forbidden fruit."

Surrounding the tube, for a distance of about fifteen feet, was a patch of scorched earth—barren and brown in a garden otherwise teeming with vegetation. "This close to the source nothing survives for very long," Shapiro told me. "We've deliberately put plants here just to see how long they would keep alive, and it's always been the same story—death in less than a week." Along the edge of the bare patch were a group of plants that were going to be spared this fate. These were young blueberry, strawberry, and peach plants, set out in pails. Shapiro explained that they had just been put in their extremely vulnerable positions and would be left there for perhaps two days, to get them started on their irradiated lives.

The tube itself towered above a platform of boards covering the pit where the cobalt 60 and its accoutrements lay. As we stepped onto the platform, Shapiro glanced at his Geiger counter; the needle didn't move. The steel cable, an eighth of an inch thick, rose beside us, barely an inch away from the tube, from a crack between two of the boards, and Shapiro plucked at it, as if at the string of a bull fiddle, causing it to quiver briefly. Nowadays, he said, if something goes wrong with the cable, it can be cut loose from the source by an electrical device operated from the shack, but until about three years ago it had never occurred to anybody that such a safety measure might come in handy. "One day, while the source was being lowered," Shapiro told me, "the cable got snarled somewhere, stranding the source right about here." He touched a spot about a third of the way up the tube. "As long as it remained there, further research in the gamma field was out of the question. We had to figure out some way of getting the source back into its shield, and what we finally decided to do was try to cut the cable in two with a bullet fired from a moderately safe distance. But the last thing we wanted was to have the bullet hit the tube, because that would probably dent it, and might easily jam the source completely. If the source itself had got stuck, and not just the cable, we'd really have been in a fix."

In the end, Shapiro went on, the hero turned out to be an expert marksman named Edward Nicholson, who at the time was a foreman in the laboratory's machine shop and a member of the Brookhaven Rifle and Pistol Club. Using a rifle with a telescopic sight, and armor-piercing ammunition, he warmed up by firing a dozen shots on an old Army range on the Brookhaven property—a relic of Camp Upton, which formerly occupied the site. When he came over to the garden, two physicists asked him how near he would have to get to the cable to stand a reasonable chance of hitting it. He said he couldn't do much at over a hundred feet, and they warned him he must not stay as near as that to the cobalt 60 for more than a minute. Nicholson nodded, and entered the garden on the double, dropping onto one knee as soon as he was within range. His first shot was wide of the mark, but with his second the cable flew apart, the source plummeted into its lead shield, and he ran back to safety and the congratulations of all concerned.

I asked Shapiro if the source simply hibernated in its underground lair during the winter months. He shook his head, and said that each November riggers are summoned to the garden to run steel cables through loops on the sides of the lead shield, whereupon a crane lifts it, with the source inside, onto a truck, and it is hauled off to Brookhaven's reactor. There the source remains, having its strength renewed by exposure to the neutrons in the nuclear furnace, until February, when the riggers return it and its shield to the pit. Shapiro plucked at the cable again, and then gazed speculatively out over the bizarre terrain—a highly intellectual sower and reaper, scanning his crops not for signs of healthy renewal but for alterations in the fruit, the leaves, and, ultimately, the seed. "A nice time of day," he observed, at last. "No gammas around, and the plants can take it easy for a few hours. I guess they can use the rest."

SPACEMAN'S SONG

To a promised planet I soar,
Its cratered valley my bed,
A pillow of mist for my head,
The unfiltered sun my hearth,
The untwinkling limbo my view.
Thus anchored again,
Citizen of somewhere else again,
I shall rest a thousand years,
Counting stars until one beckons,
And then I shall depart again,
An ancient stirring my thrust,
A trail of broken camps my wake,
My path a path to yet another earth.

CHAPTER 26 | DECEMBER, 1956

EARTH SATELLITE

AT SOME INSTANT shortly before sunset on a not yet specified day in 1958, if all goes well with the plans of a host of American scientists engaged in an undertaking called Project Vanguard, a seventy-two-foot-long, eleven-ton finless rocket—or, rather, an assembly of three rockets, known as "stages," that are adjusted to operate in sequence—will be launched from a U.S. Air Force missile test center at Cape Canaveral, near Cocoa Beach, on the east coast of Florida. In the nose of this contraption, and protected by an exceptionally tough plastic cone from the destructive effect of friction in the dense lower atmosphere, will be the pay load—a silvery sphere, twenty inches in diameter and weighing twenty-one and a half pounds, equipped with four three-foot aluminum antennae. Two minutes after the takeoff, the first, or rear, stage, having attained a speed of about four thousand miles an hour and having propelled the rocket to an altitude of thirty-six miles, out over the Atlantic, will run out of fuel, whereupon it will break away from the rest and fall into the sea north of Nassau. Now it will become the turn of the second, or middle, stage, containing the rocket's "brain"—an elaborate control mechanism for keeping the whole works on course—to take over as the propelling force. In the next two minutes, the second stage will push the rocket to an altitude of a hundred and forty miles, off Puerto Rico, and increase its speed to ten thousand miles an hour. At that point, the second stage will run out of fuel, but it will not immediately disengage itself, for the services of its brain will still be needed. The plastic nose cone, however, being no longer necessary in the rare upper atmosphere, will be jettisoned. For about five minutes, the rocket will simply coast along on its own momentum, covering a distance of seven hundred miles and rising to a height of three hundred. There the brain will see to it that the rocket levels off onto a path roughly parallel to the surface of the earth, and will start the engine of the third stage. It will then perform its ultimate service by suicidally disengaging itself and dropping into the Atlantic Ocean fifteen hundred miles east of Martinique. The third stage will streak through space, increasing its speed to eighteen thousand miles an hour in thirty seconds, and, finally, before going its own way toward eventual disintegration, it will release the spherical object from its nose. And thus, if (to hedge again) everything goes according to plan, ten minutes after leaving Cape Canaveral an infant satellite will begin revolving around the earth—a man-made celestial body newly arrived on the cosmic scene.

Encountering almost no atmospheric resistance and held to its orbit by the same delicate balance of centrifugal and centripetal forces that keeps the universe from flying apart, Earth Satellite No. 1, to give the silvery sphere its formal name, is expected to travel around the earth once every hundred minutes, or about fourteen and a half times every twenty-four hours, for at least a year. As the first heavenly body to be launched by man (unless the Russians, who may also be constructing a satellite, should beat the Americans to the punch), it will, in the opinion of many scientists, be the forerunner of a long succession of increasingly bulky and durable satellites, which may eventually carry human beings. In addition to being a forerunner, however, Earth Satellite No. 1 has a very serious immediate purpose, for it will be crammed with instruments, including a tiny radio transmitter, that will gather and report information on the zone lying between the earth's atmosphere and the almost perfect void known as outer space. This mysterious zone, called the exosphere, is the scene of many astrophysical events—involving, among other things, ultraviolet and cosmic rays, meteorites, and the earth's magnetic field—that affects the lives of all of us, but until now scientists interested in such spatial goings on have had to be content with the relatively meager data obtained by instrument-carrying research rockets. (In the United States, the launching place for many such rockets has been White Sands, New Mexico, where scientists have been conducting experiments with several dozen V-2 missiles that were taken from the Germans at the end of the war and with a series of more advanced domestic missiles.) Although in recent years some of these rockets have been able to penetrate the exosphere, none stayed up there for more than a minute or two, and the sum of the data they have furnished is negligible compared to what the satellite—"a long-playing rocket," as one scientist has called it—should collect on its very first spin around the globe. If its flight lasts a year, the satellite should provide so much information that, in the opinion of some scientists, the task of evaluating it and fitting it into our present knowledge of the scheme of things will take the better part of twenty years.

In the first few years after the war, as rockets brought back increasingly tantalizing bits of information from the exosphere, scientists in the United States and abroad became more and more firmly convinced of the feasibility of launching a satellite. Then, in 1954, the widespread theorizing began to crystallize. In October of that year, the International Council of Scientific Unions, a federation of scientific groups from nearly all the nations of the world, on both sides of the Iron Curtain, met in Rome to consolidate plans for the International Geophysical Year—or, more accurately, the International Geophysical Year and a Half, since it will last from July 1st, 1957 through December, 1958—during which a concerted effort will be made to solve various riddles of the earth and its atmosphere. In addition to approving a number of subjects for special study—among them glaciers, earthquakes, oceans, and weather—the Council unanimously approved a resolution reading, in part, "In view of the great importance of observations over extended periods of time of extraterrestrial radiations and geophysical phenomena in the upper atmosphere, and in view of the advanced state of present rocket techniques, the [Council] recommends that thought be given to the launching of small satellite vehicles, to their scientific instrumentation, and to the new problems associated with satellite experiments."

If such a resolution had been presented for consideration by the scientists of any one country or group of allied countries, it would very likely have met with a swarm of protests, for notwithstanding the blandness of its language, there is no disguising what it amounts to

—an open invitation to any government to set loose a device that will indiscriminately and repeatedly violate aerial frontiers that are normally sacrosanct. In the interests of the International Geophysical Year, however, a sort of informal truce, at least as far as the upper atmosphere is concerned, had been declared on all sides, and would-be satellite-builders were free to ignore the diplomatic niceties. Accordingly, when the American delegates to the Rome conference returned home, they recommended to the National Academy of Sciences, the nation's top scientific body, that the United States, for one, should accept the challenge. After mulling over the likelihood of success, the Academy decided to go ahead with the project, and its Committee for the International Geophysical Year thereupon proceeded to set up a host of subcommittees and panels, composed of scientists from all over the country, to tackle various phases of the work. The Defense Department, with its airfields, its hardware, and its manpower, agreed to take over the task of constructing and launching the satellite and rocket—a task that it assigned specifically to the Naval Research Laboratory, in Washington, which at once gave it the code name Project Vanguard. (This is now commonly used to designate the whole enterprise, though sticklers prefer the term Earth Satellite Program.) Then, on July 29, 1955, President Eisenhower formally announced that a satellite would be launched sometime in 1958 and that whatever information it yielded would be shared with all other countries participating in the I.G.Y. (In September, 1956, the Soviet Union disclosed that it, too, would release a satellite during the Year—it appears to be the only other nation intending to do so—but so far it has characteristically refused to let the world in on any of the details.)

American scientists—as I discovered during a recent tour of some of the cities in which parts of the satellite program are being carried out—are exhilarated by the prospect of a first-hand report on phenomena in and near the exosphere, and many of them, particularly physicists and astronomers, believe that they are on the verge of monumental discoveries. Both physicists and astronomers have always been hampered in their work by the atmospheric blanket that shrouds this planet. The molecules composing the atmosphere absorb in large measure the powerful and in some cases perilous radiations that approach the earth from outer space, and while this is, of course, fortunate for mankind, it has prevented physicists from examining the radiations in their unscreened state; as for astronomers, the density of the atmosphere has never permitted them an undistorted view of the heavens. ("We've been like so many fish, looking up at things through a rippling, baffling surface," an astronomer complained not long ago.) The high hopes that scientists have for the findings of the satellite's instruments were summed up for me by two officials of the Committee for the I.G.Y. whom I met in Washington. The Committee's chairman, Dr. Joseph Kaplan, who is also chairman of the Department of Physics and Meteorology of the University of California at Los Angeles, said flatly, "The satellite will be the greatest boon to astronomy since Galileo's telescope," and its executive director, Hugh Odishaw, pointed out that, among the satellite's other accomplishments, it should enable man, for the first time, to see his home as, conceivably, others see it. "People talk so much about space travel in the future," he said, "yet what has the earth ever been but a spaceship—hurtling through space, spinning around the sun as it, in turn, wanders the galaxy? Now, with the satellite, we may at last find ourselves in a position to disembark and get a good look at this ship we've been traveling on so long." Obviously itching to disembark, Odishaw added, "Why, the satellite will be the most significant single achievement of the century, bar none. Atomic energy is a poor second."

Several of the scientists I talked with seemed to have developed ambivalent feelings toward the satellite program—feelings that Dr. James A. Van Allen, head of the Physics Department of the University of Iowa, expressed by first exclaiming, "Isn't it remarkable that we puny people can even contemplate hurling our own moon into the sky!" and then soberly enumerating a few of the myriad details that have to be attended to before we puny people can advance beyond the point of mere contemplation. Test firings, he said, must be held at Cape Canaveral; international agreements must be negotiated for the use of patches of foreign soil by technicians engaged in tracking the course of the satellite; and harmonious relations must be maintained among the various scientific panels and a whole string of government agencies, as well as the Army, the Navy, and the Air Force.

Some of the most ticklish details are being handled by the Naval Research Laboratory, and when I visited the place I learned from Dr. John P. Hagen, its ranking Vanguard official, that arrangements have been made for the construction not merely of one satellite and one three-stage rocket assembly but of six satellites and six three-stage rockets. "There's a good chance that any particular rocket will prove to be a dud," he explained. "Some of our people are pretty confident, and think we'll succeed on the first try, but others think we'll be lucky if even the sixth rocket gets properly launched." There is a possibility that the United States will be able to launch more than one satellite during the I.G.Y., I gathered, but the experts I talked to, perhaps giving in to an unscientific fear of hexing the whole project, never referred to the little sphere except in the singular.

The job of assembling the rockets has been entrusted to the Glenn L. Martin Company, of Baltimore, and the shells of the satellites are being put together by Brooks & Perkins, a Detroit firm, while all over the country dozens of manufacturers, specialists in precision work, have been engaged to make parts and instruments. The task ahead of these manufacturers presents many formidable problems, involving, as it does, the fabrication of mechanisms that range from the miniature radio transmitter to the swiftest rocket ever built—a rocket that will reach a speed of approximately twenty-five thousand feet a second. "The present speed record for rockets is twelve thousand feet a second," Leonard Arnowitz, an engineer at the Glenn L. Martin plant, told me grimly. "We hit twenty-five or we fail."

While I was at the Naval Research Laboratory, I dropped in to see Leopold Winkler, the chief consultant on the design and construction of the satellite, who told me that one of the many important considerations that have arisen in the course of constructing "the bird," as Vanguard people usually call the satellite, is the necessity of protecting its diminutive instruments both from disruptive jolts during its trip to the exosphere and from extremes of temperature once it gets there. To minimize the effects of the former, he said, the instruments will be cushioned with foam rubber of a special kind, selected for its unequalled lightness. Providing insulation against heat and cold is a far more complex business. Although the skin of the bird will measure only about half a millimeter, or not quite three one-hundredths of an inch, in thickness, it will consist of at least four layers. The outside layer is to be silicon monoxide, a transparent substance that will help keep the bird's temperature steady; then will come a layer of aluminum, for visibility, and a supporting layer of magnesium; and, finally, the innermost layer will be of gold, which, as an exceptionally poor conductor of heat, will help conserve the warmth inside the bird. Leading me into a workshop, Winkler showed me an experimental model of the satellite, which had only a layer of gold for a skin. Vanguard officials often liken a satellite to a basketball, but as the model rested, glittering, on a battered wooden table, with its four seemingly fragile antennae sticking out from its middle, it looked to me more like an outsize bauble for a Christmas tree. "That's twenty-four-carat gold—the purest there is," Winkler said. "The gold layer is only about a thousandth of an inch thick. It covers the bird, all right, but there's not enough gold in the whole thing to fill a cavity in one of your teeth."

The expectation is that the satellite will follow an elliptical orbit. The Vanguard people would prefer a circular one, because it would simplify the interpretation of the satellite's findings, but to start it off on such a path they would have to have precise control of the speed and angle at which the bird is launched, and the art of rocketry has not yet attained anything like infallibility in these matters. Nor can the altitude of the elliptical speedway be controlled precisely, but if it draws no nearer to the earth than two hundred miles and no farther away than fifteen hundred, they will be quite satisfied, because within those limits, it is thought, the bird will remain aloft for its full year. The closer the satellite comes to the earth, the more rapidly its momentum will be dissipated by the comparatively dense atmosphere, and at only a hundred miles up its life would be over in less than an hour; if it should zoom out beyond the fifteen-hundred-mile limit, on the other hand, it would keep right on going into outer space, but for that to happen the third stage of the rocket would need to have forty per cent more power than it has.

Once the satellite is on its own in the exosphere, its existence should be a fairly tranquil one. It will not encounter buffeting winds, for the exosphere is far too rarefied to permit even the slightest breeze; indeed, the air up there is thinner than the air in a laboratory vacuum. If this were a manned satellite, the crew, while travelling at the rate of eighteen thousand miles an hour, would be no more conscious of motion than when standing still on the earth, which, together with its atmosphere, travels at the rate of sixty-four thousand miles an hour as it circles the sun. In the near-void where the satellite will have its orbit, molecules are solitary objects, each something like twelve miles from its nearest neighbor. (At sea level, a molecule's nearest neighbor is usually about a millionth of an inch away.) The sun, like other celestial bodies, shines with far greater brilliance in the exosphere than it does on earth, but it shines in darkness, for air is needed to diffuse light; here and there, where the sun's rays happen to strike a molecule, a pinpoint of light will be visible in the satellite's path, but otherwise the bird, itself dazzlingly bright where the sun strikes it, will race on engulfed by blackness. Far below it, the earth, in the daytime, will be bathed in a luminous blue glow. Speaking of this glow, Dr. Homer E. Newell, Jr., head of the Naval Research Laboratory's Division of Astronomy and Astrophysics, told me, with a musing smile, "A young couple finding themselves at the altitude of our satellite would probably prefer to gaze at the earth rather than at the moon. Our atmosphere scatters blue light, and produces a deep, lovely glow—deeper and lovelier than moonlight."

While the air in the exosphere has a constant temperature of around three thousand degrees Fahrenheit (the temperature of a substance is determined by the speed at which its molecules are moving, and the widely scattered molecules in the exosphere move fast), there is so little of it that it will constitute no danger to the bird's skin. The temperature of the satellite will, however, be affected by the direct heat from the sun above and the reflected heat from the earth below. As the bird makes its fourteen and a half daily trips around the globe, passing through the earth's day and the earth's night in the course of each revolution, its external temperature will range from a little below zero to well over a hundred, and it is for this reason that so much care must be taken to insulate its instruments. "The equipment will be happiest at room temperature," Winkler said, and added that he has good reason to believe the bird will prove capable of keeping its equipment happy. Another possible hazard is the meteorites that will pelt the satellite as it speeds along. The exosphere abounds in these fragments of metal and stone, most of them less than a thousandth of an inch in diameter, which fall to the earth at the rate of a million tons a year—a figure that scientists have arrived at by studying the age and the chemistry of sludge from the bottom of the ocean. "Those meteorites are among the things we hope to find out about," Dr. Hagen told me. "Do they come in showers or is space constantly filled with them? Most of them are just particles, but some may be the size of a pea, and a few are a whole lot bigger. What would a big one do to the satellite?" To get an idea of the force of the meteorites' impact, the designers of the bird are using a device called a resistance-strip erosion gauge, which, like all the satellite's other instruments, will be able to communicate its findings to the scientists by means of the radio transmitter. "We'll put a thin strip of metal on the bird's skin, and the amount of erosion it undergoes will indicate how heavily the meteorites strike it," I was told by Dr. Richard W. Porter, chairman of the Technical Panel of the Earth Satellite Program, which is responsible for deciding what instruments the bird will carry.

Dr. Porter went on to give me an idea of the information that the satellite is expected to pick up about radiations—specifically, ultraviolet rays, which come from the sun, and cosmic rays, which probably come from outer space. In 1958, he said, the mysterious blemishes known as sunspots will be out in full force (their activity reaches a peak every eleven years, and they are now approaching one of these peaks—a circumstance that was largely responsible for the decision to schedule the I.G.Y. at this time), and since they are usually accompanied by dramatic changes in the intensity of ultraviolet and cosmic rays, the satellite should have many momentous facts to report. Its observation of ultraviolet rays may, for instance, go a long way toward explaining how atoms absorb and expend energy, and a study of these processes, which occur under what would appear to be nearly perfect laboratory conditions in the upper regions, may, in turn, provide clues to such an age-old enigma as the nature of the glow in the night sky. The bird will carry a Geiger counter to measure the intensity of cosmic rays—those immensely powerful but little understood radiations that may eventually provide some clue to the manner in which stars come into being as well as help clear up certain matters connected with the mutation of genes, and thus with the entire process of biological evolution. What may be more readily comprehensible to many people, however, will be the findings of some other instruments that the satellite is to carry—a magnetometer, to measure the magnetic field in the exosphere, and a set of bolometers, to determine how much heat the earth absorbs and how much escapes from it. If the magnetometer performs its task, it may solve some of the riddles that now envelop the subject of magnetic storms—disturbances that cause compass needles to gyrate wildly, and disrupt radio and long-distance-telephone communications. The bolometers, too, may solve some weather problems, Dr. Porter told me. "Until we know what the earth's intake and outgo of heat is," he said, "talking about the weather is like talking about a steam engine without knowing how much pressure it's got. The information from the bolometers will enable weathermen to make far more accurate long-range predictions—about cyclones, for one thing." And Dr. J. Allen Hynek, professor of astronomy at Ohio State University, said he is looking forward to the day when, by means of more or less permanent satellites, it may be possible to keep tabs on meteorological conditions all over the world. "In that case," he predicted solemnly, "we'd all know when good weather was ahead, and plan our vacations accordingly, which would make for one hell of a lot of congestion."

Because the satellite's transmitter is expected to function for about three hundred and fifty hours, it can broadcast only for the first two weeks or so, but all year long the satellite itself will continue to be a splendid source of information for a good many scientists—particularly those concerned with geodesy, or the study of the curvature, shape, and dimensions of the earth. "For all our talk of exploring outer space, we still have only the haziest idea of where we are on earth," Dr. John A. O'Keefe, chief of the Research and Analysis Branch of the Geodetic Division of the United States Army Map Service, told me when I called on him in Washington. "We simply don't know the relationship between here and there. Our latitudes and longitudes are fuzzy because they're supposed to be determined by using the exact center of the earth as a point of reference, and how can we know where that is until we know the exact size of the earth? And we don't know that because we can't measure it exactly. In fact, we have reason to believe that on our maps the position of some of the Pacific islands is off by at least half a mile." Dr. O'Keefe said that the Map Service plans to station teams on the islands of Wake, Guam, Kwajalein, Tutuila, in American Samoa, and Luzon, to correct such errors by sightings based on the satellite. The classic method of determining geographical position, he told me, is by sightings on the sun or the stars, but while this is good enough for most practical purposes, it cannot avoid minute inaccuracies, which have long troubled geodesists. About a decade ago, they began using the moon as a reference point, but this method has not been wholly satisfactory, either. "At best, the moon has been of marginal value to us," he went on. "For one thing, it's just too far away. For another, it's greatly affected by the sun, which produces shifts in the plane of its orbit. And, for still another, the edge of the moon, as we see it, is broken by mountains and valleys, and that, too, leads to inaccuracies in our calculations. The bird will be a thousand times closer to the earth, it won't be affected by the sun, and its skin is perfectly smooth. All in all, I'd say that when we get our satellite going, we'll have an efficient moon at last."

A nightmare fear that haunts even the most sanguine booster of Project Vanguard is that once the satellite is launched, no one will be able to find it. Looking for it will be comparable to dragging the Pacific for a golf ball, and the fact of the matter is that the bird may circle the globe fourteen and a half times a day for a year or more without ever being detected. "Until we make our first sighting, things are going to be tense," Dr. Van Allen said, after assuring me, as several of the other scientists I talked with had done, that the possibility of such an outrageous anticlimax is far from purely theoretical. Elaborate precautions are being taken to minimize the risk of this fiasco. The satellite will be tracked both by a network of radio receiving stations and by a multitude of watchers, spread over much of the world. The radio tracking system, which is now being organized by the Naval Research Laboratory and is to be known as Minitrack, has certain obvious advantages (it can carry on in any kind of weather and will not be hampered by either a blinding noonday sun or the blackness of a cloudy midnight) and one obvious disadvantage; namely, that it can function only during the two weeks that the satellite's transmitter remains in action. The orbit that the satellite will select for itself is expected to remain within the zone between the fortieth parallel north of the equator (about on a line with San Francisco, Kansas City, and Philadelphia) and the fortieth parallel south of it (slightly below Buenos Aires), and in order to cover this span Minitrack will string out ten stations—a sort of radio fence—along the seventy-fifth meridian, from Washington to Santiago, Chile. During its first two weeks, the satellite will be sending out a constant signal, for tracking purposes, and each time it crosses the meridian this will presumably be picked up by at least one of the Minitrack stations. As soon as a Minitrack station detects the satellite, it will radio or teletype a report to a building on Pennsylvania Avenue, in Washington, which the International Business Machines Corporation has leased for the duration of Vanguard, and there one of I.B.M.'s most awesomely talented high-speed electronic computers will digest the information and make a rough prediction of where and when the bird will next be detectable by the trackers. As the bird passes overhead, the Minitrack station will beam a signal up to it, and the tiny transmitter will thereupon send back a message on the findings of the instruments. Though Minitrack is making its preparations with the utmost care, its director, John T. Mengel, conceded that the satellite might very well elude the trackers. "The transmitter might go haywire, or the antennae might be out of position, or any of a dozen other things might go wrong," he said.

Barring any such unwelcome development, the I.B.M. predictions will be sent on to the Smithsonian Astrophysical Observatory, on Observatory Hill, in Cambridge, Massachusetts—the headquarters of the optical tracking system, which will have a chain of twelve camera stations spread around the satellite's orbital belt, in such out-of-the-way places as Las Cruces, New Mexico; Naini Tal, India; Woomera, Australia; and Villa Dolores, Argentina. Each of these stations will be equipped with a powerful telescopic camera, as big as a deep freeze, and costing eighty thousand dollars, that embodies the latest refinements in long-range and rapid-sequence photography. Not only can these cameras spot and photograph an object the size of a tennis ball in motion at a distance of five hundred miles but their pictures are timed to within a thousandth of a second. Once the cameras have picked up the satellite, the observatory will be able to plot its orbit with astonishing accuracy. The cameras will detect the slightest change in the satellite's speed, and thus indicate the density of the atmosphere it is passing through. Moreover, they will call attention to every shift in the satellite's orbit, however small—the gravitational vagary that will help scientists measure changes caused by the slightly irregular shape of the earth (it is rather like an Edam cheese, its diameter at the equator being twenty-six miles longer than its polar axis) and by variations in the thickness of its crust.

Besides the Minitrack and camera teams, numerous other groups and individuals, professional and amateur, will be on the lookout for the bird. Astronomical observatories with telescopes of enormous power will pitch in, and so will radio hams and back-yard astronomers. And it seems more than likely that the general public will be out in considerable numbers to scan the sky. "I think it's safe to say that the satellite will have more people watching the sky than flying saucers ever did," Dr. Hynek, the Ohio State astronomer, told me. "If they catch sight of it, they will see what looks like a dim star moving so rapidly it will vanish in a few seconds."

Of all the trackers who will be at their posts at the moment the satellite is launched, probably none will be more zealous than a polyglot assortment of some thousands of men and women who have so far volunteered to serve as members of an organization, named Project Moonwatch, that has been set up under the auspices of the Smithsonian Astrophysical Observatory. These volunteers will operate as teams, and so far seventy-five teams have been organized in the United States (they vary in strength from a dozen or so to well over fifty, and include on their rosters steamfitters, schoolteachers, retired Navy officers, physicians, prep-school boys, and at least one priest), and fifty or so will probably be organized in Britain, Spain, West Germany, South Africa, and Japan. Each team will set up its own watching station—on the roof of a building, in an empty city lot, in a country field—and its members will all have telescopes about a foot long. At the center of the station will be a pole with a crossbar at its top, and, using this crossbar for orientation, each team member will watch his own small portion of sky; collectively, a team will monitor a strip of its meridian extending a hundred degrees north and south of its own station, and it is hoped that by the time the bird is launched there will be enough stations to provide fairly complete coverage of large sections of the orbital belt. When, or if, a Moonwatcher spies the bird, he will shout "Time!," whereupon the hour, minute, and second will be recorded. The watcher will then plot the position of the satellite in relation to certain stars, and, by radio or telephone, the captain of the team will relay the information to headquarters in Cambridge. Moonwatch teams are already holding periodic practice sessions, and when the launching day draws near, the Air Force is planning to simulate the satellite for them with tiny lights trailed by darkened jet planes.

However simple the equipment of the Moonwatch stations may be in comparison with the paraphernalia of the professional trackers, the morale of the Moonwatchers is high. "That bird isn't going to get past *us,*" I was assured by one of them—a meteorologist named G. R. Wright, who works in the Weather Bureau's Washington office and has a small observatory, which he built some years ago, out back of his home, in Silver Spring, Maryland. Dr. Fred L. Whipple, the director of the Smithsonian Observatory, told me that the Moonwatchers will make their most useful contribution to the program at the start of the satellite's flight, before its orbit has been accurately plotted, and toward the end of it, when the orbit will begin to wobble unpredictably. The Moonwatchers' high morale is fortunate, he said, since they will be required to rise before dawn and hurry to their posts and then, after their normal day's work, hurry back at dusk; only at sunrise and sunset, when they themselves are in shadow and the bird is brightly illuminated, will they be able to see it. In the summer, when twilight may last as long as three hours, the Moonwatchers will perhaps grow a little restless at their telescopes, but some of them may have the experience of seeing the satellite twice at a single sitting and of realizing that while they were lingering there in the dusk, the bird had made a complete flight around the earth. "It'll be hard work, no doubt about that," Dr. Whipple said, "but it'll be fun, too, as the volunteers get to know each other and share each other's excitement. And their work should bring them some solid satisfaction. No serious scientific project has ever before depended so heavily on rank amateurs."

In many places, it is business firms—insurance companies, automobile agencies, radio stations, newspapers, and the like—that are putting up the modest sums of money needed to finance community Moonwatch teams. In Phoenix, Arizona, the Valley National Bank has invited the local team to use the roof of its skyscraper, and in St. Louis a similar offer has been made by the 7-Up Company, possibly on the hypothesis that any kind of up-consciousness is good for business. And there are also some less subtle links that have been forged between commerce and the bird. Some camera shops are pushing a Satellite Special Telescope, for instance, and a recent department-store advertisement showed a teacher displaying a model of the satellite to two pupils dressed in sweaters made of Heavenly Yarn. A transparent plastic model of the satellite has been exhibited at the Coliseum in New York and is now on the road, being used as a come-on for orange festivals, industrial fairs, and the like. Warner Brothers is preparing a film to be titled *Satellite in the Sky,* and the picture's advance advertising reveals that its producers "moved Heaven and Earth to bring you The First Drama of the man-made satellite that could Rule The World!" Not long ago, an Ohio manufacturer designed a novelty napkin portraying various aspects of Project Vanguard, and, on his own initiative, submitted it to the Naval Research Laboratory for security clearance. His conscientiousness, it turned out, was all for the best. "There's practically nothing classified about Vanguard, but darned if that napkin didn't show the bit that is," Walter McDonald, one of Vanguard's information officers, told me. "How the manufacturer got hold of it I don't know—just dreamed it up, maybe." One attempt to exploit the satellite has fallen through for reasons unrelated to security. That was a request from a used-car dealer for permission from the Naval Research Laboratory to light up the bird with a neon sign advertising his wares. "The Navy never endorses any product" was the reply.

A bill—H.R. 2873—has been introduced in Congress that would

name the Earth Satellite itself something else. Sponsored by Representative Frank M. Karsten, of Missouri, the bill reads, "Be it enacted by the Senate and House of Representatives of the United States of America in Congress assembled, That Earth Satellite Number One be officially designated as the 'Astronaut.' " Since the Founding Fathers made no provision for naming satellites, the bill fluttered around a bit before landing in what is presumably the proper pigeonhole. "The House Parliamentarian didn't know which committee to refer my bill to," Congressman Karsten told me. "He favored the Interstate and Foreign Commerce Committee for a while, and then the Armed Services Committee, but he finally turned it over to Foreign Affairs, and that's where it's roosting now."

As if the Vanguard scientists weren't sufficiently occupied with the technical details of their project, they are constantly being called upon to explain what they are up to in addresses before civic organizations, fraternal lodges, high-school clubs, and so on. Complying whenever they can spare the time, they make a point of toning down the wilder notions about the bird that have got around, and of gently but unequivocally impressing upon the taxpayers the fact that this first attempt to set a satellite in motion may quite possibly end in failure. These talks are usually followed by discussion periods, and one question that the speakers are frequently asked is "What keeps it from flying off into space?" Dr. Newell, who, as a representative of the Naval Research Laboratory, has delivered his share of speeches on the satellite, assured me that he has a ready answer for this one. "I tell them the same thing that keeps the moon from flying off into space—in other words, gravity," he said. "The commonest misconception we have to straighten out is that the pull of gravity stops abruptly at a certain point. Jules Verne and his story about a trip to the moon are to blame for that one. Gravity doesn't stop abruptly, of course. It just keeps getting weaker."

Busy though the Vanguard workers are, they occasionally find time to discuss the broader implications of what they are trying to accomplish. At such moments, they sound much like the laymen they lecture to—groping and oddly unexpert. "I have a feeling that the satellite will help rid people's minds of superstitions having to do with the mystery of the heavens," the head of this nation's I.G.Y. activities, Dr.

Kaplan, observed recently. "The Eskimos—and plenty of other people, too—see the aurora and take it as a sign of God's pleasure or wrath, but if the satellite should give us an adequate explanation of this phenomenon, it would no longer be interpreted in such a misguided fashion. And the explanation should bring these people a feeling of safety—even a feeling of elation. Some months ago, a swami of the Vedanta school in Los Angeles—a friend of mine—asked me to address his following. I told them that we scientists will never learn enough about the universe to remove the need for faith in men's hearts, but that knowledge of the kind we hope to acquire from the satellite may enable us to free faith from superstition. The audience seemed pleased, and, of course, I was, too, as I always am when I've said what I believe."

In an equally pensive mood, Dr. Newell remarked to me, "This is our first step off the earth, and its possible significance is so staggering that I try to calm myself now and then by thinking of Columbus. For all he knew at the time he set out, he'd find nothing but man-eating sea serpents before his ships toppled over the edge of the world. We're a lot more fortunate. We not only know that we're stepping out into a new region but we already know what some of the things are that we're definitely going to encounter."

And Odishaw, the executive director of Dr. Kaplan's committee, wound up a talk with me by saying, "Contemplate the satellite and you inevitably think about it in terms of yourself—that is, of your destiny, and of the transience of life. I've lived with it for almost three years now, and it still excites great curiosity in me—a curiosity that is at once intellectual and spiritual."

The only concerted opposition to Project Vanguard has come from people who don't like it for religious reasons. While the fanatics among them berate the scientists as the architects of a diabolical plan to appropriate God's firmament, more temperate misgivings have been voiced by those who see the satellite as an undeniable harbinger of space travel, and wonder if we—mankind as a whole—know what we are getting into and can be sure we aren't finally pushing our cleverness too far. Quite a number of people are uneasy at the thought that the discoveries of a space age may ultimately challenge their beliefs. This uneasiness has been clearly and sympathetically put into words by a Vanguard scientist. Addressing the congregation of the First Presbyterian Church of Greenwich, Connecticut, not long ago, Dr. Porter, the General Electric consultant, frankly presented some of the questions that the exploration of outer space may eventually pose for theologians. "Our Christian doctrine is based on the importance of man and the belief that God the Creator Himself became a man for the purpose of saving all mankind from its own sin," he said. "But suppose we seriously consider the possibility of queer but intelligent creatures on some other planet. Are they, too, 'saved' . . . by the self-sacrifice of Jesus? Are their sins the same as ours? Since they very probably didn't descend from Adam, how do we know they are sinful at all?" Dr. Porter went on to say that the satellite program, "even in its early phase," may throw light on the evolution of the universe that will necessitate a sweeping reappraisal of Genesis. Evidence might be found, he suggested, to prove that the universe is still being created—an atom of hydrogen at a time—throughout the far reaches of space. Such a discovery, he pointed out, would require "a new and painful adjustment" in the believer's understanding of God and the universe. "With all these implications, perhaps it might be easier just to give up the whole idea of artificial satellites," Dr. Porter concluded. "But, unfortunately, since Eve tempted Adam to take the first bite from the fruit of the Tree of Knowledge, man has been unable to let well enough alone. We can, therefore, only hope that we will be given the wisdom to use the results for our good, rather than for our confusion and self-destruction."

In the end, the satellite will perish. Even though the exosphere may be several billion times as rarefied as the atmosphere at sea level, the resistance it offers is bound to slow the bird down in the course of its thousands of trips around the world. As its speed ebbs, the force of gravity, gaining in power, will draw it toward the earth, and its orbit will show an increasing tendency to waver. After a while, it will waver so rapidly and erratically that the telescopic cameras will no longer be able to make a coherent record of it, and then the Moonwatchers will be working harder than ever, in an effort to plot the waverings for future study. Slipping down at last to a level where the atmosphere begins to approach the density that man is accustomed to, the bird's forward motion will be slowed to a relative crawl. Then friction with the air may gradually tear it to pieces or abruptly set it ablaze; no one can be sure which will happen, but disintegration of some sort is believed certain. Its lighter parts—the aluminum antennae and the skin—will probably be the first to go, and its heavier ones, among them the long-dead transmitter, the last. Finally, it is assumed, the one-time satellite will complete its descent through the atmosphere in the form of dust, most of which, like the dust of so many meteorites, will end up as sludge at the bottom of the ocean.

CHAPTER 27 | DECEMBER, 1957

MOON IN A BOX

When Project Vanguard's first rocket—which most Americans had once confidently expected would put up the first earth satellite in history—blew up disastrously on its launching stand at Cape Canaveral on December 6, 1957, I went down to Washington, a few days after the fizzle, to find out how the vastly publicized failure had affected the scientists and engineers directly concerned. The Project's headquarters—the main scene of America's earth-satellite research and planning—is a somewhat antiquated four-story building on the grounds of the Naval Research Laboratory, and when I stopped in at a number of its offices, I discovered that the scientists had very little to contribute to the recent flood of theorizing and speculating about what went wrong. They had a very good idea of what had gone wrong, I gathered, but it was not something they could talk about publicly, because of the Project's security regulations. Whatever it was, though, the men I called on did not seem unduly upset. "A new rocket is just as apt to blow up as to go up," Roger L. Easton, a young electronics expert, told me. "Why, we couldn't make any sense out of all that stuff in the papers about how the NATO conference and the stock market were going to blow up just because our rocket blew up." Easton, who was in the blockhouse on the launching site at Cape Canaveral, Florida, when Vanguard, the three-stage rocket that was expressly designed for the Project, tipped over and burst into flames, went on to tell me that the "shoot," ill-fated as it was, was not entirely devoid of accomplishment. For one thing, it seems, the final countdown—an eleven-hour process, just before the launching, in which hundreds of complex checks were made on the rocket—went off very smoothly. For another, this was the first time that a fully assembled Vanguard had been fuelled, and that job, involving the handling of tons of dangerously inflammable propellants, also went off without a hitch. And the silvery six-inch satellite, though destined never to become a celestial body, proved as sturdy as its makers had intended it to be—plummeting eighty feet through flame that might well have melted it, landing on concrete pavement, and surviving in something close to working order. The satellite's home was now a plain brown cardboard box on the floor of a room across the hall from the office of Dr. John P. Hagen, the director of Project Vanguard, and I was taken to see it by Martin J. Votaw, a member of the Project's tracking staff, who had also been in the blockhouse at the time of the launching—and, in fact, was the man who first picked up the wounded moon. The aluminum surface of the little sphere was charred and crumpled, and the antennas protruding from it were bent, but four of its six solar batteries were still operating, Votaw told me, and its transmitters were still sending forth a signal. The signal was not audible, and Votaw told me that it never had been. "That was a lot of newspaper nonsense about the satellite lying on the ground saying 'Beep! Beep!' " he said. "The signal goes out on a frequency of a hundred and eight megacycles, and you can't hear it without a receiver. And anyway it isn't a series of beeps. It's a continuous sound."

Certainly no sign of embarrassment was to be detected in the men associated with the misfire, although letters had been coming in from the public suggesting that they would do well to take up another trade. They were, of course, sharply disappointed by the failure, but their disappointment was largely over details that might not occur to the layman. They found it particularly annoying, for example, that the second stage of the rocket, which had not yet been tested in flight, never did get a chance to prove itself, since it was in the first stage that things went wrong. (Ironically, the first and the third stages had been tested, and the tests had been successful three times in a row—an unusually lucky streak in rocketry.) Irritating as the incident at Cape Canaveral was to the scientists, however, and keenly aware as many of them were of its political consequences, they by no means considered it a catastrophic setback professionally. "This was a matter not of science but of engineering, and it can be licked," I was told by Dr. Herbert Friedman, the head of the electronic-optics branch of the Naval Research Laboratory, whose field is solar physics and whose experiments, over the preceding eight years, had depended on rocket flights. "If we didn't have a good scientific program lined up—a good set of experiments—then we'd really have reason to be embarrassed. The fact is, though, that we have a very fine program, and we want to get on with it." As for the public's chagrin, Dr. Friedman believed that it would never have been so great if more people had understood even superficially the process of trial and error that is involved in scientific work. His own career, he told me, had been strewn with mishaps, both engineering and scientific. Back in 1952, for example, he was seeking to measure the sun's X-ray and ultraviolet radiations, by means of photoelectric cells that had been installed in a Viking rocket; the rocket went off properly, but it shifted from its expected course just enough so that the photocells were turned away from the sun. "A year's work down the drain," Dr. Friedman said ruefully. "The next day, there was a cheery story in the papers about how the Viking had broken all altitude records. As if that helped me!" Dr. Homer E. Newell, Jr., the Project's science-program coördinator, told me that he agreed that ignorance of scientific methods had a lot to do with the public's strong reaction, and went on to suggest another factor. "Americans think of science in terms of its applications—things like fabrics and tail fins—not as a patient search for knowledge for its own sake," he said. "As a people, we tend to measure everything by immediate results, and that's why we're so vulnerable to setbacks. Of course, I'll grant you that in this case it wasn't exactly a test tube being quietly tossed into a wastebasket that upset the public. It was a rocket seven stories high exploding in the full glare of publicity."

That glare of publicity, I gathered, was regarded by the scientists as a sort of cultural event, *genus americanus,* rather than as the error in judgment that some critics had been calling it, and even though government leaders had been promising that the public's hopes would never again be so powerfully stimulated, all the men I talked with assumed that the same phenomenon would somehow contrive to repeat itself. "It's bound to happen when the military services are involved," one physicist told me. "As a matter of fact, you can already see the buildup for the Army's first satellite shoot mysteriously getting under way." Although the launching of earth satellites supposedly is not a military matter—it is part of America's contribution to the International Geophysical Year, itself a purely scientific enterprise—it was probably inevitable that the services, as the custodians of America's rockets and the employers of great numbers of men equipped to handle them, should have been called on to put the spheres into the air. And the military services, like practically all other government agencies, concluded a long time ago that publicity, for better or worse, is a highly effective wedge for prying funds loose from Congress. This approach, once it gains momentum, is by no means limited to the competing top echelons. Units in each of the services, fighting for their status as well as for money, enter the lists, and the press often proves a willing agent in the airing of myriad rivalries. "It gets to be a little like the tale of the sorcerer's apprentice. No one knows how to turn off the flood of handouts," the physicist said. "What's more, many scientists are learning to play the game. Science professors—men who have led almost cloistered lives in universities—come to Washington and discover that their favorite research projects will die unless they beat the drum. It's saddening to see, as I have seen, a modest, dignified scientist offer a reporter, at the end of an interview, a photograph of himself to go along with the article."

Great as the fuss and trumpeting had been, however, the scientists denied that the launching itself was timed to meet the demands of publicity, and I was assured on all sides that, whatever the rumors to the contrary, the moment for pulling the switch that set the rocket free was not advanced by a single instant. At the base at Cape Canaveral, the crews of technicians were shielded from any possible intrusion, and all but a very few visiting scientists and military dignitaries were forbidden to enter the launching area. As for newspapermen, the whole base was off limits to them, and they had to watch the launching from Cocoa Beach, three miles away. Besides, the crews were taking their orders from men who had supervised many shoots and were temperamentally impervious to buildups. "I suppose we were conscious of pressure from outside—all that high expectation," one of the scientists told me, "but there comes a time when the pressure of the engineering problem at hand is so great that any additional pressure is lost in the noise. Maybe a theoretical case could be made out for putting that sort of additional pressure down as a disadvantage—a minus quantity—because it just might fluster somebody somewhere along the line. But, all things considered, I'd say that the big buildup didn't hurt the Vanguard shoot any more than it helped it."

The Vanguard scientists made no effort to minimize American failures in the light of Russian successes, but they did point out that these successes and failures were at least partly to be explained by the different scientific climate of the two countries. They said this matter-of-factly and, it appeared to me, undefensively, and all those I talked with seemed to feel that the reasons the Russians were able to get ahead of the United States went so far back and were so broad in scope that it would be useless to try to fix the blame on any person or group. Thanks largely to America's well-publicized fizzles, the reasons, in a general way, were now familiar to the public—paltry appropriations for basic research, too much emphasis on technology instead of pure science, low salaries for teachers, and an undulant anti-intellectual fever. The Russians, on the other hand, had been pushing the development of scientists and plying their researchers with funds. "It's said that a scientist does his best work before he's thirty," Dr. James E. Kupperian, a Naval Research Laboratory physicist who specializes in upper-atmosphere studies, told me. "Well, the Russians started speeding up their training of young scientists just about ten years ago, and that program should be paying off right now. Apparently it is."

American scientists were apt to be hesitant about discussing specific aspects of the Russian feats, though perhaps not for the expected reason. Actually, their respect for the Sputniks was tinged with reservations, and they did not like to say much about these for fear of appearing graceless in the unaccustomed role of runner-up. Some scientists, for instance, felt that, considering the relatively few instruments the Sputniks seemed to be carrying, their enormous size was more theatrical than useful, but how could an American scientist point this out without being accused of crying sour grapes? In general, the scientists were wary of criticizing their opposition, but one physicist I talked with did take the Soviet scientists mildly to task for being shifty about their plans. He told me that at an I.G.Y. meeting in Washington on October

2nd, two days before the launching of Sputnik I, Dr. Anatoli Arkadyevich Blagonravov, the leader of the Soviet delegation, had delivered a talk on satellite orbits in which he had based all his calculations on the dimensions of the twenty-inch American satellite scheduled to be launched the following spring, the implication clearly being that no other model existed. Then, on Sputnik I's birthday, Dr. Blagonravov had relaxed sufficiently to say that shortly before he left for the United States, he had seen the satellite's vehicle in its launching stand "in the middle-European-latitude portion of the Soviet Union." This kind of evasiveness wasn't a pleasant thing to contemplate in a man of science, the American physicist told me, but then he added, "Of course, the dictates of the Party line can be harsh."

The American scientist on whom the burdens of the international contest lay most heavily was Dr. Hagen, who had headed the Naval Research Laboratory's atmosphere and astrophysics division before taking on his new assignment. As the director of Project Vanguard, which seemed to have become the popular symbol of America's scientific progress, he spent his time conferring with Pentagon brass, testifying before Congress, seeing journalists, and delivering lectures to civic groups, in addition to overseeing the technicalities of getting a moon up. "Before the Project got under way, I'd have predicted that John couldn't stand up under all this frenzy and pressure," a colleague of Dr. Hagen's told me. "It's amazing how well he's learned to swim in a goldfish bowl." Dr. Hagen could not get to Cape Canaveral for the recent shoot, but he was at the end of a direct telephone line to Florida, listening as his deputy, J. Paul Walsh, intoned the final seconds of the countdown. He himself was relaying what he heard to four members of his staff, crowded around him in a small soundproof room at Vanguard headquarters, and it was from one of them that I learned of those anxious moments. "Five . . . Four . . . Three . . . Two . . . One . . . Zero," Dr. Hagen had called out. "Ignition! It's left the pad. It blew up! It blew up! A lot of smoke. Some flame." Then Dr. Hagen asked Walsh, "Is everyone all right?" and, getting his answer, said to one of the staff members, "Give the reporters the news, and make sure they know everyone's all right."

I had met Dr. Hagen last winter, and in the course of my recent visit to Washington I called on him in his office—a high-ceilinged, modestly furnished room, with a desk at one end and a long conference table in the center. A large map of the world hung on one wall, and on a shelf below it were two globes, a microscope, and a black lunch pail, filled, I knew, with Dr. Hagen's daily complement of sandwiches. Dr. Hagen, who is forty-nine, is a ruminative pipe-smoker, and he wears gold-rimmed glasses, through which his brown eyes gleam cordially. His manner is calm and unhurried, his voice deliberate and even. He is slight of physique, but seems to be blessed with a metabolism that keeps him resilient for his duties. I aked him whether he had lost any weight since taking on Project Vanguard, and he said, "I don't know—I haven't had time to weigh myself."

Dr. Hagen had been attacked in various quarters for the debacle at Cape Canaveral, but he appeared to be taking it all philosophically. "Of course, I get upset a bit by needling criticism," he admitted, "but I haven't let it get me down. On the whole, the situation is not as black as it's been painted. People realize they're living in a technological age, and they want to keep up with the game, so they get agitated when they think this country is falling behind, but back of their agitation is a good deal of understanding—more and more of it all the time. Since the war, I'd say, our people have become accustomed to the idea that science costs money, and now I think they're willing to invest in pure research. How else can one explain the funds that have been appropriated for our I.G.Y. work or for something like the National Radio Astronomy Observatory?" Assuming the eventual success of Project Vanguard, Dr. Hagen said he could see certain positive advantages arising from the present situation. For one thing, Congress was consulting increasingly with scientists, and in a most constructive way. For another, an upswing in the teaching of science was clearly in the cards. "Not that I want everyone turning scientist," Dr. Hagen added quickly. "The country would be in a hell of a fix if that happened. It doesn't do for a country to be lopsided in its interests. Our youngsters must be educated in the humanities, too, and that goes for science and engineering majors. To put it in the simplest terms, they have got to learn how to express themselves. A lab, you know, is a report mill, and what good are unintelligible reports? During the war, when I was working on radar, I had some newly graduated engineers under me, and I can still remember how inarticulate most of them were. I spent so much time correcting their grammar and punctuation that I began to think of myself as an English teacher."

As for the future of Project Vanguard, Dr. Hagen said the morale of his staff was good, though that of the field men had suffered for a time, and now they were all looking forward to the next try. The first rocket's flaw had been determined, and it was not, in Dr. Hagen's phrase, "of back-to-the-drawing-board magnitude." Slow-motion movies, the debris of the shattered vehicle, and data relayed by the satellite's transmitter had enabled the Vanguard people to diagnose the cause of the explosion, and the autopsy would continue until the defect was pinpointed beyond all question. "Not that something different couldn't go wrong next time," Dr. Hagen said. The rocket that exploded was not the only fully assembled Vanguard at the Project's disposal, he went on. The Project had, of course, been prepared for the possibility of failure, and it had two other Vanguards on hand—"backup" vehicles, Dr. Hagen called them. One of these would be the next to fly. "Perhaps we should have made more of the backups in explaining the Project to the public," Dr. Hagen said reflectively, but then he shook his head. He wasn't at all certain, he said, that any one thing could have affected the turn public interest in the test had taken—namely, whether or not the satellite could be established in an orbit. Actually, he went on, the major purpose of this particular venture had not been to launch a satellite but to test the assembled rocket, and it was only last August that he and his colleagues had decided that when the test came off, it might as well include the attempted launching of a small moon. The damaged satellite had been brought to him from Florida the day after the explosion by one of his assistants, and he told me that he intended to hold on to it. "Right now," he said, "we're pleased with it for surviving its ordeal, but after we get a satellite up, we'll want it as a museum piece."

CHAPTER 28 | FEBRUARY, 1958

THIS BOOM IS SERIOUS

UNTIL SIX YEARS AGO, the village of Cocoa Beach, on the east coast of Florida, about halfway between St. Augustine and Palm Beach, consisted of a few dozen families living in a seaside never-never land of sand dunes and palmettos, where strangers rarely came, even to swim or fish. Indeed, so sparsely settled was the area that a locally celebrated hermit was able to live in practically perfect solitude a couple of miles north of the village, presumably sustaining himself on sea food and coconuts. Today, Greater Cocoa Beach, which includes the original village and its immediate environs, has a population of ten thousand, and, as the nearest community to Cape Canaveral—a swampy tract from which dozens of Atlases, Thors, Titans, Snarks, and other missiles, as well as Explorer I, America's first earth satellite, have been fired into space—it intermittently becomes what one old settler has described as "the news capital of the world." It is also, as I discovered during a visit I recently made, probably the most space-conscious locality in the United States—a locality in which most of the characteristic features of back-country Florida have been smothered by a rampant preoccupation with ballistics and astronautics.

Merely choosing a motel puts the visitor right in the prevailing Cocoa Beach mood. After driving past the Vanguard, the Sea Missile, and the Celestial Trailer Court, I pulled up at the Starlite, which has as its roadside sign a flashing neon rocket. When I was shown to a room there, I found that the floor lamp was in the shape of a rocket, too, its nose cone balancing a globular satellite much as a circus seal balances a ball. On the wall behind my bed hung three or four drawings that reminded me of a fortune-teller's gown—crescents, spheres, and orbital paths in a night sky. My towels bore the legend "Satellite Motel," and when I asked the manager about this, he said, "That's a sore point. We wanted to call the place the Satellite, but then we heard that some joker had already registered the name, so we settled for the Starlite." The restaurant was decorated with a vast—and, I was told, accurate—chart of the heavens, while the bar, a murky, L-shaped room, had murals showing the moon as seen through a telescope and the earth as seen from the moon. The bartender greeted me genially when I came in, and, no doubt spotting me as a tenderfoot, asked whether I would like a Countdown—ten parts vodka to one part vermouth—or a Marstini; I said a plain Scotch-and-water would do, and he seemed a little disappointed.

Geographically, the area around Cocoa Beach is a maze of islands, peninsulas, capes, and so-called rivers that are not rivers at all but salt-water lagoons. Cocoa Beach itself is on a narrow peninsula—seventy-five miles long and generally no more than a mile across—that starts some thirty miles to the north and runs roughly parallel to the mainland. Eight miles above Cocoa Beach, the peninsula widens to form Cape Canaveral, a restricted military zone of about fifteen thousand acres—much of it uncleared jungle, where deer and puma roam—and two miles below the village is Patrick Air Force Base, the administrative headquarters of the missile test center. To get to the mainland from Cocoa Beach, one drives along a ten-mile causeway that crosses the Banana River, Merritt Island, and the Indian River before it winds up in the established town of Cocoa, whose population has in the last few years increased from three thousand to ten thousand. For miles around, the people of this once lethargic countryside have been seized by the space obsession, and in the course of my stay I heard of the Missile Misses, a women's organization, with branches in several villages, that is dedicated to good works and bridge parties; the Miss L. Ranger, a deep-sea fishing boat operated for Air Force personnel; and a contest to select Miss Satellite—a more up-to-the-minute, if less comprehensive, title than Miss Universe. In Cocoa, a sign outside the offices of the Chamber of Commerce, antedating the orbiting Explorer I by many months, jauntily announces that reservations are being accepted "for space aboard the first globe-circling satellite," and a few miles to the north, on Highway 1, a new species of Florida tourist trap has come into being—the Spacarium, a rather ramshackle alfresco museum, owned by two automobile mechanics, whose prize display is a collection of burned-out components of Cape Canaveral rockets, purchased from a junk dealer. South of Patrick Air Force Base, there is a new settlement, of about two hundred people—mainly missile workers and their families—that incorporated itself last October under the name of Satellite Beach. Two months later, just after the first Vanguard fizzle, the mayor and the city council of the young community reassuringly wrote President Eisenhower that they had no intention whatsoever of renaming the place Sputnik Beach, and they received a grateful acknowledgment from Sherman Adams, the President's assistant, who said, "Your pledge to assist in any way to establish technological goals is indeed appreciated."

High-flying nomenclature is merely one sign of the general transformation that the missile program has wrought in the Cocoa area. Only two years ago, the Chamber of Commerce that is now booking spaceship passengers was almost wholly concerned with the job of boosting Cocoa as "the salt-water trout capital of the world." It still alludes to trout, of course, but in its paeans they now run a poor second to rockets. Rockets account for everything that is currently marvellous about Cocoa—its swelling population, its scores of new businesses, the housing developments that have supplanted orange groves, and the money being put into circulation by the Air Force, whose local payroll comes to six million dollars a month. A few Cocoans seem to miss the leisurely old days, when the only strangers in town were well-to-do Northerners who came down to bask in the sun or sit on the banks of lagoons, fishing for trout or pompano. "It used to be that when I walked down the street, I knew everybody, native or visitor, but now I hardly recognize a soul," Mrs. Marie Holderman, a great-grandmother who has been publisher of the Cocoa *Tribune* for the past forty-one years, told me ruefully. (In deference to the accelerated pace of Cocoa life, she recently began putting out her paper three times instead of twice a week.) Mrs. Holderman's nostalgia is not shared by many of her fellow-townsmen, however. A far more common attitude was summed up for me by the owner of a Cocoa gift shop, who said cheerfully, "These newcomers don't bother us at all. Remember, they're quiet, brainy guys, and they're not interested in boozing or kicking up a fuss or running around to honky-tonks. They do have money to spend, though, and we figure we might as well make as much as we can while we can. Before you know it, everybody around here will be taking off for the moon."

About fourteen thousand people are now employed at Cape Canaveral and Patrick Air Force Base, and eighty per cent of these are civilians working either directly for the Air Force or for one or another of the firms that are handling various aspects of the space program, among them Lockheed, Convair, and Douglas, which manufacture missiles; the Radio Corporation of America, which electronically computes such things as the missiles' air speed, their rate of internal heating, and their skin (or surface) temperature; and Pan American World Airways, which handles housekeeping and maintenance chores for the Air Force at the test center. At the end of the working day, the peninsular roads and the causeway are jammed with traffic. By no means all the drivers live in Cocoa Beach itself; indeed, a surprising number of them commute from places as far away as Orlando, a drive of an hour and a half. A synthetic community, with its roots in space, Cocoa Beach lacks certain amenities of modern life; though it now has three drugstores and three gas stations, all set up since 1954, it has no school, no library, and no hospital. A Convair official, whose job it is to keep his company's flock in the Cocoa area happy, told me, "We have six hundred-odd men here, and most of them are in their mid-thirties. They have young children, and want to be near schools and hospitals, so they're willing to travel a long way. Besides, Cocoa Beach isn't much of a place for shopping. You've seen the shopping area, haven't you? A few stores, with humdrum merchandise, huddled around a stop light." Another effective deterrent to living in Cocoa Beach, I discovered, is the price of land. Ocean frontage costs as much as twenty times what it did a few years ago. One eighty-acre tract I saw had been bought for four thousand dollars back in 1954; it was sold a month later for eighteen thousand, was resold six months after that for fifty-six thousand, and is now on the market for a hundred and sixty thousand. In the circumstances, it is not surprising that a handful of alert real-estate operators have compared the missile boom to a gold strike. "Mine is a success story," I was told flatly by John J. Kabboord, formerly a used-car dealer in Kalamazoo and now the president of the Ocean Realty Company, which occupies one of the stores huddled around the stop light. "Three years ago, I got clued in that the missile program was going to be big, and I believed it. So last year I sold nine million dollars' worth of land. It used to take me three days to make sixty dollars on a car, but down here I've made as much as fifty thousand dollars in a morning." While Kabboord and other local real-estate operators do not expect the honey to keep flowing at its present rate forever, they are pretty bullish about the future all the same. "This isn't any freak boom that's going to blow over one, two, three," I was told by a portly ex-sergeant, who used to be stationed at Patrick and now has a hand in running three motels. "Man, this place is the jumpoff port for interplanetary travel. This boom is *serious*."

There are sixteen motels in and around Cocoa Beach, and every one of them is thriving; indeed, the aircraft companies and the other civilian firms involved in missile work have standing reservations throughout the year for more than half the motel rooms in town. The motels look as if they had been designed for pleasure-minded tourists—particularly the Vanguard and the Starlite, which have swimming pools and shuffleboard courts—but few of their guests give much thought to pleasure. The visitors are predominantly high-ranking engineers, scientists, and military men who come down from Washington or from their company headquarters to supervise some phase of the recurrent tests. One motel manager told me that not long ago a dozen generals had shown up at his place and registered under patently assumed names—no doubt, he thought, to avoid disclosing that a certain rocket merited all that high-level attention. The length of the guests' stay depends on the weather and the thousand other variables attendant on a shoot. Ordinarily, as soon as they check in, they rent a car and drive off to Cape Canaveral, and they are rarely seen around the motel except at breakfast. Each shoot, representing months of planning, is a tremendous gamble. The missiles cost millions of dollars each, and, more important, there are billions in contracts ahead for the companies that turn out the best-behaved rockets. The men are too wrapped up in their immediate duties to spend much time speculating about America's race with the Russians, and they tend to be clannish; the members of each company's contingent usually spend their moments of relaxation together, their great bond apparently being the combined expertise that may or may not tame their rocket. Those moments occur in the evening over drinks and dinner, but there aren't many of them, and the groups that share them are seldom convivial. Their collective mien is one of stern competence, and I got the impression that even their small talk is strictly shop talk.

The news of the arrival of any particular contingent in Cocoa Beach gets about fast, for "bird-dogging," as the sniffing out of an impending shoot is known, is a flourishing local sport; if a team of Chrysler engineers flies in from Michigan, for example, it can only mean that a Redstone rocket—a Chrysler product—is about to be fired. Once the word is out, a kind of missile fever ensues, spreading to outlying towns, and even to tourists passing through them, a number of whom have been known to revise their itineraries and make for Cocoa Beach. The Starlite's manager told me that one woman had offered to pay double for her room if he could arrange to have a rocket go off during her stay. The fever is especially virulent among a special breed of buffs, who over the months have done some boning up on rockets and who sometimes claim to be able to identify a missile in flight by its trajectory, its vapor trail, and the noise it makes. Members of this cult are known as "bird watchers," and a few weeks ago they were loosely, and prankishly, organized into the Greater Cape Canaveral Astrophysical Debating, Marching, Waiting and Bird-Watching Society, Unincorporated. As it happens, "bird watching" is an ambiguous term around Cocoa Beach, since the region is an ornithologist's paradise. For three years now, the local chapter of the Audubon Society has won the parent organization's annual bird-count championship hands down, having spotted more varieties of avian life than any other chapter—ibis, avocet, plover, turnstone, egret, and heron among them. Relations between the two types of bird watcher seem to be fairly easy. "We don't mind those missile bugs calling themselves bird watchers," William Hueston, a retired steel executive and an Audubon Society official, told me, with a good-natured smile. "We don't even mind the missiles. They flush the birds when they go off, but the birds come back. There are so many fish around here that the birds just can't pass them up."

The launching of missiles from Cape Canaveral is visible from the sands to the north of Cocoa Beach, and spectators are permitted to come within three miles of the launching site. Not long before a rocket is scheduled to be fired—the length of time varies with the type of rocket—a sphere of red nylon, about three feet in diameter, is run up a ninety-foot pole on the Cape as a warning to fishing and shrimping boats and other sea traffic within five miles to clear out. Since the red ball is visible to the surrounding countryside as well, it serves the incidental purpose of informing bird watchers that their hour is at hand, and they are quick to respond. Cars skim along the hard, flat beaches, and the drivers maneuver for vantage points. In the distance, the poised rocket stands perpendicular and alone—no longer encumbered by the scaffolding that surrounded it while its crew was preparing it for flight. Whole families turn up on the beach, and the younger children may play with toy missiles as they romp about, totally uninterested in the real thing a few miles off. The serious bird watchers scan the rocket with field glasses and wait. The waiting time varies, and sometimes the red ball is lowered, which means that, for one reason or another, the shoot has been postponed; barring such a development, the bird watchers are likely to stand fast for a good part of the day, on the reasonable supposition that the countdown going on in the test center's blockhouse may have struck a snag. This is not invariably true, however. A year or so ago, a launching was delayed for several hours when a pilot, who had been sent up to make sure that there was no interference on the frequency over which the missile would radio data back to R.C.A. technicians on the ground, reported that the channel was jammed. He took what is called a directional fix, and traced the interference to a radio station that had just opened in Goose Bay, Labrador; the test center's command brought the crisis to the attention of the Department of Defense, in Washington; the Department of Defense made a hurried phone call to Goose Bay; and the radio station was prevailed upon to shut down long enough for the shoot to proceed.

As the spectators' vigil wears on, they are likely, in this chill

Florida winter, to keep themselves busy and warm by building small bonfires and by forming impromptu glee clubs. The size of the turn-out depends pretty much on the hour. When Explorer I went up in darkness on January 31st, 1958, there wasn't much of a crowd on the beach, although people rushed out to inspect the skies when they heard the roar of the rocket, and lights stayed on in most homes until one in the morning, when the news came through that the satellite had gone into orbit. The second Vanguard test, a few days later, drew an even smaller crowd, for it took place at 2:33 A.M.—an hour when even the most determined bird watchers are in bed. For daytime launchings, though, the crowds generally number in the hundreds, and on the morning of December 6th, 1957, when the first Vanguard was fired, thousands of people were on the beaches and cars were strung out clear across the causeway from Cocoa. There are usually a good many out-of-state cars interspersed among the Florida vehicles, and one afternoon a New York car materialized alongside the rented Chevrolet in which I was sitting, waiting for an Atlas to go up. Its driver, who wore a dark-blue beret, a Hawaiian shirt, and blue slacks, got out of his car, approached mine, and asked anxiously, "Have they fired it yet?" He was greatly relieved when I said no. "Good, good," he said, staring in the direction of the Cape. "I'm just down this way on vacation, but while I'm at it I want to feel I'm a part of history."

When a long-range rocket, satellite-bearing or not, is launched, it leaves its stand hesitantly, as if it were straining to ascend, and bird watchers are apt to urge it on with a chant of "Go, go, go." If it does go, it makes a graceful spectacle indeed. Its base a small sun of shimmering fire, it rises straight into the air and then describes a long arc, leaving a vapor trail that helps onlookers track it with the naked eye. (Binoculars are a nuisance once the rocket is in flight.) As it gathers speed, a thunderous roar, like some immense surf, shakes the motels and even the sturdiest of homes nearby; in towns within earshot of the roar, shopkeepers and their customers rush out into the streets to see if they can spot the rocket as it soars through the clouds, now hidden by them, now exposed in the blue sky. With a final surge, it vanishes into the loftiest clouds or, more likely, hurtles through them into the clear empyrean. The show takes three or four minutes, and when it comes to an end, the spectators on the beach exchange congratulatory looks, and then disperse and make for their cars.

The now invisible rocket flies southeast down a prescribed corridor, and on eleven islands from Grand Bahama, off Palm Beach, to Ascension, off the southern coast of Brazil, the Air Force has set up a chain of outposts, called down-range stations, to track it and pick up its signal. The rocket may go five thousand miles—the full length of the corridor—or a good deal less, depending on its range and performance and the nature of the test, but whatever the distance, Air Force pilots will have made as certain as they can that the course is clear of shipping, and the Civil Aeronautics Administration will have seen to it that commercial flights anywhere near the rocket's path have been rerouted. So far, there have not been any accidents, or even any narrow escapes, an Air Force public-information officer assured me. "Can you imagine how we'd look if we hit someone?" he asked, horrified.

The launching of a rocket always means a welcome break in the monotonous existence led by the men at the down-range stations. Major John D. Ogle, Chief of the Military Training Division at Patrick Air Force Base, who has spent a year on one of the islands and has visited all of them except Ascension, told me that there are anywhere from a hundred to three hundred men at each station—all civilians except for the base commander, who is an Air Force officer—and that during a flight they may be at their posts for twenty hours at a time. They receive a substantial bonus for serving on the hot, lonely islands, but the torpor of their life there makes it necessary for Pan American, which keeps house on the islands as well as at Cape Canaveral, to dream up further inducements in order to keep the turnover of employees within bounds. As often as possible, the men are flown to the mainland for weekend leaves; on the islands, Pan Am shows them a different movie every night, and provides them with fishing boats and equipment for various hobbies, including, Major Ogle said, bird watching. "The old-fashioned kind," he added.

Probably the most stimulating projectile to come the men's way, Major Ogle said, was not Explorer I but the runaway Snark that was launched in December of 1956. The down-range stations have electronic equipment for bringing down an erring missile—the same sort of equipment that the Vanguard men at Cape Canaveral used to blow up their defective rocket—and almost all of them had a stab at commanding the Snark to commit suicide. Major Ogle, who was base commander at Mayagüez, in Puerto Rico, at the time, took part in the effort. "That crazy Snark!" he said. "You have to be awfully careful about destroying one of these things—they're so damn expensive—but my orders were to destroy it if it approached a populated area, and that's what our radar showed it was doing. It was streaking at forty thousand feet toward Hispaniola—the island shared by Haiti and the Dominican Republic. I had two buttons in front of me that were supposed to bring that Snark down, and I jabbed and jabbed and jabbed at them, but I might as well have been pushing a doorbell with nobody home. That Snark stayed on our radar screen until it was over the northern coast of South America. Then it disappeared. I've never heard an explanation of the incident, and the corpus delicti has never been produced. Maybe it's in the Brazilian jungle, maybe it's a satellite."

At the conclusion of a test, the Department of Defense usually issues an official communiqué describing the missile's behavior, but anyone in Cocoa Beach can tell whether it was good or bad by looking at the faces of the visiting engineers. If things have gone poorly, the engineers are a study in glumness; if all is well, they throw a party, although, as befits a party thrown by men with a serious purpose in mind and an incalculable amount of work still ahead of them, it tends to be sedate and to break up early. On the evening of one successful launching recently, a group of engineers gathered at a corner table in one of the local restaurants. They had two drinks each, ate a substantial dinner, talked quietly but with obvious satisfaction, and then went off to their motel rooms to get a good night's sleep before setting off in the morning for the company's headquarters, where they would start planning the next shoot—a shoot, they hoped, that would also end with a quiet, two-drink party in a Cocoa Beach restaurant.

CHAPTER 29 | NOVEMBER, 1958

MAN IN SPACE

IN SPITE OF ALL the serious investigation that our scientists and engineers are devoting to the possibilities of space travel, the would-be voyager to Mars or Venus need not pack his bags quite yet—or so I gathered after looking into the progress of what is known to researchers, in and out of the U.S. government, as "the man-in-space program." One thing that is holding up the program is the machine; engineers have been turning out better and better experimental rocket planes, but they are by no means ready to launch a really spaceworthy ship—a passenger-carrying vehicle capable of making its way through the earth's atmosphere into outer space and coming back to terra firma, itself and its cargo reasonably intact. Formidable as this part of the job is, however, most of the experts assume that, sooner or later, it will be accomplished; all that is required is technological improvement. Many scientists are a good deal more puzzled, I have discovered, over what to do about the one element in space travel that is technologically unimprovable. This element is none other than the space traveller—man.

Man's age-old physical and psychological needs and frailties, it seems—"the human factors," as man-in-space experts call them—make him a rather poor risk for space voyaging, and some of the scientists I have talked to, or whose treatises I have read, have expressed mild disappointment with man for not coming up to the astronautical mark. "Man's functional system cannot be fooled by gimmicks and gadgets," a comprehensive report on space flight got up for the Air University Command and Staff School, in Alabama, remarks. "He cannot be altered dimensionally, biologically or chemically. None of the conditions necessary to sustain his life-cycle functions can be compromised to any great extent." Wherever man is and whatever his circumstances, the report says, in effect, he simply must have many of the things that sustain him here below—air, food, and a certain amount of intellectual and physical activity. "Encapsulated atmosphere is what we're after," one scientist told me, and went on to explain that the space traveller—whether wearing a space suit in an airless cabin or, as most scientists would prefer, wearing ordinary clothes in a pressurized cabin—would have to have enough of the familiar earthly environment to see him through his voyage. "A spaceship," this scientist said, "must, you see, be a 'terrella,' a little earth."

The human factors in space travel are being studied on a broad front, and at every level from the immediately practical to the highly theoretical, by special groups set up within America's armed services, universities, and private aircraft companies—groups like the Space Biology Branch of the Air Force Aero Medical Field Laboratory, in Alamogordo, New Mexico, and the Human Factors Engineering Group of the Convair Division of General Dynamics Corporation, in San Diego, California. The assignments these groups have taken on are myriad, and practically every one of them necessarily involves guesswork, or what one man calls "the vagueness of imagination," to a degree that most scientists abhor. Nonetheless, the job is being tackled, in its various aspects, by biochemists (who are concerned with the space traveller's physical care and feeding), radiobiologists (who worry about the effects of cosmic rays in outer space), sanitary engineers (who are figuring out how to dispose of wastes and insure the cleanliness of the terrella), anthropometrists (who measure the functional capacities of man), astrobotanists (who are attempting to discover what sort of food, if any, the space man might find on other celestial bodies), and psychologists (who tend to doubt whether a man can roam extra-terrestrially for years, months, or even weeks without going batty). Physiologists, chemists, pharmacologists, physicists, and astronomers are also making contributions to the man-in-space program, as are sociologists, whose responsibilities would seem to be remote at the moment but who foresee all kinds of catastrophic dilemmas in the future. "What will happen to a man's wife and children when he embarks on a prolonged space trip, perhaps for years, with every chance of not returning?" one scholar asked not long ago, in a symposium called "Man in Space: A Tool and Program for the Study of Social Change," which was held in the sober halls of the New York Academy of Sciences. "How long a separation in space would justify divorce, and if he should return, how will the [possible] Enoch Arden triangle be handled?" At the same symposium, Professor Harold D. Lasswell, of the Yale Department of Political Science, envisioned an even more drastic jolting of the status quo. He asked his learned audience to imagine what might happen if a spaceship's crew landed on a celestial body whose inhabitants were not only more than a match for us technologically but had created a more peaceable political and social order. "Assume," he said, "that the explorers are convinced of the stability and decency of the . . . system of public order that exists alongside superlative achievements in science and engineering. Suppose that they are convinced of the militaristic disunity and scientific backwardness of earth. Is it not conceivable that the members of the expedition will voluntarily assist in a police action to conquer and unify earth as a probationary colony of the new order?"

Before the space traveller can return to earth, with or without a police force at his back, he must go into space, and psychologists are now engaged in a sharp debate as to just what type of person would be best suited to embark on a long extraterrestrial trip. Addressing a meeting of the American Association for the Advancement of Science in Indianapolis a few months ago, Dr. Donald N. Michael, a psychologist who has been doing research on the effects of automation, estimated that a journey to Mars might take about two and a half years, and concluded that our culture was unlikely to produce anyone with that much patience; good space men, he said, might be found in "cultures less time-oriented and more sedentary"—in a Buddhist monastery, perhaps, or among the Eskimos. Reasoning along other lines, Dr. Philip Solomon, chief psychiatrist at the Boston City Hospital, has come out for extrovert space voyagers. Like other medical men in all parts of the country, Dr. Solomon has been conducting what are called "sensory-deprivation experiments"—specifically, confining volunteers of various personality types in iron lungs to see how they bear up in isolation—and in a recent issue of *Research Reviews,* a monthly put out by the Office of Naval Research, he writes: "It appears that the self-centered introvert, whom you might expect to be quite content in the respirator, holed up in his own little world, so to speak, is precisely the one who breaks down soonest; whereas the extrovert, who is more strongly oriented to people and the outside world, can stand being shut off, if he has to, more readily. Sensory deprivation places a strain on the individual's hold on external reality, and it may be that those who are jeopardized most by it are those whose ties to reality are weakest."

Women have notoriously strong ties to reality, and for this reason, among others, some experts are convinced that they would fare better than men on a pioneering journey through space in cramped quarters. Another reason is that women live longer than men, and some of the envisioned journeys would take an extended period of time; still another is that women could probably weather long periods of loneliness better, because they are more content to while away the hours dwelling on trivia. Writing in the *American Psychologist* a couple of months ago, Dr. Harold B. Pepinsky, a psychology professor at Ohio State University, came up with the notion that the ideal space voyager would be a female midget with a Ph.D. in physics. When I asked a physiologist what he thought of this idea, he not only supported it heartily but embellished it. "It would be good if this midget woman Ph.D. came from the Andes," he said. "We're going to have to duplicate the traveller's normal atmosphere in the ship, and it's easier to duplicate a rarefied fourteen-thousand-foot atmosphere than a dense sea-level atmosphere." The cards, though, seem to be stacked against any woman's blasting off ahead of a man. One important offcer, Lieutenant Colonel George R. Steinkamp, of the Space Medicine Division at the Air Force School of Aviation Medicine, in San Antonio, Texas, said recently, "It's just plain not American. We put women on a pedestal, and they belong there." The pedestal apparently should be anchored firmly to the ground.

As for the Ph.D. in physics, I gathered that while it would definitely be an asset, some of the experts are worried lest a physicist might not know all he should about astronomy. An astronomer, on the other hand, might be weak in meteorology, and a meteorologist might well bungle some vital engineering problem. An engineer might know how to operate and maintain his ship but would probably not be able to cope with any illness that happened to befall him. The possibility of illness in outer space is receiving its share of attention, to judge by a paper that Drs. Donald W. Conover and Eugenia Kemp, of Convair's Human Factors Engineering Group, submitted to the American Rocket Society several months ago, in Los Angeles. "Space men and women must have almost perfect health in order to avoid bringing disaster on the flight by physical incapacity," they declared, and went on to say that even these paragons of fitness should "be trained in self-medication and, particularly, the use of antibiotics." From that point of view, the ideal traveller would seem to be a physician, but Professor Lasswell, the Yale political scientist, has a different idea. An anthropologist-linguist, he feels, would make a good space traveller, especially when it came to communicating with the inhabitants of remote celestial bodies; other candidates the Professor has nominated include individuals gifted with extrasensory perception—perhaps members of the Society for Psychical Research, Western parapsychologists, or Eastern mystics.

Naturally, all these difficulties would be cleared up if the vehicle carried a physicist, an astronomer, a meteorologist, an engineer, a physician, and the rest, but at the moment it seems likely that the first spaceships will carry a crew of only one, because present computations show that half a ton of fuel and metal must be provided for every pound of cargo. Still, some farsighted psychologists are pondering the intangibles that would make a large spaceship a happy one. The crew members, living close to disaster at all times and needing all their resources to forestall it, will have to be able to get along with one another, and various experts have told me that this state of affairs will not be as easy to achieve as it might sound. One question they are mulling over is what size crew would prove most efficient and congenial, and the question, I learned, has its facets. A group of five or six, research discloses, would be better in some ways, and worse in others, than a smaller one. Studies now in progress at various universities, though their results are anything but definitive, seem to show that half a dozen men thrown together in close confinement tend to form a highly standardized, if miniature, community, taking on and retaining social patterns through a desire to conform. The members of a smaller group, being less concerned about neighborliness and conformity, are apt to attack the business at hand, whatever it may be, with greater zest and intelligence. "It's something of a dilemma," I was told by Luigi Petrullo, who heads up the Group Psychology Branch of the Office of Naval Research, an agency that has for many years observed the behavior of submarine crews. "The factors that make for harmony—a nice clubby atmosphere, if you will—won't necessarily make for efficiency, while those that make for efficiency will probably lead to jangled nerves. The particular character of a mission, I suspect, will have a lot to do with determining the size of the crew."

Whatever the crew's size, its members will have no escape from one another's likes, dislikes, normalities, abnormalities, and day-to-day moods for weeks, months, or years, in which long stretches of boredom will be interrupted only by moments of stark terror. Such a situation, as the military services have discovered from observing the behavior of men assigned to long-drawn-out perilous missions, does not ordinarily make for camaraderie; indeed, familiarity may breed feelings even stronger than contempt. One of the psychologists who pointed this out to me referred to a passage from *Kabloona,* in which the author, Gontran de Poncins, a French anthropologist and explorer, describes his change of attitude toward a trader, Paddy Gibson, with whom he spent part of an arctic winter:

> I liked Gibson as soon as I saw him, and from the moment of my arrival we got on exceedingly well. He was a man of poise and order; he took life calmly and philosophically; he had an endless budget of good stories. In the beginning we would sit for hours . . . discussing with warmth and friendliness every topic that suggested itself, and I soon felt a real affection for him.
>
> Now as winter closed in round us, and week after week our world narrowed until it was reduced—in my mind, at any rate—to the dimensions of a trap, I went from impatience to restlessness, and from restlessness finally to monomania. I began to rage inwardly and the very traits of my friend . . . which had struck me at the beginning as admirable, ultimately seemed to me detestable.
>
> The time came when I could no longer bear the sight of this man who was unfailingly kind to me.

In an effort to learn more about the way groups of men react to prolonged togetherness, the military services, some universities, and various aircraft companies have been incarcerating crews in mockup space gondolas right here on earth, and the findings, though inevitably sketchy, have, on the whole, been illuminating. After a day or two, most of the subjects—even pilots with considerable flight experience—begin to show signs of listlessness and frayed nerves. Several experiments of the sort have been conducted by the Air Force Aero Medical Laboratory, in Dayton, Ohio, each involving the isolation of a five-man crew for five days, and as the time wore on, the crews, whose talk was recorded, revealed a preoccupation with food that eventually bordered on the obsessive. I was told about these experiments by Charles Dempsey, the head of the laboratory's Escape Division, which is studying the habitation of space vehicles and emergency escapes from them. "The men seemed to be living to eat rather than eating to live," he said. "Their schedule provided for fifteen minutes of work each hour for sixteen hours, with the remaining forty-five minutes spent sitting around, after which they had eight hours off duty, eighty per cent of this time spent in sleeping. At the start, they discussed everything under the sun. In due course, though, they just about talked themselves out, and then there seemed to be only one subject that still interested them—food. Each man had his own five-day supply of food to eat when he wished, and, as things turned out, practically every one of the men soon started watching what his companions were doing with their food. Each seemed uncertain whether he was using good judgment about his own supply—whether he was eating too much of it at once or too little. Living on the kind of schedule they did, their stomachs became confused, and they kept debating whether it was breakfast time or suppertime or what. Yes, food got to be quite a deal. I'd say it was on their minds three-quarters of the time they were awake."

The food that the earth-bound astronauts were given at the Aero Medical Laboratory was familiar, varied, and tasty, including such items as brownies and salted peanuts. In space, the voyager would be unlikely to have such interesting fare. In fact, no one knows at this point what he would have in the way of food. On the assumption that the spaceship would have automatic controls, Dr. John Lyman, associate professor of engineering at the University of California, has gone so far as to suggest that if a space man were bound for Mars, say, he might be given a still undeveloped drug that would lower his body temperature and put him to sleep until he got there; such a hibernating man, with his breathing and heart action slowed, would require relatively little food and water, and what he did need could be automatically injected into his veins. In an article in the *Bulletin of the Atomic Scientists,* Dr. James B. Edson, assistant to the director of Research and Development of the Department of the Army, goes even further, envisioning a synthetic nutrient that could make breathing as well as eating and drinking unnecessary. After speculating for a time on how the nutrient might work, Dr. Edson does relent a bit. "It may, however, prove necessary," his article says, "to breathe at least a little, so as not to get out of the habit."

In contrast to Dr. Lyman and Dr. Edson, some of the Navy's scientists take a decidedly old-fashioned view. With a conscious, lively space crew in mind, these men insist on a normal terrestrial diet, including all possible trimmings. "We do not completely understand why," Captain C. P. Phoebus, a physician assigned to the Naval War College, in Newport, has written, "but we have found in dealing with submariners that the mere provision of enough calories, bulk, vitamins and minerals, and other essentials is not enough to keep a man physically and mentally healthy. It is very important that some of these needs be supplied in the form of fresh food, that the types of food and cooking techniques be varied, that the diet be balanced, and that the food be as tasty as that served at home. If it is not, the crew's performance and morale are not at their best." And that, these Navy men seem to think, would be just as true in outer space as underwater.

Captain Phoebus and his submariners notwithstanding, one type of nutrition that is being seriously considered is about as far a cry from blueberry pie as can be imagined. This is the botanical group called the algae, one of the earth's most primitive forms of vegetation. In many respects, algae would make the ideal food for the astronaut, though they might not appeal to his palate. Algae contain proteins, fats, and carbohydrates, and could easily be grown aboard the ship

—in small tanks irradiated by intense light. Moreover, they might solve the difficult problem of disposing of human waste, by using it as fertilizer. And, to mention another of algae's virtues, they can photosynthesize—that is, re-form the molecules of carbon dioxide breathed out by the space traveller, thereby releasing oxygen. Less than two months ago, during the world's first international symposium on submarine and space medicine, which was held by the American Institute of Biological Sciences at the naval submarine base in Groton, Connecticut, some researchers reported the discovery of a new strain of algae that can increase itself by cell multiplication a thousand-fold daily; the previous high had been eight times. The taste of algae, it might be mentioned, varies; one strain, for example, has a black-peppery tang, and another tastes something like mushrooms. "Algae have it all over pemmican," one man who has sampled both told me. But he hadn't eaten algae month after month in a spaceship.

This whole scheme of spaceship farming is patterned after nature's cycle here on earth, where time and the sun's energy, through the chemical changes they bring about, convert animal wastes and dead plants into crops. "What better method [of producing food] is there than to emulate the system already found in existence on the earth?" is a rhetorical question asked in "Closed Cycle Biological Systems for Space Feeding," a paper put out by the Quartermaster Food and Container Institute for the Armed Forces, in Chicago. "Man will be supplied food, water and oxygen from biological and chemical systems. He will eat the food, turning out the same wastes in the spaceship that are produced on the face of the earth." One expert I met, Dr. Harvey E. Savely, director of the Aero Medical Division of the Air Force Office of Scientific Research, confessed to me that the prospect of having our space men grow and harvest algae strikes him as anachronistic. "To think," he said, "that we may develop so advanced a machine as a spaceship and then have to fall back on so primitive a calling as agriculture."

Of all the strange experiences that may await the astronaut, none will be quite so strange, the experts agree, as weightlessness. This phenomena will occur as soon as the spaceship reaches a speed at which the rocket's centrifugal force cancels the pull of the earth's gravity, and when it does, the space man, whether settling into orbit or making for Venus or Mars, will know for certain that he has arrived in outer space. He will weigh nothing. The air in his cabin will weigh nothing. The warm carbon dioxide he breathes out, being no lighter than the air in the cabin, will not rise, so he will have to exhale forcibly. Momentum, the force whirling the ship on its course, will rule its interior as well, and with possibly weird results. All objects that are not in some way fastened down—a map, a flashlight, a pencil—will float freely, subjecting the space man to a haphazard crossfire. If he were to drink water from an ordinary tumbler, the water might dash into his nostrils, float there, and drown him. Ordinary tumblers will not be used, however; plastic squeeze bottles will. ("The proper-size orifice is being worked out," I was told by Major Henry G. Wise, of the Human Factors Division, Air Force Directorate of Research and Development.) Far more startling than the movement of objects, though, will be the space man's own movements. Normally, in making a movement of any kind, a man has to overcome the body's inertia plus its weight; a weightless man has only the inertia to overcome, and the chances are that it will take a long time for his muscles to grow accustomed to the fact. "What would be a normal step on earth would . . . send the 'stepper' sailing across the cabin or somersaulting wildly in the air," the Air University Command and Staff School study declares. "A mere sneeze could propel the victim violently against the cabin wall and result in possible injury."

Actually, very little is known about weightlessness. Until a few years ago, it was something that man had experienced only in very special circumstances, and then for no more than a fraction of a second—at the start of a roller coaster's plunge, for example, or at the instant of going off a high diving board. With the man-in-space program moving along, however, weightlessness has been deliberately arranged in certain flights undertaken at the Air Force School of Aviation Medicine, in San Antonio; in these, jet planes, flying along a prescribed parabolic course, manage to escape the effects of gravity for as long as thirty seconds. The exposure to weightlessness, brief as it is, has had widely varying effects on the airmen. "The sensation can best be described as one of incredulity, or even slight amusement," a colonel with a great deal of flying experience has reported, ascribing this reaction to "the incongruity of seeing objects and one's own feet float free of the floor without any muscular effort." Another airman, who was a gymnast in college, was reminded of "having started a back flip from a standing position and then become hung up part way over—looking toward the sky but not completing the flip." The sensation, he said, gave him "no particular enjoyment or dislike"—only "a feeling of indifference." Other airmen have found the experience extremely unpleasant—accompanied by nausea, sleepiness, weakness, sweating, and/or vertigo—and, to confuse matters, still others have discovered that their reactions differ on different flights. All told, one expert estimates, about a third of the subjects regard weightlessness as "definitely distressing," while a fourth regard it as "not exactly comfortable."

The experts realize, of course, that weightless voyages lasting a good deal longer than half a minute would have physical and mental results that can only be guessed at now. "Most probably, nature will make us pay for the free ride," one scientist has said, almost superstitiously. For one thing, a long trip would raise hob with a man's muscles. In any earthly condition of inactivity, no matter how extreme, they still have the job of resisting gravity, and without this they are bound to grow flabby. Moreover, the space man's sense of balance would be thrown out of whack; this sense is governed by a liquid in our inner ear, and without gravity that liquid, floating freely in the chambers of the ear, could not be relied on to do its work. Not only would the space man be uncertain of where he was in his cabin at any particular moment, I learned from Lieutenant Colonel Robert Williams, a consultant in neurology and psychiatry to the Surgeon General, but he would run the risk of losing his "body image." This image, Dr. Williams told me, is the deeply rooted conception that we all have of ourselves as a physical entity; it is one of the major constituents of our equanimity. "Without a body image," he went on, "a person has difficulty in determining what is inside oneself and what is outside, in distinguishing one's fantasy life from one's real environment. In losing it, we face a possible complete disruption of personality."

Assuming that the space traveller returns to earth with his personality undamaged, other difficulties may be in store for him. "A man who has been weightless for a couple of weeks would find it as hard to move around as a hospital patient taking his first steps after a long siege in bed," Dr. Savely told me. "If he were to travel in a cooped-up posture over a long period of time—and, for all we know now, that may be the only way he can travel—the whole architecture of his skeleton might change. Of course, we simply cannot allow that to happen." In view of such forebodings, it is not surprising that the man-in-space people are seeking to avoid weightlessness, altogether or in part, by developing an artificial substitute for gravity, but they don't seem to have made much headway. According to one scheme, the space man's cabin would be attached to the rocket by a long cable and would be swung around it continuously, thus creating a field of gravity that would restore the passenger's weight and, presumably, his efficiency. Discussing this in the *Scientific American,* Dr. Heinz Haber, of the Air Force School of Aviation Medicine, guesses that it would work only as long as the passenger stood absolutely still. "Every voluntary movement," he writes, "would give the traveller the peculiar illusion that he was being moved haphazardly." Another approach would be to have the astronaut tread a magnetized floor in iron shoes, but Dr. Haber isn't too sanguine about this one, either. Not only would the magnetism throw off the ship's electronic instruments, he points out, but it would "probably add to the traveller's confusion, for while his shoes would be attracted to the floor, his nonmagnetic body would not."

If the problem of weightlessness is solved, the pilot may know where he is in the cabin, but, owing to the vastness of space, he will still be uncertain of his whereabouts in the universe. This will be so, I was told, regardless of how informative the ship's instrument panel may be. A trip to Venus, around it, and back to earth would require a million miles of travel every day for three years, Dr. Seville Chapman, director of the Physics Division of the Cornell Aeronautical Laboratory, told me, and went on to say that the human mind may find the simple statistics of space baffling. "Suppose I tell you that our nearest star, Proxima Centauri, is four and two-tenths light-years away, a light-year being the distance a beam of light travels in twelve months at about a hundred and eighty-six thousand three hundred miles per second," he added. "Just what does that mean to you?" (Compared to such destinations, writes Major General Dan C. Ogle, the Surgeon General of the Air Force, our present space-travel aspirations—merely reaching the moon, for example—are "relatively provincial," taking in no more than "our own back yard.") Certainly nothing the space man will see is going to make him feel at home. He will have no horizon to look out on; in fact, he will be engulfed by blackness, for space has none of the air particles that diffuse the sun's rays to give us our daylight. In this nightlike setting, the sun itself will be painfully brilliant, and the constellations will seem to be spread out flat and to take on bizarre shapes. There will be stars both above and below, but they will not twinkle, for twinkling is caused by the same air particles. They will appear, rather, as steady points of light, and in their true colors—red, blue, yellow, white.

The ship will be moving at well over a hundred times the speed of sound, but it will be breaking no sound barriers; air is needed to carry sound, and seventy-five miles up, there is no such thing as a sound wave. And no matter how fast he is going, the space man will be unaware of moving at all. Speed itself will take on new meaning for him. He will not be able to measure it as an airplane pilot can; the speed that a plane's indicators show is computed on the basis of air resistance and altitude above sea level. "In space, there is no air and no sea, so most of the pilot's old indicators won't mean a thing up there," I was told by Dr. Max W. Lund, head of the Engineering Psychology Branch of the Office of Naval Research. "Instrument panels will have to be redesigned so that they show not miles per hour but simply the passage of minutes, hours, days, or even fractions of light-years. And, of course, that isn't all. Take the matter of destination. An approach to a point somewhere in space won't be made in a straight line, you know—nothing like the way we fly from one city to another. Celestial bodies don't stand still; the spaceship will have to describe a parabola, and we've been testing a screen that would show the space pilot the proper curve to follow in order to reach his destination. In fact," he went on, "we might even devise a screen that could flash him the answers to broad, vital questions like

'Where am I?,' 'How am I doing?,' and 'What should I do next?' He's going to be under a great strain, and his mind shouldn't be cluttered with more detailed information."

The space traveller will be under a very great strain indeed if he lets his mind dwell on the dangers surrounding him. For the first part of the journey, at least, cosmic rays will be bombarding the ship, without letup, and the space pilot may return to earth—if he returns at all—a physically impaired man. One authority, Dr. Hermann J. Schaefer, of the Navy School of Aviation Medicine, declared in the course of a California symposium last year that "not even informed guesses are possible" concerning the power of cosmic rays in space, but some idea of his respect for those rays can be deduced from his warning that "commercial airlines should not risk flight above ninety thousand feet, as they could not prove that any mutations or stillbirths following such flights were not caused by cosmic radiation." Farther out in space, the pilot might run into meteors, which, according to the Air University study, would present "an additional psychological problem to the would-be space traveller"—to say nothing of a physical problem. Some meteors are the size of a pea, and these, the study estimates, would score no more than "two hits per month per spaceship." Still, they might puncture a ship, causing a loss of pressure and possibly injuring or killing the traveller. But there are also meteors weighing tons and flying at speeds of up to three hundred and sixty thousand miles an hour, and the study notes that a hit by one of them "means sudden death." Another depressing consideration for the space man is that outside his ship—which may seem to him no more than a cockleshell—the temperature will range from 67 degrees below zero to 26,000 degrees above. As the Air University study observes, "The prospect of being cooked alive is not an attractive one."

Inside his cabin, the space man—if, of course, he is not in hibernation—may find temporary distraction from his lethal surroundings in the performance of his chores. He will have to check his cabin for pressurization, temperature, and humidity, as well as for noxious gases given off by the ship's equipment and by his own metabolism; he will have to watch his oxygen supply, perhaps keeping track of the photosynthetic process by which it is being maintained; and every now and then, depending on his course, he may need to provide his ship with a rocket assist by letting out a charge of fuel. Essentially, though, the space pilot will be a passenger, a man wafted through the dark, silent emptiness by momentum, and he will have a great deal of time on his hands. All that leisure is a matter of concern to the experts. Our senses must be stimulated or they will die, and in space there won't be even the simplest things that ordinarily keep a man's senses alert—the day's changes in temperature, for instance, or the different pressures we experience when we lie, sit, stand, and move. Ways of keeping the space man alert are being considered, and one of them, I was told by Dr. Richard Trumbull, head of the Physiological Psychology Branch of the Office of Naval Research, will be a system of "programming" his time. The idea is to give the space traveller a reasonably full schedule of things to do, at fixed times—including made work, self-study courses, and such recreational activity as listening to records and playing pinball.

If the space man is in a pressurized cabin, one big advantage he will have is that sound will travel normally, but if he is in an airless cabin, rigged up in his space suit, the only sounds he is likely to hear are those he makes himself, and the sound of his breathing might be as loud to him as Niagara. The silence prevailing in such a cabin, I was told, might be comparable to that of an anechoic chamber—a super-soundproof room, with walls that do not reflect sound, that researchers use for testing an individual's ability to withstand one form of sensory deprivation. Lieutenant Bruce E. Pinc, a physiologist who spent an hour in an anechoic chamber at the Aero Medical Laboratory in Dayton, told me that he would far rather find himself in "a high-stress situation where you don't know if the equipment will work but where you're at least in touch with people." Nor did he think his reaction was exceptional. "A psychiatrist who had been testing others at the lab tried the chamber himself, and in a matter of minutes he was so disturbed he had to be let out," Lieutenant Pinc told me. "He was disgusted with himself. He kept muttering that he had to face something in himself that he hadn't known about before."

In the silence and isolation, the space man is likely to be afflicted with hallucinations; he may see strange shapes and hear strange voices. That, at least, was the experience of a group of students at the University of Texas who voluntarily took part in an isolation experiment, and one report prepared by General Dynamics says that it will be necessary "to convince future space men that the hallucinations they may experience are the normal responses of . . . isolated people and not a cause for worry." Paradoxical as it may seem to the layman, ear surgery has been proposed as a method of forestalling visual illusions, and nerve-soothing drugs are being studied, as well as drugs to regulate the metabolic rate and the appetite. Another effect of isolation is profound fatigue, I was told, and here, again, it is hoped that drugs may be the answer, though a recent experiment with one powerful substance would seem to indicate the need for further research. The experiment has been described in a paper called "Fatigue, Confinement, Proficiency and Decrement," by Dr. George T. Hauty, of the Department of Experimental Psychology at the Air Force School of Aviation Medicine. A group of subjects used the stimulant to good advantage for twenty-four hours, Dr. Hauty discloses, but then delusions and hallucinations set in and proficiency vanished. "Since these operations [the delusions and hallucinations] occur with a normal sensory environment," he concludes, "it may be that such will occur to a greater degree in a closed ecological system associated with sensory deprivation as it is found in space flight with nullified gravitation [weightlessness], in a hermetic cabin, surrounded by the perpetual silence of space."

Perhaps the greatest danger of all is that the space man will fall victim to the "breakoff phenomenon"—an eerie and sometimes fatal by-product of isolation and boredom, which, according to a paper published in the *Journal of Aviation Medicine,* has caused some airplane pilots, flying well within the confines of the earth's atmosphere, to experience an unsettling "loss of identification with the earth." Upon becoming thus disconnected from the home planet, the flier grows uninterested in survival and falls into something like a trance, staring with apparent concentration at his instruments or out his window. Skin divers, Dr. Trumbull told me, undergo a counterpart of the breakoff phenomenon in what Jacques-Yves Cousteau, the French writer and underwater explorer, has called "the rapture of the depths"—a beckoning power that more than one diver has heeded, with fatal results. Colonel David G. Simons, now chief of the Space Biology Branch of the Aero Medical Field Laboratory, in Alamogordo, experienced the breakoff phenomenon in 1956, when he made his famous balloon ascent to an altitude of a hundred thousand feet. In describing the sensation to me, he likened it to the grip of a daydream. Judging only by his own experience, he said, he doubted whether the breakoff phenomenon would trouble any space traveller who managed to keep occupied. "When I was busy—and if ever anyone was busy, for thirty-two hours I was, what with making observations and reading dials and maps—I wasn't bothered by breakoff," he said. "But when I was tired and took a short break, I did feel that peculiar sense of detachment."

Even if the grand objective of a man in space is not attained for a long time to come, many of the scientists on the project are convinced that their work will bring about some fairly immediate benefits on earth. Animals that are to be catapulted into space in the near future, for instance, will have instruments attached to their bodies that will send back data on their physiological reactions, and these instruments—very possibly like those that the Russians attached to the late Laika—may have their medical uses here and now. Heart action, brain waves, reflexes, changes in both deep and superficial reflexes, and a wide variety of other information will be recorded, and the effort to develop instruments for this purpose, in the opinion of General Ogle, is hastening the improvement (the miniaturization, for one thing) of many appliances used in terrestrial diagnostic procedures. Moreover, he said, devices that will eventually be used for transmitting data from spaceships may soon be used to send information to centralized hospitals, where panels of specialists can diagnose difficult cases no matter how far away the patients are. "Maybe they'll save the life of an Ozark woman whose hill doctor is stumped," General Ogle remarked. Another doctor general, Don Flickinger, who is director of Life Sciences for the Air Research and Development Command, told me that wired monkeys, mice, and rats have already been rocketed and ballooned to high altitudes, though within the earth's atmosphere, and these, he said, may one day furnish leads for cancer research. He was particularly interested in the fact that certain black mice, dispatched from the Holloman Air Force Base, have white streaks in their fur where cosmic rays hit it. The black fur has never grown back, and this interests the General. "The white streak isn't just an ordinary burn," he said. "It represents a deleterious transfer of energy from ray to rodent, and it produces a basic alteration in cell function, though the cells continue to live. Well, what the cancer-research people are doing, to put it in basic terms, is to find out all they can about what influences and stimulates and changes the cell. We're hoping—and they are, too—that our black mice will contribute something to the answer."

Another study that has been speeded up by the man-in-space program is that of the stress hormones, like adrenalin, which accelerate our mental processes and quicken our reflexes. Fear triggers the flow of adrenalin, and adrenalin thereupon intensifies some of the side effects of fear—a faster heartbeat, for instance, and a tendency of the blood to clot. Now some scientists are calculating that if a man were to be given small doses of the stress hormones, he might develop a tolerance for them, and the dangerous effects of anxiety would be brought more or less under control—an achievement that, an Air Force physiologist told me, would benefit people here as well as out in space. "Certainly a space man is going to get the quakes," he told me, "but no worse than those poor wretches who were tossed to the lions in ancient Rome. A fellow can get just so scared and no more." As various medical discoveries give us increasing control over the nervous system, General Flickinger said, it may become possible to predict human performance under pressure. "This question is a dilly," he said. "To tackle it, one has to deal with the whole spectrum of personality, from a genius to an African Bushman, say —a simple fellow with a stomach that tells him he's hungry and eyes that tell him when the sun goes down. We know right now that if the heart does this and the cerebral cortex does that, then, as a functional organism, a particular fellow can do this and that. But to translate this into terms of human performance, of what he *will* do when the chips are down—that's something else again. It's possible that I will have a hand in picking our first space operator, and in any case he'll surely be someone who has passed all the tests and has a record of behaving well under stress. But how he'll behave once he gets up there —well, all we can do is hope."

Interesting though the terrestrial by-products of space research may be, the experts are concerned principally with the big prize. They want a man in space, and nothing less will do. Some of them have even begun to wonder exactly why. Some laymen are intrigued by the idea that space stations might have a military value, but not many scientists. In fact, Dr. Lee A. DuBridge, president of the California Institute of Technology, speaking at the Second Symposium on Basic and Applied Science in the Navy, held a few months ago in San Diego, dismissed the whole idea. If any military commander looks forward to launching missiles from Fortress Moon, Dr. DuBridge said, "Well, more power to him! He'll find the temperature a bit variable—boiling water by day, dry ice by night. And the days and nights are each two weeks long! He will find the lack of air, water and any appreciable or usable source of energy a bit inconvenient. And he will be bothered by the logistic problem of shooting his materials and supplies and weapons and personnel up there in the first place. Why shoot a load of explosives plus all auxiliary equipment two hundred and forty thousand miles to the moon, then two hundred and forty thousand miles back to hit a target only five thousand miles away? I'll guarantee to shoot a thousand missiles from the U.S. to any point on earth while our moon man is waiting twelve hours, more or less, for the earth to turn around and bring the target into shooting position. Finally . . . a bomb projected on a zero-angular-momentum path from the moon to the earth will take just five days to get there. . . . And we will hope the bombardier can figure correctly which side of the earth will be *up* by then."

To Dr. Edson, the assistant to the director of Army Research and Development, the exploration of space presents itself not as a potential means of mutual annihilation but as a chance—perhaps our last—to perpetuate the race. His position is that if we can no longer take to the hills, perhaps we can take to the planets. "In olden days," he told me, "a defeated people could always find a new green valley in which to start life afresh, but that is hardly feasible today. I see but two approaches to our plight. One is to reduce human destructiveness through some international plan. The other is the old one of finding a new green valley, of expanding the range of human habitat, and this can be done only through astronautics. People sense that the race is in peril, and this, I believe, is a powerful, if unstated, reason for the widespread interest in space and space travel."

Colonel John Paul Stapp, chief of the Aero Medical Laboratory in Dayton and the man who, a few years back, rode a rocket sled at nearly the speed of sound, suspects that "survival euphoria" may be at the bottom of it all—a desire to win out over the near-death that a space journey would involve. "The Chinese say that narrow escapes are like cutting off the Devil's tail," he told me, and I was not surprised when I learned later that he has already volunteered to go into space if and when the time comes. A colleague of his had a less adventurous approach. "Live, intelligent individuals have got to go up or we won't get the information we need," he said. As for General Ogle, he told me that the urge to send a man up is largely explained by half a sentence from the President's Science Advisory Committee's "Introduction to Outer Space," a White House document issued last spring: ". . . the thrust of curiosity that leads men to try to go where no one has gone before." Then, perhaps visualizing a man in space with an algae garden and a still unknown defense against weightlessness, he invoked another quotation, this one from Einstein: "The fairest thing we can experience is the mysterious. It is the fundamental emotion which stands at the cradle of true science. He who knows it not and can no longer wonder, no longer feel amazement, is as good as dead."

INDEX